FLORA OF HERTFORDSHIRE

The Chiltern Gentian (*Gentianella germanica*)   Oddy Hill   LYLE E. PERRINS

FLORA
OF
HERTFORDSHIRE

THE WILD PLANTS OF THE COUNTY OF HERTFORD
AND THE ADJOINING AREAS INCLUDED IN
WATSONIAN VICE-COUNTY 20

By

JOHN G. DONY

HITCHIN MUSEUM

1967
HITCHIN URBAN DISTRICT COUNCIL

TO
CHRIS

Printed by
White Crescent Press Ltd, Luton

CONTENTS

PHOTOGRAPHS

(following page 48)

FOREWORD

It is a pleasure to comply with Dr. Dony's request to contribute a foreword to the present work which is a memorial to both his industry and his skilful handling of the mass of material that has accrued over the years.

The first Flora of Hertfordshire, by Webb and Coleman, appeared in the middle of the nineteenth century followed, some forty years later, by that of Pryor. Perusal of these works reveals the changes then already taking place. My own recollections of the county flora go back to my childhood, some seventy years ago, so that many of the salient changes of more recent years, I myself have witnessed. The most pronounced were due to the falling water-table and the increasing population pressure. To the former we can attribute the decline or disappearance of many marsh plants such as Grass of Parnassus, *Triglochin palustris* and *Pulicaria vulgaris*. To the decline of the marsh plants the neglect of many ponds, upon which the watering of stock once depended, has contributed whilst the adaptation of the surfaces and widths of roadways to the needs of motor traffic has greatly diminished the extent and character of the wayside sanctuaries of wild life. With the advent of the motor-car, in the early years of this century, heath fires became more frequent so that the thickets of heather and gorse, which formerly presented barriers to excessive pedestrian activity, on commons such as those of Harpenden, Nomansland and Gustard Wood, largely disappeared. The abrasive effects of footwear have depressed or eliminated many of the smaller open-habitat species whilst the increasing toll taken of the more conspicuous and attractive flowers has sadly curtailed their capacity for replacement by seed, as was evinced by the spectacular resurgence of the Pasque Flower in the immediate post-war years.

Dr. Dony has provided, in many instances, the dates when diminishing species were last observed and this, it may be hoped, should serve as a challenge to field botanists to discover overlooked survivors and as a warning to all who prize our floral heritage that preservation, of the flora that remains, demands an active and not merely a passive support.

Just as many, so-called native, species have become uncommon or extinct, introductions during recent years, such as Common Field Speedwell in the arable fields, the Pineapple Weed by the roadsides, *Impatiens capensis* by our canals, or the American Pondweed in our streams, have become abundant. So that the decline of species, long regarded as wild, and the spread of new introductions, that may become completely integrated with the established vegetation, alike are essential parts in a process of continual change in the relationship between the flora of an area and the altering environment. It is towards the documentation of this process that the present flora of Hertfordshire makes a valuable contribution.

Some kinds of plant, such as the more characteristic species of exposed mud, are notoriously intermittent in their occurrence and therefore the fact that they have not been seen in a locality for a number of years may not imply actual extinction, but it is to be hoped that these pages stimulate observation and recording of diminutions or increases, whether permanent or fluctuating. The best acknowledgement that can be offered the author for his admirable presentation of existing data, is to augment them. The maps of distribution should be regarded, not merely as a summary of past records, but as a basis for further observations on distribution and the process of never-ceasing change that the plant population evinces.

Edward J. Salisbury

PREFACE

My *Flora of Bedfordshire* was published in 1953 and two years later I took over the work so ably begun by Mr. G. L. Evans of collecting material for a similar study on Hertfordshire. The task at first appeared to be a more difficult one. There had been no earlier adequate account of the Bedfordshire flora but now I had to consider the detailed description of the Hertfordshire flora by Pryor which had been published in 1887. Pryor's Flora, it should be noted, is by no means rare. To have repeated the whole of this work and added all the subsequent records would have resulted in a book of considerable size which with increased printing costs could not have been published. On the other hand there were recently compiled lists of the bryophytes by Dr. T. D. V. Swinscow and of the fungi by Dr. P. H. Gregory and Miss Holden. I had no need to account for these.

In the meantime there appeared the *Atlas of the British Flora*. This was undoubtedly the greatest achievement in the study of plant distribution in Britain and the most noteworthy as it sounded the death knell of the Watsonian system which had restricted progress for half a century. The Atlas was the result of a survey organised by the Botanical Society of the British Isles based on the use of a grid of 10 km. × 10 km. Mr. E. S. Edees was already using a grid of 2 km. × 2 km. for a study of the Staffordshire flora and this I finally adopted for the Hertfordshire survey. By this means it has been possible to use maps to show the present distribution of most of the more common species. The text has been reserved for detailed notes on the distribution of the more rare species and matters of historical interest. It is hoped that these departures from what has been normal in local floras for so many generations may be acceptable to older botanists who have become accustomed to previous practice and prove useful, especially to younger workers.

The collection of records was made possible only by the assistance of a great number of workers who are acknowledged early in the book. My thanks are also due to many landowners, and especially the British Transport Commission, for allowing me access to their property. I trust that others who may be led to look for plants in places described in this work will first seek permission, where it is necessary to do so. I wish also to thank Mr. W. H. Fordham who, at the beginning of the survey, donated £50 to the Hertfordshire Natural History Society to be spent on collecting data for the Flora. During the past five years my wife has been my co-worker in the field and in preparing the work for publication. Without her great assistance and co-operation the Flora would have been less complete and have taken longer to prepare.

The records made in the preparation of the Flora are by no means complete and I shall be pleased to hear of any current or past records which may have escaped my attention. An interleaved copy of the Flora in which additional information will be entered will be housed at Hitchin Museum and Art Gallery with the original field record cards which were compiled during the survey. It is also my intention to deposit at the Museum a complete set of distribution maps of all species including those not reproduced in the Flora.

The publication of the Flora has been greatly assisted by a grant of £300 from the Royal Society. Miss M. E. Gibbs made a gift of £100 collected as a testimonial by the Hertfordshire Natural History Society in recognition of her long service as secretary of the Society. It was Miss Gibbs' wish that this should be used for illustrations for the Flora. The Society added a similar sum for the same purpose. Since 1965 I have been in receipt of a travelling grant from the National Environment Research Council to allow me to study the relationship between area and species. The first stage of this work is summarised in Map 56g.

I am especially grateful to Mr. P. J. Ellison for his great care in preparing the maps, which are so important in the interpretation of the Flora, and for his assistance in many other ways. I wish also to thank Mrs. Bowden, Mrs. White and Mr. H. Meyer for providing the photographs, a number of which were taken at my special request, and Dr. L. E. Perrins for providing the photograph for the coloured frontispiece.

I am also grateful for the assistance I have received from members of the staff of the British Museum (Natural History) including Mr. J. E. Dandy in matters of nomenclature and Dr. W. T. Stearn and Mr. A. C. Jermy in problems of arrangement. I have received kindly assistance on many occasions from the staffs of the Linnean Society and the Rothamsted Experimental Station and from Mr. N. H. J. Clarke of the County Planning Department of the Hertfordshire County Council. I am grateful also to a number of my friends who have checked parts or the whole of the manuscript or proofs, and in so doing have made valuable suggestions to improve the text.

Publication itself has produced its minor difficulties and in overcoming these I have had the willing co-operation of the White Crescent Press Ltd.

I wish finally but by no means least to thank the Hitchin Urban District Council for publishing the Flora. In so doing it has followed the lead already given by Luton Borough Council in publishing the *Flora of Bedfordshire* and it is to be hoped that this will encourage more local authorities to publish similar accounts of local natural history. I received much assistance from Mr G. L. Evans during the period that he was Curator of Hitchin Museum and Art Gallery and to Miss M. M. Kershaw, the present Curator, and Miss M. Gadd, her assistant, I am grateful for easing in many ways the process of publication.

Luton March 1967   J. G. Dony

THE STUDY OF THE HERTFORDSHIRE FLORA

It is generally accepted that William Turner, who died in 1568, was the first British botanist, for before his time the sole interest shown in plants was in their medicinal and other uses. Turner's attention was drawn to the study of plants for their own sake and his books give us the very first records of the British flora. The history of the study of plants in Hertfordshire may be said to begin with the mention Turner makes in his *Names of Herbes* (1548) of the spindle tree 'in moste plentye between Ware and Barkway,' where it was probably seen by him on a journey from London to Cambridge. There is, however, evidence of natural vegetation in the county long before this and some pioneer work on the examination of a prehistoric flora was undertaken near Hitchin by Clement Reid in 1897. Many place names, some dating back to the period of the Anglo-Saxon occupation, are derived from plants and at a later period plants are mentioned frequently in documents such as manorial rolls. This early evidence is interesting and worthy of even more study but it gives no proof of a continuity of the flora which can only be built up with certainty from the time of Turner.

Herbalists flourished in the sixteenth and seventeenth centuries and the more exact of these made some attempt to account for the natural occurrence of plants. Gerard (1597), Parkinson (1640), Johnson (1641) and Culpeper (1652) among the better known writers of herbals gave a few records of Hertfordshire plants but from one more obscure herbalist came some very detailed information. This was William Coles whose *Adam in Eden, or Nature's Paradise* (1657) mentions no fewer than twenty-five plants to be found in or near St. Albans. The care with which these were recorded may be shown in the case of Yellow Archangel (*Galeobdolon luteum*) which he noted 'under a hedge on further side of a Meadow near St. Albans, near the Causey that leadeth from thence to Mr. Cotton's House on the left hand, a little before you come to the turning of the way, up to Windridge, where I shewed (it) to my worthy friends, Dr. Arris, a Doctor of Physick, and Mr. Dichfield, a School-master of St. Albans'.

Coles had a celebrated contemporary in Isaak Walton who noted in *The Compleat Angler* (1653) about ten plants from his favourite ground at Amwell on the River Lea. Isaak Walton's pre-occupation was angling but Moses Cook, gardener to the Earl of Essex at Cassiobury, had a more direct interest in plants and in *The Manner of Raising . . . Trees* (1676) he gives for the first time details of a number of Hertfordshire trees.

Botany was in the meantime being developed into a scientific study and William How's *Phytologia Britannica* (1650) added a few records but still more came from John Ray (1627–1705) and his correspondents. The first edition of Ray's *Synopsis* (1690) included observations made by Ray himself with details sent to him by Dr. Eales, who lived at Welwyn, and Leonard Plukenet (1656–1706). Plukenet was a well-known botanist who had a farm at Horn's Hill, below Rickmansworth and just inside the county boundary. The third edition of the Synopsis, edited by J. J. Dillenius in 1724, contained further records from Thomas Knowlton, Samuel Dale and Samuel Doody.

THE EIGHTEENTH CENTURY – JOHN RAY TO JOSEPH SABINE

A period in the development of the study of British botany which must be associated with Ray comes to a close with the work of John Blackstone (1713–53), who lived for some periods of his life at Harefield, just over the county boundary in Middlesex. His two works *Fasciculus Plantarum circa Harefield* (1737) and *Specimen Botanicum* (1746) show little respect for the consideration of county boundaries and Pryor was no doubt justified in thinking that many of Blackstone's records could have referred to Hertfordshire as easily as to Middlesex.

Blackstone's work is of added interest as the *Specimen Botanicum* was the last book to be published in English using the pre-Linnaean names of plants. Names, whether Linnaean or pre-Linnaean, presented no problem to two early botanists, Edward Steele and William Ellis, both of whom recorded plants from the Gaddesden area but used vernacular names.

Lieut.-Col. J. H. Busby, of Finchley, has drawn my attention to a manuscript list in Edward Steele's Notebook in the Bodleian Library which is headed 'A Catalogue of some plants spontainiusly growing near Barkhamsted or Gadsden'. It lists twenty-six species most of which can be readily identified e.g. 'Spurge Lawrill. Plentifull in all these parts. Bearesfoot near Gadsden Church in the Hedges.' Colonel Busby thinks that the list could have been compiled as early as 1710 but I have preferred to consider it to have been later.

William Ellis, of Little Gaddesden, was a prolific and popular writer on agriculture whose books contain many references to wild plants. Most of the weeds that he mentions are difficult to identify but he leaves no doubt when he is dealing with trees. Ellis's works contain a great deal of botanical information and I regret that I have not been able to give them greater attention.

In 1748 Ellis received a visitor in Pehr Kalm, a pupil of Linnaeus, who was accompanied by Lars Jungström, a gardener and fellow-countryman. Their visit, which was extended to North America, was financed by Baron Bielke, a Swedish nobleman, who wished to know more of the new farming methods advocated by Ellis. Kalm appears to have had a poor opinion of Ellis which was confirmed by other farmers of the neighbourhood. This was not so much in criticism of the principles expounded by Ellis but that he did not practise what he preached. Kalm's return to Sweden was to the joy at least of Linnaeus who is said to have been cured of an attack of gout in the excitement of examining the collection of plants which Kalm had brought back with him.

The adoption of the Linnaean system and the publication of Withering's *Botanical Arrangement* (1771), the first major botanical work written in English, did much to promote the study of plants. For the second edition of Withering, edited by J. Stokes, many Hertfordshire records were provided by Thomas J. Woodward. There were occasional records in such standard works as Hill's *British Herbal* (1756) and Curtis's *Flora Londinensis* (1777–1791). In the meantime Stanesby Alchorne (1727–1800) made some notes in a copy of Blackstone's *Specimen Botanicum* and Charles Abbot, the author of *Flora Bedfordiensis* (1798), provided a few additional records.

Lists of Hertfordshire plants, containing little that was original, appeared in Gough's edition of Camden's *Britannia* (1789) and in various travellers' accounts of their journeys. In 1805 Dawson Turner and L. W. Dillwyn published the *Botanist's Guide* which collected together much that had been published elsewhere and added some further records supplied mainly by Joseph Woods (1776–1864). This was soon followed by an expanded list compiled by Joseph Sabine (1770–1837) for Robert Clutterbuck's *History . . . of the county of Hertford* (1815). Sabine's list is what it claims to be, namely 'Rare plants found in the county' and included 88 flowering plants and four 'lichens'. Sabine, who was a Hertfordshire man and born at Tewin, must have been familiar with the ordinary plants of the Hertfordshire countryside but did not consider them to have been important enough to record elsewhere. In any case the botanists of this period did not consider that counties were suitable units for the basis of plant recording. The early botanists were no more careful than most of us are now to be sure from which county they were recording their plants and it is no surprise that Sabine should have received from James Dickson and W. Anderson a number of interesting records of plants growing at Tring, Hertfordshire, which must have grown on the hills to the south-west of that town in Buckinghamshire.

As interest in field botany grew it became popular to have a collection of dried plants known at the time as a *hortus siccus* and now more generally as a herbarium. Many of these must have been compiled in Hertfordshire. Most of them have since been destroyed but those which have survived are of great importance in the study of the flora of the county. One such collection is the Franks Herbarium, made between 1820 and 1823, of plants growing at or near Beechwood, near Flamstead. It arrived eventually at Epsom College and was presented to Luton Museum in 1954. A complete list of the specimens, not all of which came to Luton, was entered in a copy of Forster's *Botanical Pocket Book* now at the British Museum (Natural History). The handwritten title page describes it as 'List of Augustus W. Franks' Herbarium'. As Sir Augustus Wollaston Franks (1827–97) was not born until after the collection was made it could not have been compiled by him but there can be little doubt that it was made by his mother, Frederica Sebright (b. 1796). She was the daughter of Sir John Sanders Sebright, of Beechwood, who had more than a passing interest in scientific matters. Her younger sister, Emily (b. 1797), married Frederick Franks of Hatfield on 30 March 1822 and died on 4 November 1822 (Debrett makes it appear that it was Frederick Franks who died on that date). Frederick Franks then married Frederica Sebright, an irregular contract at that time, which accounts for the Beechwood collection's ending in 1823 and could account for Sir Augustus having been born at Geneva and having spent his childhood abroad. The herbarium is indeed a valuable one, consisting of excellent and carefully documented specimens.

A similar collection of plants was in the meantime being made by William John Blake (1805–75) of Danesbury, Welwyn. It was apparently begun in 1818 and carried on until 1824 after which few specimens were added. A number of Blake's plants were collected at Beechwood and some of Frederica's were from the Welwyn area. I have not been able to establish the connecting link between the Blakes and the Sebrights but it may well have been Dr. W. H. Wollaston (1766–1828), the well-known pioneer chemist and geologist who was secretary of the Royal Society. He is said to have been the godfather of Sir Augustus and it is interesting to note that William Blake's younger brother was named Henry Wollaston Blake (1815–99). On the other hand the connection may have been a political one as Sir John Sebright was a Whig member of parliament for Hertfordshire and William Blake was later member for Newport, Isle of Wight, also as a Whig – he eventually lost his seat by only two votes. In returning to Blake's botanical interests it must be noted that his herbarium, which was very carefully compiled, finally found its way to G. C. Druce who cut a number of the sheets and stamped what remained 'Herb W. J. Blake circa 1820' or scribbled on the sheets so cut that same bare information. In this way there was lost some very useful details of first records for many Hertfordshire species but it is at least certain that many of the dates given in Pryor's Flora for Blake's records are much later than they should have been. I hope elsewhere to be able to present a fuller account of the botanical work of both William Blake and Frederica Sebright.

It is possible that Blake was also connected with J. A. Hankey who collected mainly in Middlesex but also made some excursions into Hertfordshire. His specimens went to Haileybury and most have been incorporated into the Druce Herbarium.

Another collection made by Samuel Rudge (1728–1817) of undated specimens from the Elstree area is now incorporated in the British Museum (Natural History) Herbarium as is also a small collection of plants made from the neighbourhood of Sawbridgeworth between 1827 and 1836 – see Kent, D. H. (1957).

A considerable interest in field botany begins in this period among members of the Society of Friends mainly in Hertford and Hitchin. Lucy Manser, of Hertford, who made many records and compiled a useful herbarium, married Alfred Ransom, one of a family of Hitchin Quakers who were likewise botanists. Other members of the Ransom family included Maria (see Saunders, J. (1897)) and William who founded in 1846 a firm of herb growers which still continues as manufacturing chemists. Connected with the Mansers and Ransoms were other botanical Friends including Thomas Corder (see *Flora of Bedfordshire*, 23) and Septimus Warner, of Hoddesdon. The younger Ransoms attended a school at Hitchin which was opened in 1838 by a Quaker schoolmaster, Isaac Brown (1803–95), who was an excellent botanist and made field studies an important part of the curriculum. The school, which lasted until 1845, turned out some good field workers in Henry Brown (not related to Isaac), Joseph Pollard and Arthur Lister, later a well-known mycologist, whose brother Lord Lister was another scholar. After his school closed Isaac Brown left Hitchin but in addition to his previous scholars he left behind a team of workers, among them William Dawson, who were to have a continued interest in the countryside. Brown never lost his affection for Hertfordshire and when he died left his herbarium to the Hertfordshire Natural History Society. In the meantime Irvine's *London Flora* (1832) contained a few Hertfordshire records and others were added by J. D. Morell, c. 1835, on sheets from the *Botanist's Guide*.

COLEMAN AND HIS CONTEMPORARIES

In the same year that Isaac Brown started his school at Hitchin, William Higgins Coleman (c. 1816–63) compiled a manuscript list, now at the Linnean Society, of plants to be found growing in the neighbourhood of Hertford. The list, which gives details of 515 species to which more were added in 1839, is the first reasonably complete account of the flora. Coleman, who was an excellent botanist, is supposed to have expanded the list in 1839 into an unfinished Flora which I have not been able to find. He was at this time a classics master at the Bluecoat School at Hertford and was already associated with Richard Holden Webb (1805–80), Rector of Essendon. In May, 1840, they announced in a local newspaper their intention of compiling a full Flora of the county and in 1843 they published a slim volume of only twelve pages but containing a mine of information entitled 'A report on the progress made in the investigation of the Flora of Hertfordshire with a catalogue of species known or reported to have been found'. This makes reference to a list of 1839, presumably Coleman's, in which 619 species had been recorded compared with 885 they now accounted for. Both men were influenced by H. C. Watson who at this time was striving to save field botany from being an idle pastime by laying the sound foundations of a serious study. By the system for all time to be associated with his name Watson was giving a new significance to the county as a basis for plant recording. In the meantime the Coleman–Webb partnership was strained as workers elsewhere, being aware of Coleman's botanical superiority, assumed that the proposed new Flora would be his work. This supposition Coleman went to great lengths to deny (*Phytologist* 3 (1848) 320).

Coleman left Hertford in 1847 to become an assistant master at the Grammar School in Ashby-de-la-Zouch and the work on the Flora would have ceased but for the enterprise of Webb who in March, 1848, published or secured the publication of the first part of *Flora Hertfordiensis* adding Coleman's name as co-author. Co-operation was then resumed and Coleman checked the proofs of the remaining three parts, the last of which was published in January, 1849. The Flora was remarkable and in many respects made history. A geographical introduction had already been prepared by Coleman and this described a division of the county based primarily on three river drainage systems (Lea, Colne and Ouse) with these further divided into twelve approximately equal areas each with a town or large village as its centre. This was the first time that a county had been divided for the purpose of a botanical survey and most authors of future local Floras saw fit to make divisions of the areas of their study. The body of the Flora had verses at the head of each natural order, these having been sought out by Webb and probably intended to be a compromise with the old sentimental approach to the subject which the Flora itself was to play no small part in destroying. English names for the plants were given side by side with the Latin ones, the derivations of which were added. The habitats of the species were given and localities added for all but the most common plants. The various other persons who provided records were credited with their discoveries by their initials being given. There were no fewer than thirty-eight of these and an additional nine were given in a supplement, almost entirely the work of Webb, which appeared in 1851. The use of initials instead of full names was almost the only criticism that Watson could make of the Flora which it is interesting to note in conclusion claimed a total of 933 species for the county.

Both Webb and Coleman compiled herbaria and some of Coleman's specimens, on which his neat handwriting is unmistakable, have found their way into various other collections. The greatest number that I have been able to find together have been incorporated into the Bolton Museum Herbarium. Webb contributed two papers to the *Phytologist* giving additions to the Flora and in 1859 provided a second supplement to the Flora itself. He lived just long enough to become one of the pioneer members of the Hertfordshire Natural History Society when this was formed in 1879, and to the Society his widow presented his botanical correspondence, manuscripts and herbarium, which was supposed also to contain much of Coleman's material. It is much to be regretted that these valuable sources cannot be traced.

The *Flora Hertfordiensis* gave a great impetus to the study of the plants of the county and papers were contributed by Edward Edwards (1812–86) of Marford, near Wheathampstead, and Richard Chambers who wrote of the plants of the Tring area. Robert Bentley (1812–91), who was born at Hitchin and became professor of botany at King's College, London, co-operated at one stage with Webb. H. Harpur Crewe (1830–83), better known as an entomologist, was rector of Drayton Beauchamp for over twenty years and knew well the plants of the Wilstone area. Henry Fordham (1803–94), of Royston, made valuable records from that area as did also Elizabeth Twining, of Therfield, and Mrs. Morice, of Ashwell. Alicia M. Barnard who made records from the Ashwell area was a descendant of Sir J. E. Smith. Records from the St. Albans neighbourhood came from John Coales, a local doctor, and H. D. and Charlotte Henslow, brother and sister of Professor J. S. Henslow. G. C. Churchill also contributed records from Harpenden. Mrs. E. Shute, of Watford, observed the arrival of *Elodea* to the county and at Easneye T. Fowell Buxton, son of the slave emancipator, and members of his family were keen botanists.

John Ansell, who lived for a time at Hertford, gave his records to Webb and Coleman but appears mostly to have worked independently. He made a large herbarium which ultimately went to Druce and from notes on some of the sheets in the Blake Herbarium it would appear that this at some time passed through his hands.

Visitors to the county included William Pamplin (1806–99), of Soho, London, who printed the Flora and also published the *Phytologist*, and G. S. Gibson, of Saffron Walden, author of the *Flora of Essex*. From Essex too came Edward Forster (1765–1849), a banker at Woodford, who made visits over a long period of time. In the background always was W. W. Newbould (1819–86) who wrote little but seemed ever ready to help others. Of T. Walker, of Abingdon, who found *Teesdalia* in 1859, and J. Walker, of Tunbridge Wells and formerly of Hunsdon, I know nothing more.

There was less interest in the flora of the county for a brief period until 1874 when Arthur Reginald Pryor (1839–81) decided to assist Webb in preparing a new edition of *Flora Hertfordiensis* but this project was soon abandoned in favour of the preparation of an entirely new Flora. Pryor, who was born at Hatfield, was never in good health but he had private means and after he left Oxford University he was able to devote the whole of his time to Hertfordshire botany. In the short space of six years he completely revised the Flora by checking all the available literature, examining herbarium material and spending as much time as possible in the field. He played a large part in the work of the Watford Natural History Society when that body was formed in 1875 and articles and notes from his pen appeared in its Transactions and those of the Hertfordshire Natural History Society, which from 1879 continued the work of the Watford Society. Pryor was an excellent botanist having soon a reputation that went far beyond the county. It is obvious that he intended to spend many years on the Flora but alas he died at Baldock at the early age of forty-one leaving his manuscripts, herbarium and £100 to the Hertfordshire Natural History Society, obviously intending that his Flora should be published. Publication, however, presented the Society with a major difficulty as the work was not in a condition which was ready for the press. The material went first to James Britten, one of the foremost botanists of the day, but after two years he returned it having made no progress. It then passed to John Hopkinson, secretary of the Society, who in two more years had provided a geographical introduction but nothing more. It went finally to B. Daydon Jackson (1846–1927), at that time botanical secretary of the Linnean Society, and with the help of A. E. Gibbs, who performed the wearisome task of transcribing the whole of the manuscript, the work was edited and the new Flora finally published six years after Pryor's death. Neither the manuscript nor the very valuable herbarium can now be found.

Pryor's *Flora of Hertfordshire* (1887) proved to be a disappointing work compared with the *Flora Hertfordiensis* but the faults in it lie less with Pryor than in circumstances arising out of his untimely death. The twelve districts of Webb and Coleman were replaced by six based solely on the river-drainage systems. Pryor's districts are very variable in size and one, Lea, occupies almost half the county while another, Brent, is so small that very few records had been obtained from it. Daydon Jackson was a bibliophile rather than a botanist and being so kept strictly to the manuscript regardless of the difficulties that this entailed. Far too many stations are given for a number of the species, especially closely allied ones that Pryor was apparently studying. Had Pryor lived there can be no doubt it would have been a very different Flora. The most unfortunate feature is that no English names are given for the species and this omission is made worse as the scientific names which are used are sometimes so unusual that even a competent botanist is left in doubt as to the species intended. The Flora has been the standard work on its subject for eighty years and notwithstanding its weaknesses the county may consider itself fortunate that it was the work of two men as careful as Pryor and Daydon Jackson.

Pryor was assisted by a number of botanists some of whom had already helped Webb and Coleman. The Quaker influence at Hertford continued with Daniel Peirson (1819–99) and was soon to be carried on by his son, Henry Peirson (1852–1915), and son-in-law, William Graveson (1862–1939). At High Down, near Pirton, Joseph Pollard (1825–1909), one of Isaac Brown's scholars, was building up a valuable herbarium, now at Hitchin Museum, and corresponding with other botanists. Thomas Bates Blow (1854–1941), of Welwyn, provided useful records when he was not in Japan or Madagascar or British Guiana studying charophytes. From Luton James Saunders (1839–1925) made frequent excursions into the county, as did also D. Martha Higgins (c. 1856–1926). John Benbow (1821–1909) did a great deal of work in Middlesex which often extended over the county boundary to the south of Rickmansworth and Henry Groves (1855–1912), a well-known London botanist, made visits sometimes in company with T. B. Blow and at other times, alone. J. E. Littleboy sent in a number of records to the Watford Natural History Society and Ada Selby, of Aldenham, supplied useful reports for the earlier volumes of the Transactions of the Hertfordshire Natural History Society. Useful records also came from S. Pidcock, a Watford doctor.

At the turn of the century there was comparatively little work being done and not much of note had been written on the flora since Pryor's death. There was little to come for a number of years. *The Fauna and Flora of Haileybury* (1888) and Kingston's *Royston Heath* were ambitious but contained nothing new. On the other hand Eyre de Crespigny's *New London Flora* (1877) gave a useful and first-hand description of some Hertfordshire localities. For the article on Botany in the *Victoria County History of Hertfordshire* (1902) John Hopkinson was chosen as editor but only repeated what was already in Pryor. Sections on the mosses and liverworts by A. E. Gibbs and the mycetozoa by James Saunders contained much original material. In the meantime Daydon Jackson provided some useful papers on the history of botanical study in the county which have proved to be invaluable to me in writing this section.

THE INFLUENCE OF DRUCE

The comparative decline in the interest in Hertfordshire botany reflects a state of affairs existing in the country as a whole. H. C. Watson had directed attention to the need for a serious study of plant distribution and his place was now taken by G. C. Druce (1850–1932) who stressed the importance of splitting (i.e. the study of minor differences to be found in plants) and the need to add more and more alien plants. There was a danger that field botany would become once more an idle but harmless kind of pastime. The Drucean period may be said to have lasted from approximately 1901 to about 1939 and of the workers of this time who were influenced by Druce it can at least be said that they knew their plants well and were meticulously careful in their observations – they were, however, at their best when they showed some individuality.

Most of the serious work which was done in the county in this period emerged from Letchworth and Hitchin and the most distinguished botanist was without any question Joseph E. Little (1861–1935). He was an excellent classical scholar who in 1885 became headmaster of Hitchin Grammar School, a post he relinquished in 1897. He was not temperamentally suited to be a schoolmaster. From time to time he undertook occasional work at Rugby and Haileybury but continued to make his home in Hitchin. He had always been interested in natural history and from about 1910 this interest increased and he specialised in botany. His special studies were made of trees but this was closely followed by a study of the Ivel District in both Bedfordshire and Hertfordshire. He split when there seemed some purpose in splitting and he considered aliens only when they came his way. His papers are a testimony to the soundness of his work but his contribution to the *Natural History of the Hitchin Region* was a disappointment to him as he had reasonable hope that scholarship as rare as his, on a theme so important in the general purpose of the work, would merit a larger share. Little's field notes are housed at Hitchin Museum and his large and valuable herbarium is incorporated with those of many of his co-workers in the collection at the Botany School, Cambridge. Perhaps his greatest contribution to the study of Hertfordshire botany was the compilation of four manuscript volumes entitled 'Flora of Herts – Supplementary Records'. It was, however, much more than he modestly claimed it to be and it could well have been the basis for a new Flora of the county.

17

Little gathered around him a group of workers as interested in plants as he was even if they were less capable. Among these were Margaret Brown, of Luton, daughter of Henry Brown, H. C. Littlebury and his own daughter, Katherine; but the greatest enthusiasm came from the Phillips family – Mrs. Margaret S. Phillips (1857–1937), her daughter, Mrs. E. Macalister Hall (d. 1941) and her son Hugh Phillips (still living). Mr. Phillips made a large herbarium in which the critical groups and alien species were well represented and this he has kindly presented to Hitchin Museum. Little also received a number of records from persons who did not consider themselves to be botanists.

Natural history played an important part in the early development of the First Garden City at Letchworth. This has continued, thanks to the Letchworth Naturalists' Society, formed in 1908, and to the services given by the Museum which was opened in 1914 and had for many years a natural history bias. Among the earlier botanists at Letchworth mention may be made of A. G. Brunt, T. A. Dymes, who made a valuable collection of seedlings, and Richard Morse, previously of Hitchin and still living, who was for many years editor of *Country-Side*.

The attention of botanists in the Hertford area was turned mainly to the alien flora which was being made more evident as disused gravel pits became increasingly used as refuse tips. A few records came from R. Thornton Andrews (1839–1928) who had a wide interest in local affairs and played a large part in getting Hertford Museum started. William Graveson's main contribution was a chapter on plants in *The Natural History of Hertfordshire* (1925). His son, Arthur W. Graveson (still living), began in 1908 to compile a herbarium but local specimens featured less in this after he ceased to live at Hertford and his visits to the county at holiday times became of shorter duration. Notwithstanding this it is a very valuable collection for the interpretation of the flora of the county. Mr. Graveson informs me that it is his intention to present it to Bridport Museum. For a few years around the period of the First World War a number of records were made by J. W. Higgens, probably of Hertford. At Hoddesdon another Quaker, H. F. Hayllar (still living), worked with much enthusiasm from about 1910 to 1917 on the alien flora. He has continued to keep a watching brief on a few native plants.

G. C. Druce made a number of visits to Charlotte G. and Alice Trower at Stansteadbury. The two sisters were good botanists and Charlotte (1855–1928) painted flowers with a skill that delighted Druce so much that he persuaded her to have some reproduced in *British Brambles* (1929). Well-known botanists who visited the county in the Drucean period included C. E. Britton, C. E. Moss, E. F. Linton and Mrs Wedgwood but it was a local non-botanist, K. R. Wooster, who found our only Lizard Orchid. Some useful records were also made by A. H. Carter and J. E. Cooper, visitors from London.

THE ECOLOGICAL INFLUENCE

The Hertfordshire Natural History Society was very active in this period especially in initiating valuable work in many branches of natural history but its efforts were less directed than they had been before to the traditional study of field botany. It had played an important part in the establishment of the County Museum at St. Albans in 1899, with A. E. Gibbs as its first curator of natural history, and although the Society recognised no town as its headquarters it began to meet more often at St. Albans. From about 1910 to 1930 the biggest botanical influence in the Society was E. J. (now Sir Edward) Salisbury, who was born in the county at Harpenden. He joined the Society in 1908, was its secretary for six years from 1914 and later its president. Sir Edward was at this time laying the foundations for a new study of botany known as plant ecology and the papers listed in the Bibliography give some indication of the amount of this pioneer work which was done in Hertfordshire. A noteworthy achievement of the Society in the early days of this new influence was a survey entitled *St. Albans and its neighbourhood* (1911) in which an account of the vegetation of Colney Heath written by Salisbury demonstrated the application of these new methods. Plant ecology was by no means the limit of Sir Edward's botanical work in the county and papers were contributed in the more traditional pattern on the variations in Hertfordshire gentians, blue pimpernels, water-crowfoots and wood anemones. Annual reports contributed by him to the Transactions of the Society included records from various correspondents among whom were H. F. Hayllar, M. Eyles and Charles Oldham, who was primarily a conchologist.

In the early years of the Second World War H. W. Pugsley, one of the best botanists of his day, stayed for a long period with his son who was then living at Allens Green, near Sawbridgeworth. It was at about this time also that W. C. R. Watson made a number of visits to study brambles. In the meantime L. J. Tremayne and Mrs. A. White, who later lived in the county, were making annotated copies of the *London Catalogue*.

In 1941 Dr. A. G. Harrold began, with the good wishes of the Society, to collect material for a new Flora of the county but limited progress was made as he soon emigrated to Australia. The Council of the Society felt the need for a revision of the Flora which was emphasised by its own publication of excellent accounts of other organisms such as a vertebrate Fauna of the county in 1947 and P. H. Gregory's *Fungi of Hertfordshire* (1951). An approach was made in 1951 to Mr. G. L. Evans, then Curator of Hitchin Museum, who, aware of the richness of the botanical collections in his own care, undertook to begin the work again. He entered quickly into correspondence with previous workers and received from Dr. Harrold his unfinished material. A card index was made consisting of two volumes of Pryor's Flora which were cut up and pasted on the 'cards' and J. E. Little's notes were added. Mr. Evans began to build up a new herbarium to supplement those already at the museum, intending that this should house mainly the more critical groups and species which needed voucher specimens. In time he found it difficult to undertake the increased field work which became more and more necessary. My revision of the Bedfordshire Flora was finished and in February, 1955, I took over the work. I became honorary keeper of botany at Hitchin Museum as this was clearly the only centre from which the work could be directed. My task was made the easier by the large amount of work that Mr. Evans had already done. He also encouraged me to pursue the revision when at times it seemed to overwhelm me.

THE REVISION OF THE FLORA

For about four years I was finding my way in a county which was largely new to me having decided after two years that it would be impossible to search some parts of the area satisfactorily without a car. The method I finally adopted for the survey of the flora is described in some detail in a later section and it remains for me here to account for the botanical work done during the past fifteen years other than that on the Flora and to acknowledge the assistance given to me by a large number of fellow workers.

In 1955 the Natural History Society published an account by R.D.S. English of Bricket Wood and it is appropriate that this recent botanical contribution to its Transactions should be devoted to the locality which over the years has absorbed its attentions more than any other. Between 1951 and 1957 the *Handlist of plants of the London area* by D. H. Kent and J. E. Lousley appeared in the *London Naturalist*, the journal of the very active London Natural History Society, a body formed in 1913 by the amalgamation of two older societies. The London Natural History Society studies the wild life in an area twenty miles radius from St. Paul's Cathedral and this includes a great deal of Hertfordshire. The Handlist, which is the next best thing to a Flora of London (for which there is incidentally a great need), is the source of many valuable Hertfordshire records.

In the meantime the Bishop's Stortford and District Natural History Society, formed in 1935, had an active botanist in R. T. Anstead among its early members. In 1952 the Society published a Flora of the area in which it was then interested, namely a ten-miles radius of Bishop's Stortford. It has since amended the area of its activities to a block of ten-kilometre grid squares. The Welwyn Natural History Society, formed in 1962, is more recent but very active. It has also made itself concerned with an area based on the National Grid. Of considerable importance was the formation in 1964 of the Hertfordshire and Middlesex Trust for Nature Conservation. It is to be hoped that, supported by the various natural history societies, it will be able to save much of the flora that would otherwise be lost.

It remains for me to acknowledge the assistance I have received from many fellow naturalists. This is done with reference to the places at which they were living at the time of the revision of the Flora which is not necessarily where their work for the Flora was done.

ROYSTON.   Useful records have come from Mr. W. Darling who has been active in the work of the Trust. Therfield Heath has been visited for a number of years by members of the Botany School at Cambridge including Dr. (now Prof.) C. D. Pigott, Mr. P. D. Sell and Dr. S. M. Walters all of whom have contributed valuable information.

LETCHWORTH AND BALDOCK. Mr. H. and Miss D. Meyer have continued the records begun by the pioneers in Letchworth and when the present survey began they arranged these records into a tabular form. This was taken over by Mrs. H. Bowry who extended the system to include about forty tetrads and thus provided very valuable assistance. Mr. W. H. Fordham, of Odsey, great-nephew of Henry Fordham, has made records in addition to giving the financial assistance acknowledged elsewhere. Col. A. Gavin Jones and Mr. D. W. Brunt, both of Letchworth, have provided occasional records.

HITCHIN.   The revision of the Flora was watched in its early days with keen interest by the late Katherine D. Little who was able to refind many plants known to her father. The work of the flora has been intimately associated with Hitchin and useful records have been made at various stages by Mr. G. L. Evans. In more recent days Mr. F. Bentley and Mr. C. W. Burton, of Pirton, have given valuable assistance.

DUNSTABLE AND LUTON. Miss G. Elwell, of Dunstable, made herself responsible for providing complete records for the detached Watsonian vice-county portion lying to the south of Dunstable in addition to doing useful work in a wider area. Mr. L. J. Margetts, formerly of Caddington, Mr. P. Taylor, now of the Royal Botanic Gardens, Kew, and formerly of Luton, and Mr. T. C. E. Wells, also formerly of Luton and now of the Nature Conservancy, have provided records as have Mr. J. Adams and Mr. D. Stanbridge, of Luton. My own work has been centred on Luton and Mr. B. Clay accompanied me on some of my early excursions into Hertfordshire and Mr. H. B. Souster has been my companion on many occasions throughout the period of the survey.

TRING AND BERKHAMSTED. Mr. J. E. Dandy, Keeper of Botany at the British Museum (Natural History), has lived at Tring for the past twenty-five years and in addition to providing valuable records of aquatic species has contributed other useful material. Further records have come from Mr. E. G. Rance, of the Tring Museum and Mr. P. E. Richards, of West Leith, Tring. Miss H. Catchpole, of Little Gaddesden, Mr. H. E. Bannister, of Potten End, the first secretary of the Trust, and Mr. J. Wilson, of the National Trust, have introduced me to a number of sites in the Ashridge area and Mr. R. I. Sworder, of Little Dudswell, has contributed further records. Great perseverance was shown by Brig. E. A. Glennie, of Berkhamsted, to discover that *Spiranthes* still appears in the county.

HEMEL HEMPSTEAD. Mr. R. B. Benson, an entomologist of repute, lived at Felden until 1962. He supplied complete records for two tetrads and showed me some of the more important sites in the south-west of the county. Miss E. Salisbury, of Boxmoor sent many records made over a number of years and some supplemented those made by her brother, Sir Edward Salisbury.

ST. ALBANS AND HARPENDEN Mrs. J. Foster, of St. Albans, made herself responsible for complete records from four tetrads in unpromising country to the south of the city and in so doing gave valuable assistance. Further records came from Mr. J. Willé, Mr. T. G. Skinner, formerly of St. Albans County Grammar School, Mr. P. D. Coker and Mr. W. P. Gatward, now of St. Albans but who lived previously at Harpenden. Occasional records have come from members of the staff at Rothamsted including earlier members of the staff now deceased, Dr. W. Brenchley, Dr. K. Warington and Dr. H. F. Barnes. Miss J. F. Thurston, also of Rothamsted, has given me assistance with the genus *Avena*. Records have also come from Mrs. Clark and Mrs. C. Swain, of Harpenden, and Mr. J. Lovell, who has also accompanied me on a number of excursions. Mr. M. J. Richardson, formerly of Redbourn, Mrs. R. Charter, still living there, and the Rev. N. E. G. Cruttwell, formerly of Radlett and now in Papua, have provided further records.

WELWYN AND HATFIELD. Very valuable assistance and records made over a number of years came at the beginning of the survey from Dr. E. G. Kellett, of Welwyn Garden City. Mrs. L. Crewdson, of Welwyn, made some useful records in the early days of the survey and in the period immediately before the survey began additional records were being made by Miss H. D. Garside, of Welwyn Garden City. Occasional notes have come from Mr. F. A. Robinson, of Welwyn, and Dr. B. Jennings, working through the newly-formed Welwyn Natural History Society, provided many additional records for a large block of thirteen tetrads. During the past four years Mr. M. Mylecreest, of Hatfield School has completed records for two tetrads and Dr. J. Timson, previously of Hatfield College of Technology has sent in further records.

STEVENAGE AND KNEBWORTH. Dr. T. D. V. Swinscow, of Knebworth, studied the ferns of the county before his interests were turned to the bryophytes, for which he has provided a complete list for the county, and more recently to the lichens and mycetozoa. Mr. G. Bloom, also of Knebworth, and his son Michael have provided many records. Throughout the period of the survey I have had much assistance from Mr. A. Carlton Smith, of Stevenage, whose special interest has been orchids, and, in the last few years before he left Stevenage in 1964, Michael Mullin, a young botanist whose work showed great promise, gave valuable assistance. Records also came from Mr. D. Eastham, likewise of Stevenage.

HERTFORD AND WARE. At the beginning of the survey Mrs. S. C. Mortis, of Hertford, handed over to me all her very useful records made during a long period of years. Mr. A. G. Brown and Mr. H. Williams of the John Innes Institute persevered for about three years to compile a complete list of the wild plants of the Bayfordbury Estate. Mr. K. A. Beckett, previously of Bayfordbury, sent in additional records. Miss J. Eldridge, formerly of Ware Grammar School and still living at Hertford, has provided many records and introduced me to a number of sites of considerable interest. From the very beginning of the survey and throughout there has been great assistance from Dr. L., Mrs. M. and Trevor Lloyd-Evans, of Ware. Before I had a car they took me to sites I could not have visited otherwise and more recently they have accompanied my wife and me on numerous excursions and have explored independently many parts of the county. Some records attributed to Dr. Lloyd-Evans could have been claimed equally for other members of the family and their joint extensive knowledge of many branches of natural history has at no time diminished their interest in the flora.

Through the Lloyd-Evans family I have also received records from Mr. A. R. Paterson, of Woodhall Park. Further notes on plants in this area have come from Miss M. B. Bing, of Fanhams.

BISHOP'S STORTFORD. I have had much assistance from Mr. J. L. Fielding, of Little Hallingbury, whose herbarium also supplied records from previous workers in B. J. Adams and H. J. Holland. Mr. E. J. Douglas, of Hadham Hall School, has sent in useful records and others have come from Mr. J. Doyle, also of Hadham Hall School, and Mr. H. J. Killick, previously of Bishop's Stortford. In the early days of the survey some interesting records came from Mr. J. Hopkins, of Much Hadham.

BARNET AND BOREHAM WOOD. In this area records have come mainly from naturalists who have explored the small islands which still retain a natural history interest in a region given over to urban development. These workers have included Mr. D. J. Hinson, of Whetstone, Mr. J. Sparling, of East Barnet, Mrs. Clarke, of Boreham Wood, Mrs. Trayner, of Barnet, Mr. J. Mason, of East Barnet and Mr. E. B. Bangerter, also of East Barnet and formerly president of the London Natural History Society and general secretary of the Botanical Society of the British Isles.

WATFORD. Mr. B. Goater, of the Haberdashers School, supplied a complete list of records for the grounds of Aldenham Park as well as others from further afield and Mr. P. J. Ellison, of Watford, in addition to his great assistance with the maps made many interesting records. In the early days of the survey a young and promising botanist, Miss C. M. Leach, then living at Watford, made numerous valuable records. Mrs. R. Altham has kept me supplied with notes on changes in the flora on the tunnel top north of Watford, near her home and Mr. E. Grant Longman reported changes in the flora at Bushey Heath. Miss W. F. Buckle, formerly of Watford, made complete records for one tetrad.

RICKMANSWORTH. A complete list of the plants of Moor Park was made by Mr. G. Day who has also supplied further records made by his brother, F. M. Day (1890–1962), during his visits to the county. Mr. R. F. S. Hooker, of Rickmansworth, completed so fully my records for the major TQ/09 square that my subsequent visits to this interesting area have been few. Mr. R. F. Turney, of Chorley Wood, has drawn on an intimate knowledge of that neighbourhood to provide valuable records. Mrs. A. T. Peppercorn, of Amersham Common, and Mr. L. F. Stearn before he left the county have added to our knowledge of the flora of the Chorley Wood area. From a short distance over the county boundary Rex A. Graham (1915–58), then living at Northwood, made some profitable visits into Hertfordshire. Dr. A. W. Exell, who lived at Rickmansworth, provided more records.

VISITORS. The nearness of London to the open country of Hertfordshire has given an added interest in the flora and much valuable assistance has come in this way. The greatest contribution of any visitors came from Mr. P. C. and Mrs. J. Hall who devoted the greater part of two seasons to provide full records for more than forty tetrads. The psychological effect of this was as great as the physical achievement, for it encouraged me to persevere with the tetrad system of recording at a time when it seemed that the task was too great to be completed. Mr. J. C. Gardiner contented himself with the more modest number of six tetrads but the thorough way in which these were studied is reflected in the large number of records which stand to Mr. Gardiner's credit in the Flora. Mr. D. E. Allen and Mr. P. Sheasby each took over two tetrads and sent in complete records. The greatest authority on the flora of the north London fringe is Mr. D. H. Kent, whose very complete Flora of Middlesex awaits publication, and it is needless to say that many records and much valuable information have come from him. Mr. D. McClintock, a great-grandson of Thomas Fowell Buxton, has family connections still in Hertfordshire and during visits has added many records. Mr. B. F. C. Sennitt's visits have been few but profitable. Other visitors have included Mr. A. C. Jermy and Mr. J. E. Lousley while Mr. E. Milne-Redhead has joined me on a number of excursions. In more recent years Mr. B. Wurzell, having a special interest in aliens and casuals has added still more records. All of these visitors are, or have been, members of the Botanical Society of the British Isles. This society has arranged about six one-day meetings in Hertfordshire for its members and the Wild Flower Society one such meeting during the period of the survey. These meetings added many records.

Other visitors from the London area include Mr. R. M. Payne, who in the early days of the survey made many visits, the late Iolo A. Williams, Mr. J. P. M. Brenan, of the Royal Botanic Gardens, Kew, Mrs. L. M. P. Small, secretary of the London Natural History Society, Sir George Taylor, Director of the Royal Botanic Gardens, Kew, who lived for some time in the county, Mr. R. A. Boniface, Lady Anne Brewis, Miss A. M. Hugh-Smith, Mr. S. Phelp, Mr. B. Pickess, Mr. F. C. Studley and Professor E. Warmington.

Visitors from further afield include Mr. P. M. Benoit, of Barmouth, who has stayed for five holidays with us and has a keen eye especially for hybrids and the water starworts. He has added considerably to the completion of the Flora. Dr. F. Rose, of East Malling, Kent, on a number of visits to Dr. Swinscow has added many records, and useful records have also come from Mrs. B. H. S. Russell, of Duton Hill, Essex, Mr. R. S. R. Fitter, of Chinnor Hill, Oxon, Dr. L. M. Harley, now of Bristol University, Mr. L. H. Pinkess, of Birmingham, and Mr. R. P. Libbey, of King's Lynn, Norfolk.

Hertfordshire is a small English county, the area of the present administrative county being 403,803 acres. The areas of the neighbouring administrative units are:

Greater London	397,269 acres	Bedfordshire	305,056 acres
Essex	978,091 acres	Cambridgeshire	315,168 acres
Buckinghamshire	479,407 acres		

For the purposes of maintaining a continuity of records botanists have followed a system based on vice-counties which was originally adopted by H. C. Watson in 1859. Much of the usefulness of this is now lost and a new basis for recording is long overdue. The Watsonian system, which excluded detached portions of counties, was related to the county boundaries as they were in 1859 and these must still be respected when plant records are related to that system. In Watson's system Hertfordshire was designated v.c. 20 Herts. and the adjacent vice-counties were:

v.c. 18 South Essex
v.c. 19 North Essex These are the names used by Watson and
v.c. 21 Middlesex it would have saved some confusion if he
v.c. 24 Bucks. had been consistent and called v.c. 20,
v.c. 30 Bedford Hertford, and v.c. 24 Buckingham.
v.c. 29 Cambridge (which
    included the Isle of Ely) The area of the vice counties is not known.

This work is a Flora of the administrative county of Hertfordshire to which are added those parts of the Watsonian vice-county 20 Herts. which are now in other administrative areas and a small area which was in the administrative county from 1904 to 1965 and is now in Greater London (See Maps Ia and Ib and inset Map 9). The area covered by the Flora is about 421,000 acres (1,704 square kilometres).

The county has been much affected by a growth in its population which is shown in the following returns:

| | 1801 | 97,577 | 1851 | 167,298 | 1901 | 258,423 |
| | 1951 | 609,775 | 1965 (estimated) | 865,000 | | |

Notwithstanding the considerable urban development during the past hundred years some parts of the county are still rural and support a more or less natural vegetation. This has been studied in some detail with special consideration given to those factors producing change and variation. Some of these factors have been shown in maps e.g. altitude (Map 2a), rainfall (Map 2b) and river drainage (Map 3a).

The geology of the county is on the one hand simple, as the solid rock throughout is Chalk except for small areas in the extreme north and west, where it is replaced by the Gault. On the other hand the surface geology is most complicated as the Chalk is overlain in the greater part of the county by various deposits which form no simple pattern. Mr. P. Evans is in the process of preparing a much-needed interpretation of the geology of the county and has in the meantime assisted me considerably in presenting a geological basis for the flora. The soils follow very closely the geological formations and these have been described elsewhere by Thomasson and Avery (1963). Their map is unfortunately not related to the National Grid and takes no account of the soils of the built-up areas in which a number of wild plants grow.

Important as are the various physical factors in affecting plant growth and distribution in Hertfordshire they are of little consequence compared with the influence of man. In the more rural parts of the county the somewhat intense cultivation seriously limits the growth of wild plants and a native vegetation survives only in woodland, old pasture and roadside verges. The urban areas have usually some derelict land and waste places and in these it is often difficult to decide whether native plants are survivors or invaders. A study of Map 56g will show that the more floristically rich parts of the county are usually those of the greatest urban development where flooded gravel pits, rubbish dumps, derelict building sites, cemeteries and town gardens give a great assortment of plants of at most only a semi-permanent nature.

The survey of the vegetation which follows is based on a division of the county, made for me by Mr. P. Evans, into six approximately equal areas in each of which one geological formation is a prominent feature. These regions (see Maps 4–9) are by no means homogeneous and they have been adopted, firstly, because they enable a very reasonable interpretation to be made of the distribution of a number of the more interesting species of the county and, secondly, because they avoid the very large differences in size of divisions, such as those used by Pryor, based on river drainage systems.

THE HABITAT STUDIES

The vegetation of each of the regions has been studied mainly by a system of Habitat Studies. Each of these was made of an area of five yards radius which was visited at two different times of the year. A total of over 450 species was recorded in the various studies, most of them natives, and it is hoped that the account given here of the plant associations of most of the more important species of the county may be of greater future significance than it is now.

Abbreviations used in the Habitat Studies

42/M etc.	A tetrad reference (see Maps 4, 5, 7, 8)	l. ab	abundant in one part	r-o	rare to occasional
L. Ll-E.	Dr. L. Lloyd-Evans	f	frequent	L	in one part only
M. Ll-E.	Mrs. L. Lloyd-Evans	lf	frequent in one part	1 (2) etc.	one (two) plant(s), etc.
C. M. D.	Mrs. J. G. Dony	f-o	frequent to occasional	M	on the margin
l. dom.	locally dominant	o	occasional	<	not more than
ab	abundant	r	rare	sp.	an unidentified species

The Natural Regions

A. THE CHALK REGION (Map 4)

This forms two detached portions the larger one of which is in the extreme north of the county and the smaller in the extreme west. In addition to the Chalk it includes two small areas of Gault, one in the neighbourhood of Mob's Hole, the most northerly point in the county, and the other in the valley of the R. Thame near to Long Marston. I have not concerned myself with the various zones of the Chalk as these seem to have little effect on the flora. The Chalk and the Gault give rise to comparable vegetations and what variety there is appears to be mainly the result of drift deposits (principally Glacial Gravel) and land usage.

The larger portion of the Chalk Region lies between Hexton and Royston. It is mainly cultivated but chalk downland is to be seen at its best in Hertfordshire in the long escarpment to the south-west of Royston known as Therfield (or Royston) Heath. Much of the downland here is dominated by *Bromus erectus* which has increased considerably in recent years and the floristically richer parts of the heath are at each end i.e. at Church Hill towards the western limit and near the rifle range to the south of Royston. Two habitat studies were made on Therfield Heath.

The name of the parish is given only if it does not appear in the name given for the Habitat Study.

Habitat Study 1   Therfield Heath
TL/342 404 (34/K)   Alt. 320 ft.
                         Soil: Middle Chalk (pH 8·0)
Surveyed: 10 June 1962 with C. M. D., 9 Aug. 1962. The study was made about twenty yards above a track made by horses exercising from Royston. The point chosen was immediately below the tumuli on the crest of the hill where there is a gradual north-facing slope with a gradient of about 1 in 8 to the main road below. On the margin of the study there was some disturbance caused by the horses but the only apparently intruding species was *Diplotaxis muralis*.
Abundant: Bromus erectus.
Frequent: Dactylis glomerata, Daucus carota, Helianthemum nummularium, Koeleria cristata, Plantago lanceolata, Sanguisorba minor, Thalictrum minus.
Occasional: Agrostis stolonifera, Briza media, Cirsium acaulon, Diplotaxis muralis, Festuca ovina, Filipendula vulgaris, Linum catharticum, Lotus corniculatus, Plantago media, Scabiosa columbaria.
Rare: Campanula rotundifolia, Carex flacca, Centaurea nigra, Helictotrichon pratense, Hippocrepis comosa, Lolium perenne, Polygonum convolvulus, Primula veris, Prunella vulgaris, Ranunculus bulbosus, Reseda lutea, Rumex acetosa, Sonchus sp.

The second study was made on Church (or Pen) Hill.

Habitat Study 2   Church Hill, Therfield Heath
TL/332 395 (33/J)   Alt. 300 ft.
                         Soil: Middle Chalk (pH 7·9)
Surveyed: 9 June 1962 with C. M. D., 9 Aug. 1962 with J. Russell and C. M. D. The study was made about twelve yards from the top of the hill on its south-facing slope.

There is a steep gradient here of about 1 in 4 and at the time of the survey there was evidence of considerable rabbit grazing.
Frequent: Asperula cynanchica, Briza media, Bromus erectus, Campanula glomerata, Carlina vulgaris (L), Linum catharticum, Sanguisorba minor, Scabiosa columbaria, Thesium humifusum, Thymus drucei.
Occasional: Astragalus danicus, Campanula rotundifolia, Cirsium acaulon, Festuca ovina (o-f), Helianthemum nummularium, Hieracium pilosella, Hippocrepis comosa, Koeleria cristata, Lotus corniculatus, Plantago media, Prunella vulgaris, Pulsatilla vulgaris (o-f), Senecio jacobaea.
Rare: Bellis perennis (1), Bromus mollis, Carex caryophyllea, C. flacca, Centaurea nigra (1), Chrysanthemum leucanthemum, Crataegus monogyna (1) 1 in., Filipendula vulgaris, Galium verum, Helictotrichon pubescens, Leontodon hispidus, Ophrys apifera (1), Picris hieracioides, Pimpinella saxifraga, Plantago lanceolata, Polygala vulgaris, Primula veris, Ranunculus bulbosus, Senecio integrifolius.

Most of the less steep slopes of the Chalk have at some time been cultivated but on being allowed to return to pasture they develop a vegetation similar in many respects to the longer established chalk downland. The previously disturbed areas when no longer grazed revert quickly to scrub.

Habitat Study 3 Chalk slope below Tingley Wood, Pirton
TL/135 305 (13/F)   Alt. 420 ft.
                         Soil: Middle Chalk (pH 7·3)
Surveyed: 10 May 1962 with L. Ll.-E., 19 July 1962 with P. M. Benoit and C. M. D. This study was made on the west aspect where there is a slight gradient of about 1 in 10. Immediately to the south of the site chosen there is a depression made by a disused chalkpit.
Frequent: Asperula cynanchica, Briza media, Cirsium acaulon, Festuca ovina, Koeleria cristata, Leontodon hispidus, Lotus corniculatus, Sanguisorba minor (f-ab), Viola hirta.
Occasional: Campanula rotundifolia, Carex flacca, Filipendula vulgaris, Galium verum, Helianthemum nummularium, Helictotrichon pratense, Linum catharticum, Ononis repens, Plantago lanceolata, Thymus pulegioides.
Rare: Acer pseudo-platanus (1) 6 in., Agrimonia eupatoria (1), Agrostis stolonifera, Brachypodium sylvaticum, Bromus erectus, Campanula glomerata, Carlina vulgaris, Centaurea nigra, Chrysanthemum leucanthemum, Crataegus monogyna 1 ft., Euphrasia nemorosa, Galium mollugo, Gentianella amarella, Heracleum sphondylium (1), Hieracium pilosella, Knautia arvensis (M), Medicago lupulina, Pastinaca sativa, Polygala vulgaris, Primula veris, Prunella vulgaris, Quercus robur 6 in., Rosa canina, Scabiosa columbaria, Taraxacum officinale (1), Viburnum lantana 1 ft.

An area of planted woodland felled about 1945 reverted rapidly to scrub and provided an interesting habitat. The site was unfortunately cleared and ploughed in 1966. As the bare chalk produces little humus colonist species survive in the felled-woodland habitat a long time before giving way to the native flora.

Habitat Study 4   Bury Plantation, Wallington
TL/277 345 (23/S)   Alt. 335 ft.
           Soil: Middle Chalk (pH 7·4)
Surveyed: 24 June 1962 with C. M. D., 25 Aug. 1962 with C. M. D. The site of this study was reached by following the main trackway from the entrance at the south-west corner of the plantation for a distance of about 80 yards and then proceeding along a pathway to the right for a further 30 yards. At the time of the study there was evidence of intensive grazing by rabbits.
Frequent: Agrimonia eupatoria, Arrhenatherum elatius, Centaurea scabiosa, Clinopodium vulgare, Festuca rubra, Hypericum perforatum, Leontodon hispidus, Linum catharticum, Pimpinella saxifraga.
Occasional: Agrostis stolonifera, Crataegus monogyna <2 ft., Epilobium angustifolium, Knautia arvensis, Plantago lanceolata, Poa pratensis, Senecio erucifolius, Trisetum flavescens, Vicia hirsuta.
Rare: Achillea millefolium, Cerastium fontanum, Cirsium vulgare, Dactylis glomerata (1), Daucus carota, Erigeron acer, Euphrasia nemorosa, Galium mollugo, G. verum, Gentianella amarella, Hieracium pilosella, Holcus lanatus, Lathyrus pratensis, Ligustrum vulgare <3 ft., Linaria vulgaris, Medicago lupulina, Orobanche elatior, Phleum bertolonii, Potentilla reptans, Prunella vulgaris, Rosa canina, Rubus sp., Sanguisorba minor, Senecio jacobaea, Silene vulgaris, Swida sanguinea, Torilis japonica, Veronica arvensis, Vicia angustifolia.

Similar conditions are produced in disused chalkpits of which there are many in the county. The nature of the chalk and the age of the pit make considerable differences to the vegetation. Two contrasting sites were studied but each illustrated how conducive such habitats are to orchids.

Habitat Study 5   disused chalkpit, Ashwell
TL/251 396 (23/P)   Alt. 180 ft.
           Soil: Lower Chalk (pH 7·5)
Surveyed: 7 July 1962 with C. M. D., 8 Sept. 1962 with C. M. D. The site of this study was reached by entering the pit by a gap in the hedge on the eastern side and then proceeding along a path running parallel to the hedge for a distance of about fifteen yards. Hawthorn scrub had developed to the extent of making much of the area impenetrable.
Frequent: Centaurea nigra, C. scabiosa, Convolvulus arvensis (L), Leontodon hispidus, Linum catharticum (L), Lotus corniculatus, Ononis repens, Trisetum flavescens, Vicia cracca.
Occasional: Achillea millefolium, Arrhenatherum elatius, Briza media, Bromus erectus, Crataegus monogyna <6 ft., Galium mollugo, Holcus lanatus, Plantago lanceolata, P. media, Primula veris, Trifolium pratense, Veronica chamaedrys (L).
Rare: Agrimonia eupatoria, Agropyron repens, Anacamptis pyramidalis, Campanula glomerata, Carex flacca, Cirsium acaulon, C. arvense, Dactylis glomerata, Festuca rubra, Galium aparine, G. verum, Gymnadenia conopsea, Heracleum sphondylium, Knautia arvensis, Medicago lupulina, Pastinaca sativa, Poa pratensis, Polygala vulgaris, Potentilla reptans, Sanguisorba minor, Prunella vulgaris, Prunus spinosa <2 ft., Rosa canina, Sambucus nigra, Scabiosa columbaria, Silene vulgaris, Tamus communis (M), Torilis japonica, Urtica dioica, Vicia sepium.

Habitat Study 6   Grove chalkpit, Hitchin
TL/192 308 (13/V)   Alt. 200 ft.   Soil: Lower Chalk (pH 7·9)
Surveyed: 9 June 1962 with J. Lovell, 8 Aug. 1962 with C. M. D. This study was made on the flat base of the old

quarry and there was evidence that the limited vegetation had been affected by fire in the winter of 1961–2. The pit was taken over by Hitchin U.D.C. for a refuse tip in 1965 and the natural vegetation has already disappeared.
Frequent: Agrostis stolonifera (f–l.ab), Arrhenatherum elatius, Daucus carota, Linum catharticum, Melilotus altissima, Pastinaca sativa, Trifolium pratense, Tussilago farfara.
Occasional: Achillea millefolium, Dactylorhiza praetermissa, Leontodon hispidus, Plantago lanceolata, Picris hieracioides, Poa angustifolia, Prunella vulgaris, Senecio erucifolius.
Rare: Anagallis arvensis, Anthyllis vulneraria, Blackstonia perfoliata, Calystegia sp., Centaurea nigra, Cirsium arvense, Convolvulus arvensis, Crataegus monogyna <1 ft., Cynosurus cristatus, Dactylis glomerata, Festuca rubra, Hieracium pilosella, Holcus lanatus, Hypericum perforatum, Leontodon autumnalis, Linaria vulgaris, Medicago lupulina, Orobanche minor, Poa compressa, Rubus sp., Salix caprea (2) <10 ft., Sonchus asper, Sinapis arvensis, Taraxacum officinale.

Some sites on the Chalk are in a constant state of disturbance but this does not prevent unusual species surviving under such conditions. This is the case with the wind-swept ancient earthwork, Arbury Banks (23/U), which provides the only known Hertfordshire station for *Seseli libanotis*. Wilbury Hill, another earthwork, is on a road junction on the outskirts of Letchworth and is the western limit in Britain of *Phleum phleoides*.

Habitat Study 7   Wilbury Hill, Letchworth
TL/201 325 (23/B)   Alt. 275 ft.
           Soil: Glacial Sand overlying Middle Chalk (pH 7·6)
Surveyed: 9 June 1962 with J. Lovell, 8 Aug. 1962 with C. M. D. This study was made at about the middle of the bank on the eastern side of the road. The sides of the bank at this point slope steeply on both faces.
Abundant: Koeleria cristata.
Frequent: Festuca rubra, Galium verum, Scabiosa columbaria.
Occasional: Agrostis stolonifera, Helictotrichon pratense, H. pubescens, Lolium perenne, Lotus corniculatus, Medicago lupulina, Phleum bertolonii, Plantago lanceolata, P. media, Poa pratensis, P. trivialis, Ranunculus bulbosus, Rumex acetosa, Senecio jacobaea, Trisetum flavescens.
Rare: Achillea millefolium, Arenaria serpyllifolia, Arrhenatherum elatius, Bromus erectus, B. mollis, B. sterilis, Campanula rotundifolia, Centaurea nigra, C. scabiosa, Cirsium acaulon, Crepis capillaris, C. taraxacifolia, Cynosurus cristatus, Dactylis glomerata, Festuca ovina, Galium aparine, Hieracium pilosella, Hippocrepis comosa, Ononis repens, Papaver dubium, Phleum phleoides, Polygonum aviculare, Prunus spinosa < 3ft., Reseda lutea, Rubus sp., Senecio vulgaris, Sisymbrium officinale, Taraxacum officinale, Tripleurospermum maritimum, Vicia angustifolia.

There are few other places in this Region where there is an established turf for while there is plenty of meadowland on the flat plain of the Gault at Hinxworth and Ashwell End it has all been recently improved. Relics of what was once an interesting flora may still be seen on some roadside verges. By contrast the meadows by the River Purwell at Hitchin have an undisturbed vegetation.

Habitat Study 8   Purwell Meadow, Hitchin
TL/200 299 (22/E)   Alt. 180 ft.
           Soil: Alluvium overlying Lower Chalk (pH 7·7)
Surveyed: 9 June 1962 with J. Lovell, 31 July 1962 with C. M. D. This study was made 220 yards up-stream from

the bridge crossing the main road and six yards above the stream on its right bank.

Frequent: Centaurea nigra, Cynosurus cristatus, Holcus lanatus, Juncus inflexus (l.ab), Plantago lanceolata, Ranunculus acris, Trifolium repens.

Occasional: Agrostis stolonifera, Bellis perennis, Briza media, Carex hirta, Cerastium fontanum, Cirsium palustre, Leontodon taraxacoides, Lolium perenne, Lotus corniculatus (L), Medicago lupulina, Mentha aquatica (M), Poa trivialis, Potentilla anserina (L), Rumex acetosa, Trifolium pratense.

Rare: Achillea millefolium, Arrhenatherum elatius, Carex flacca, C. spicata, Cirsium arvense, Dactylis glomerata, Deschampsia cespitosa, Epilobium parviflorum, Equisetum arvense, Festuca pratensis, Galium verum, Helictotrichon pubescens, Lathyrus pratensis, Myosotis scorpioides, Phleum bertolonii, P. pratense, Plantago major, Prunella vulgaris, Ranunculus repens, Scrophularia auriculata (M), Taraxacum officinale, Trisetum flavescens.

Habitats of the kind just described merge with a high water level into marsh or swamp. Such conditions are produced on the left bank of the river almost opposite the site of the previous study.

Habitat Study 9   marshy depression, River Purwell, Hitchin
TL/200 299 (22/E)   Alt. 180 ft.
        Soil: Alluvium overlying Lower Chalk (pH 7·3)
Surveyed: 9 June 1962 with J. Lovell, 31 July 1962 with C. M. D. This study was made at a point continuing the line of the fence by the watercress beds for a distance of six yards.

Frequent: Equisetum palustre (l. ab), Galium uliginosum, Juncus subnodulosus (l. ab), Lotus uliginosus, Rumex acetosa.

Occasional: Carex acutiformis, Cerastium fontanum, Holcus lanatus, Juncus inflexus, Lathyrus pratensis, Poa trivialis, Valeriana dioica, Vicia cracca.

Rare: Alopecurus geniculatus, Anthoxanthum odoratum (M), Arrhenatherum elatius, Carex disticha, C. hirta, C. nigra, Centaurea nigra, Cirsium arvense, C. palustre, Epilobium parviflorum, Festuca pratensis, F. rubra, Filipendula ulmaria, Helictotrichon pubescens (M), Lychnis flos-cuculi, Nasturtium officinale, Potentilla anserina, P. erecta, Ranunculus acris, R. ficaria, R. repens, Rumex conglomeratus, R. crispus, Scrophularia auriculata, Senecio vulgaris, Sonchus arvensis, S. oleraceus, Stellaria media, Trifolium pratense, Triglochin palustris, Veronica beccabunga.

The largest marshy area in association with the Hertfordshire chalk is Oughtonhead Common (13/Q) which is rapidly drying out. Its few remaining wet portions have a vegetation similar to that described above. Small marshy areas of a like nature may be seen at Old Ramerick Bottom (13/S) and Ickleford Common (13/W). The most interesting marsh in this part of the county is one still fortunately preserved in the middle of Letchworth on Norton Common.

Habitat Study 10   marsh, Norton Common, Letchworth
TL/218 332 (23/B) Alt. 220 ft. Soil: Boulder Clay (pH 7·5)
Surveyed: 21 June 1962 with H. and D. Meyer, 5 Sept. 1962 with H. and D. Meyer and C. M. D. This study was made at a point twenty-five yards along the ditch from the end of the marshy area.

Abundant: Hydrocotyle vulgaris (L), Molinia caerulea.

Frequent: Juncus subnodulosus, Oenanthe lachenalii, Valeriana dioica.

Occasional: Arrhenatherum elatius, Dactylis glomerata, Deschampsia cespitosa, Festuca arundinacea, F. rubra,

Galium uliginosum, Lathyrus pratensis, Mentha aquatica, Poa pratensis, Potentilla erecta, Rubus sp., Vicia cracca.

Rare: Agropyron repens, Centaurea nigra, Cirsium arvense, Dactylorhiza praetermissa, Equisetum palustre, Heracleum sphondylium, Listera ovata, Ophioglossum vulgatum, Pastinaca sativa, Potentilla anserina, P. reptans, Sonchus arvensis, Tamus communis, Tussilago farfara.

Woods are few in the larger portion of the Chalk Region. Fox Covert, adjoining Church Hill (Habitat Study 2), is a rare example of beech woodland but it was originally a mixed plantation of pine and beech. It is now fortunately managed by the Hertfordshire and Middlesex Trust for Nature Conservation as a nature reserve. Its limited flora includes *Cephalanthera damasonium* and *Sanicula europaea*.

Drift deposits overlying the Chalk are frequently wooded. Ravensburgh Castle (12/E), an earthwork mainly on a shallow deposit of Glacial Gravel, is planted with trees as are the sides of the large valley to the east of it. A native flora survives on the margin of the woodland and in clearings within it. Tingley Wood which supports a mixed flora is on a pocket of Boulder Clay overlying the Chalk.

Habitat Study 11 woodland ride, Tingley Wood, Pirton
TL/138 303 (13/F) Alt. 400 ft. Soil: Boulder Clay (pH8·0)
Surveyed: 10 May 1962 with L. Ll.-E., 19 July 1962 with P. M. Benoit and C. M. D. This study was made 75 yards along a wide grassy ride to the west of the main junction of rides in the wood. The ride studied is twelve yards wide at this point and marginal species probably more properly belonged to the woodland.

Frequent: Agrimonia eupatoria, Clinopodium vulgare, Glechoma hederacea (f-ab), Hypericum hirsutum, Potentilla anserina, Ranunculus repens, Veronica chamaedrys.

Occasional: Acer pseudo-platanus 1 ft., Ajuga reptans, Bromus ramosus (M), Centaurea nigra, Crataegus monogyna (seedlings), Dactylis glomerata, Fragaria vesca, Mercurialis perennis (M), Ononis repens, Plantago lanceolata, Poa trivialis, Potentilla reptans, Rubus sp., Urtica dioica (M), Viola hirta.

Rare: Acer campestre (1M) 10 ft., Achillea millefolium, Agrostis stolonifera, Alopecurus myosuroides, Arrhenatherum elatius, Bellis perennis, Brachypodium sylvaticum, Bromus sterilis, Carex spicata (1), Centaurea scabiosa, Cerastium fontanum, Corylus avellana (1) 12 ft., Crataegus monogyna (1 M) 6 ft., Euonymus europaeus (1 M) 8 ft., Festuca rubra, Galium aparine, G. mollugo, G. verum, Geranium dissectum (1), Geum urbanum, Helianthemum nummularium, Holcus lanatus, Knautia arvensis (1), Leontodon autumnalis (1), L. hispidus, Luzula campestris, Matricaria matricarioides (1), Medicago lupulina, Odontites verna, Origanum vulgare, Plantago major, P. media, Phleum bertolonii, Potentilla sterilis, Primula vulgaris, Prunella vulgaris, Quercus cerris (1 M) 10 ft., Rosa canina, Rubus caesius, Sanguisorba minor, Sanicula europaea, Senecio jacobaea, Silene vulgaris (1), Swida sanguinea (1 M) 15 ft., Taraxacum officinale, Trifolium pratense, Trisetum flavescens, Ulmus sp. (1 M) 30 ft., Viola riviniana (M).

The very large number of species recorded in the above study should be compared with the few obtained in a nearby one.

Habitat Study 12   Tingley Wood, Pirton
TL/138 303 (13/F) Alt. 400 ft. Soil: Boulder Clay (pH 5·5)
Surveyed: 10 May 1962 with L. Ll.-E., 28 July 1962. This study was made twenty yards to the north of Habitat Study 11. Here woodland conditions alone with oak (*Quercus robur*) and elm (*Ulmus* sp.) apparently the only trees and growing to a height of 75 ft.
Dominant: Mercurialis perennis.

Frequent: Endymion non-scriptus, Poa trivialis.
Occasional: Anemone nemorosa, Galeobdolon luteum, Ranunculus ficaria, Urtica dioica (L).
Rare: Acer pseudo-platanus < 2 ft., Arctium sp., Crataegus monogyna < 2 in., Sambucus nigra < 8 ft., Sanicula europaea, Viola hirta.

One of the most striking features of the Chalk Region is the weed flora of its arable fields. Given suitable conditions there may appear abundantly the small-flowered fumitories (*Fumaria micrantha, F. parviflora* and *F. vaillantii*), the fluellens (*Kickxia spuria* and *K. elatine*), *Papaver hybridum, Valerianella dentata, Legousia hybrida, Silene noctiflora* and *Ajuga chamaepitys*. To the east of Baldock the genuine cornflower (*Centaurea cyanus*) appears regularly as a cornfield weed and close by on a roadside verge *Lepidium latifolium* has been long established. Roadside verges and the tops of disused chalkpits are the usual habitats of the greater broomrape (*Orobanche elatior*). The most noteworthy colonist of the Chalk is *Bunium bulbocastanum* which appears in arable fields but more frequently in rough chalky pastures.

The smaller portion of the Chalk Region stretches westwards from the village of Aldbury to the county boundary. The valleys here are more pronounced and although the area is small it contains some of the most attractive and botanically more interesting parts of the Hertfordshire countryside.

The flat plain of the Gault in the valley of the R. Thame, which has for convenience been included in the Region, has some well-established pasture with a flora rarely seen elsewhere in the county.

Habitat Study 13 meadow, Long Marston, Tring Rural
SP/886 167 (81/Y) Alt. 260 ft. Soil: Gault (pH 6·1)
Surveyed: 15 May 1963 with C. M. D., 18 Aug. 1963 with C. M. D. This study was made eight yards inside the field from the fence by the railway and opposite the first telegraph pole beyond the disused station.
Frequent: Alopecurus pratensis, Anthoxanthum odoratum (f-ab), Cynosurus cristatus, Plantago lanceolata, Ranunculus acris, Trifolium pratense.
Occasional: Agrostis stolonifera, Bellis perennis, Centaurea nigra, Dactylis glomerata (o-f), Deschampsia cespitosa, Holcus lanatus, Leontodon autumnalis, Lotus corniculatus (o-f), Luzula campestris (o-f), Ranunculus bulbosus, Rumex acetosa, Saxifraga granulata, Taraxacum officinale, Trifolium repens (o-f), Trisetum flavescens.
Rare: Achillea millefolium, Agrostis tenuis, Arrhenatherum elatius, Briza media, Cardamine pratensis, Carex caryophyllea, C. flacca, Chrysanthemum leucanthemum, Festuca pratensis, Filipendula ulmaria, Helictotrichon pubescens, Hypochoeris radicata, Leontodon hispidus, L. taraxacoides, Lolium perenne, Phleum bertolonii, Plantago major, P. media, Primula veris, Prunella vulgaris.

The Chalk itself forms a fine escarpment to be seen at its best in this part of the county at Aldbury Nowers a well known hill above Tring Station.

Habitat Study 14 Aldbury Nowers
SP/950 132 (91/L) Alt. 575 ft.
Soil: Middle Chalk (pH 7·7)
Surveyed: 8 June 1962 with C. M. D., 11 Aug. 1962 with D. E. Allen and C. M. D. This study was made six yards south-west from a dip in the path alongside the wood. The hill here was rabbit-grazed. It has a south-west aspect and a gradient of about 1 in 4.
Abundant: Sanguisorba minor.
Frequent: Briza media, Festuca rubra (f-ab), Galium verum, Helianthemum nummularium (f-ab), Koeleria cristata (f-ab).

Occasional: Asperula cynanchica (o-lf), Bromus erectus, Centaurea nigra, Cirsium acaulon, Festuca ovina, Helictotrichon pratense (L), H. pubescens, Hieracium pilosella, Leontodon hispidus, Plantago lanceolata, P. media, Polygala vulgaris, Prunella vulgaris, Scabiosa columbaria, Thymus pulegioides.
Rare: Achillea millefolium, Aesculus hippocastanum (1) 6 in., Agrimonia eupatoria, Arenaria serpyllifolia, Brachypodium sylvaticum, Bromus sterilis, Campanula rotundifolia, Carex caryophyllea, C. flacca, Cirsium vulgare, Clinopodium vulgare, Crataegus monogyna < 3 ft., Filipendula vulgaris, Fragaria vesca, Fraxinus excelsior < 6 in., Galium mollugo, Linum catharticum, Lolium perenne, Origanum vulgare (1), Pimpinella saxifraga, Quercus robur (1) 3 in., Ranunculus bulbosus, R. repens (1), Rosa sp. 1 ft., Senecio jacobaea, Sonchus oleraceus (1), Taraxacum officinale, Veronica chamaedrys, Viola hirta.

By a roadside to the south of Tring there is a small hill with a very different flora from the above.

Habitat Study 15 Oddy Hill, Wigginton
SP/934 109 (91/F) Alt. 600 ft.
Soil: Middle Chalk (pH 7·9)
Surveyed: 8 June 1962 with C. M. D., 11 Aug. 1962 with D. E. Allen and C. M. D. This study was made on a north-facing gradual slope ten yards from a bank in a flattened hollow on the top of the hill. There was a short close turf on the hill but no visible signs of grazing.
Frequent: Asperula cynanchica, Briza media, Cirsium acaulon, Koeleria cristata, Linum catharticum, Lotus corniculatus (o-f), Sanguisorba minor.
Occasional: Campanula rotundifolia, Carex caryophyllea, C. flacca, Carlina vulgaris, Euphrasia pseudo-kerneri, Gentianella amarella, G. germanica, Helictotrichon pratense, Leontodon hispidus, Pimpinella saxifraga (o-f), Plantago media, Polygala vulgaris, Prunella vulgaris, Scabiosa columbaria, Thymus pulegioides.
Rare: Agrostis stolonifera, Anthoxanthum odoratum, Bellis perennis, Crataegus monogyna (1) 1 in., Festuca ovina, Fraxinus excelsior < 3 in., Helictotrichon pubescens, Hieracium pilosella, Listera ovata (1), Medicago lupulina, Plantago lanceolata, Ranunculus bulbosus, R. repens, Rosa sp. (1), Trifolium pratense.

There is very little woodland in this part of the Region but it is of an excellent quality. Beech wood which has developed on the top of Aldbury Nowers supports an interesting flora.

Habitat Study 16 wood, Aldbury Nowers
SP/954 133 (91/L) Alt. 600 ft.
Soil: Middle Chalk with washdown of Clay-with-Flints (pH 4·8)
Surveyed: 8 June 1962 with C. M. D., 11 Aug. 1962 with D. E. Allen and C. M. D. This study was reached by proceeding 90 yards along the path from the gate at the southern entrance to the wood and then six yards to the east of the path.
Frequent: Galium odoratum (L), Mercurialis perennis.
Occasional: Anemone nemorosa, Crataegus monogyna (seedlings), Endymion non-scriptus, Epilobium montanum, Fraxinus excelsior (seedlings), Melica uniflora, Rubus sp., Rumex sanguineus, Viola riviniana.
Rare: Acer pseudo-platanus (1) seedling, Ajuga reptans, Arctium sp. (1), Brachypodium sylvaticum, Carex sylvatica, Circaea lutetiana, Crataegus monogyna (1) 20 ft., Deschampsia cespitosa, Epilobium angustifolium, Fagus sylvatica (2) 40 ft., Festuca gigantea, Fragaria vesca, Fraxinus excelsior (2) 50 ft., Geranium robertianum. Geum urbanum, Glechoma hederacea, Ilex aquifolium (2) < 1 ft., Oxalis acetosella, Poa nemoralis, Quercus robur

(3) 40 ft., Rosa canina, Swida sanguinea < 2 ft., Ulmus sp. (1) 6 in.

The finest beech woods in the county are to be seen south of Tring in Grove and Stubbings Woods. They are fortunately owned by Tring Urban District Council and it is to be hoped that because of this they may be saved for all time.

Habitat Study 17   Stubbings Wood, Tring Urban
SP/917 100 (91/A)   Alt. 575 ft.
          Soil: Middle Chalk (pH 7·7)
Surveyed: 6 May 1962 with P. C. and J. Hall and C. M. D., 21 July 1962 with P. M. Benoit and C. M. D. This study was made on the west side of a rough road passing through the wood in a deep ravine. The exact site was at the top of the ravine ten yards below the level of a telegraph pole – the only one actually in the ravine itself. There is a gradual slope of about 1 in 10 away from the roadway. The habitat supported little ground vegetation.
Locally abundant: Hedera helix, Rubus sp.
Frequent: Galium odoratum (L), Sanicula europaea, Viola riviniana,
Occasional: Brachypodium sylvaticum, Bromus benekenii, B. ramosus, Festuca gigantea, Mercurialis perennis, Poa nemoralis.
Rare: Acer campestre (M) 10 ft., Acer pseudo-platanus <1 ft., Aesculus hippocastanum (2) <2 ft., Anemone nemorosa, Anthriscus sylvestris, Arrhenatherum elatius, Arctium sp., Circaea lutetiana, Clematis vitalba, Corylus avellana (1) 6 ft., Crataegus monogyna <2 ft, Daphne laureola (1) 2 ft., Deschampsia cespitosa, Epilobium angustifolium, E. montanum, Epipactis leptochila (3), Fagus sylvatica (3) 50 ft., Fragaria vesca, Fraxinus excelsior <3 ft., Geum urbanum, Lolium perenne, Mycelis muralis, Poa annua, Prunus avium <1 ft., Ranunculus acris, Rosa arvensis, Senecio jacobaea, Solanum dulcamara, Sorbus aria (1) 3 ft., Stachys sylvatica, Swida sanguinea < 3 ft., Tamus communis, Taraxacum officinale, Tussilago farfara, Veronica chamaedrys, Viburnum lantana <4 ft., Viola reichenbachiana.

No less interesting than the downland and woodland flora of this part of the Chalk Region is its aquatic and marsh vegetation. Much of this arises from the reservoirs and the canals which they were made to serve. The Cow Roast Lock in the Tring Gap is the highest point in the Grand Union Canal system and it is to keep up the level of water in the canals that the reservoirs are necessary. The reservoirs have been made into the only National Nature Reserve in the county but its merits are supposed to be ornithological rather than botanical. To the west of Wilstone Reservoir and unfortunately outside the reserve is a small marshy field known as Rushy Meadow. It is possible that it is a remnant of a once larger marsh which existed before the reservoir was made. On the other hand the farmer who owns the field considers that it is seepage of water from the reservoir that has made the meadow wetter than it would otherwise have been. However it was caused it is the only marsh of its kind in the county. Two studies were made, one in a drier part of the meadow and the other in a wet depression.

Habitat Study 18   Rushy Meadow, Tring Rural
SP/903 127 (91/B)   Alt. 340 ft.
          Soil: Lower Chalk (pH 7·8)
Surveyed: 6 May 1962 with P. C. and J. Hall and C. M. D., 21 July 1962 with P. M. Benoit and C. M. D. This study was made three yards to the north of a ditch crossing the field and 55 yards along the ditch from the field boundary opposite the reservoir.

Frequent: Agrostis stolonifera, Glyceria plicata (lf – l. ab), Juncus subnodulosus (f-ab), Lathyrus pratensis, Lemna minor (L), Mentha aquatica (L), Poa trivialis.
Occasional: Anthoxanthum odoratum, Cardamine pratensis, Carex distans (L), C. hirta (L), Centaurea nigra, Equisetum palustre (o-lf), Filipendula ulmaria (o-f), Galium uliginosum, Juncus effusus, J. inflexus (L), Plantago lanceolata, Potentilla anserina, Rumex acetosa, Trifolium pratense, T. repens, Vicia cracca.
Rare: Carex flacca, C. lepidocarpa, C. panicea, C. spicata, Cerastium fontanum, Cirsium palustre, Deschampsia cespitosa, Epilobium parviflorum, Festuca arundinacea, F. rubra, Galium mollugo, Holcus lanatus, Hypericum tetrapterum, Juncus articulatus, Lotus uliginosus, Luzula campestris, Molinia caerulea, Phleum bertolonii, Poa pratensis, Primula veris, Pulicaria dysenterica, Ranunculus acris, R. ficaria, R. repens, Rumex obtusifolius, Scrophularia auriculata, Taraxacum officinale, Valeriana dioica, Veronica beccabunga.

Habitat Study 19   marshy depression, Rushy Meadow, Tring Rural
SP/903 127 (91/B)   Alt. 340 ft.
          Soil: Lower Chalk (pH 7·5)
Surveyed: 6 May 1962 with P. C. and J. Hall and C. M. D., 21 July 1962 with P. M. Benoit and C. M. D. This study was made halfway along a depression crossing diagonally the south end of the meadow.
Locally dominant: Juncus subnodulosus.
Frequent: Carex acutiformis (L), Festuca arundinacea, Filipendula ulmaria, Holcus lanatus, Juncus inflexus.
Occasional: Agrostis stolonifera, Cirsium palustre, Equisetum palustre, Festuca rubra, Galium uliginosum, Lathyrus pratensis, Mentha aquatica, Trifolium repens, Veronica beccabunga (L), Vicia cracca.
Rare: Angelica sylvestris, Arrhenatherum elatius, Caltha palustris, Cardamine pratensis, Carex distans, C. disticha, C. flacca, C. lepidocarpa, Cerastium fontanum, Dactylis glomerata, Dactylorhiza incarnata, D. praetermissa Deschampsia cespitosa, Epilobium hirsutum, E. parviflorum, Equisetum arvense, Hypericum tetrapterum, Juncus articulatus, Lolium perenne (1), Lychnis floscuculi, Lycopus europaeus, Phalaris arundinacea, Plantago major, Poa pratensis, Prunella vulgaris, Ranunculus acris, R. ficaria, R. repens, Rumex conglomeratus, Salix sp. (1) 6 in., Senecio sp (1), Taraxacum officinale (1), Trifolium pratense, Trisetum flavescens, Veronica arvensis.

The reservoirs have a limited aquatic flora but their muddy shores always repay investigation. A study was made of one such site readily accessible from a road.

Habitat Study 20 muddy shore, Startops End Reservoir, Tring Rural
SP/920 135 (91/G)   Alt. 340 ft.
          Soil: Lower Chalk (pH 7·8)
Surveyed: 8 June 1962 with C. M. D., 11 Aug. 1962 with D. E. Allen and C. M. D. This study was made five yards from the water's edge. The water level varies greatly from year to year and season to season and the zones of vegetation will consequently also vary not only in their extent but in their relation to the water's edge. Comparatively large patches were occupied by one single species and these are shown as localised in the list.
Locally dominant: Eleocharis palustris, Glyceria maxima, Juncus compressus.
Frequent: Agrostis stolonifera (L), Galium palustre (L), Limosella aquatica (L), Lycopus europaeus (L), Mentha aquatica, Myosoton aquaticum (L), Polygonum amphibium (L).

Occasional: Cirsium arvense, Poa trivialis. Potentilla anserina, P. reptans, Rorippa islandica, Rumex crispus, Solanum dulcamara.

Rare: Agropyron repens, Bidens tripartita, Calystegia sp., Chenopodium rubrum, Crataegus monogyna seedlings, (1) 3 ft., Deschampsia cespitosa, Epilobium hirsutum, E. parviflorum, Filipendula ulmaria, Geranium dissectum, Glechoma hederacea, Gnaphalium uliginosum, Holcus lanatus, Juncus inflexus, Medicago lupulina, Plantago major, Poa pratensis, Polygonum aviculare, Ranunculus repens (1), R. sceleratus, Rosa sp. (1), Senecio erucifolius (1), Sonchus asper, Taraxacum officinale, Trifolium campestre, T. repens, Tripleurospermum maritimum, Urtica dioica, Veronica anagallis-aquatica, V. catenata.

B. THE BOULDER CLAY REGION (Map 5)

This region has a comparatively uniform vegetation as the Boulder Clay is itself relieved by few other geological features. Apart from a number of small chalk outliers and some choice marshy areas there is little to give variety to the flora. It is at the same time the most rural part of the county and it would be difficult to find any area of comparable size in the Home Counties that is so little developed. Most of the Region is devoted to arable farming with a small amount of improved pasture and there is very little park land. A deficiency in the flora which results from this is compensated for by the comparatively large amount of woodland that remains or has been planted. There are also a few unspoiled areas which well repay study. Judged by the total number of species it produces the Boulder Clay Region has a limited flora but nevertheless it contains many of the more interesting plants of the county.

The chalk outliers may be located by observing the distribution of some chalk-loving species such as *Scabiosa columbaria, Origanum vulgare* and *Helianthemum nummularium.* Two chalk banks were studied.

Habitat Study 21 chalk bank, Benington High Wood
TL/284 234 (22/W)   Alt. 300 ft.
                            Soil: Upper Chalk (pH 7·8)
Surveyed: 13 May 1962, 20 July 1962 with P. M. Benoit. This study was made at about the middle of the first clearing at the side of the rough track through the wood from the road. The plant growth here forms a close community. The bank has a slight gradient facing westwards. There was no evidence of grazing.

Frequent: Agrimonia eupatoria, Arrhenatherum elatius, Festuca rubra, Origanum vulgare, Rubus caesius (L), Sanguisorba minor, Trisetum flavescens.

Occasional: Carex flacca, Clinopodium vulgare, Dactylis glomerata, Fragaria vesca, Glechoma hederacea, Holcus lanatus, Medicago lupulina, Plantago lanceolata, Poa trivialis, Trifolium repens, Veronica chamaedrys.

Rare: Acer campestre <3 ft., Agrostis stolonifera, Ajuga reptans, Arenaria serpyllifolia, Bellis perennis, Brachypodium sylvaticum, Carpinus betulus (1) 3 ft., Cerastium fontanum (1), Corylus avellana (2) 2 ft., Crataegus monogyna <3 ft., Deschampsia cespitosa, Euonymus europaeus (1) 2 ft., Galium mollugo, Helianthemum nummularium, Hypericum hirsutum, H. perforatum, Pastinaca sativa, Phleum bertolonii, Poa pratensis, Potentilla anserina, P. reptans, Primula vulgaris, Prunella vulgaris, Prunus spinosa < 2 ft., Quercus robur (1) 1 ft., Ranunculus bulbosus, R. repens, Rhamnus catharticus <2 ft., Rosa canina, Rubus sp., Rumex crispus, R. sanguineus, Senecio jacobaea, Silene vulgaris, Swida sanguinea (1) 2 ft., Viburnum lantana (1) 2 ft., Viola hirta.

The flora of the second bank was influenced to some extent by a shallow cap of gravel overlying the Chalk.

This no doubt accounted for the comparatively large number of annuals which were observed.

Habitat Study 22   bank by Sawtrees Wood, Thundridge
TL/387 181 (31/Z)   Alt. 240 ft.
Soil: Glacial Sand and Gravel overlying Upper Chalk
                                                    (pH 7·8)
Surveyed: 26 May 1962 with H. B. and G. Souster and C. M. D., 22 July 1962 with P. M. Benoit and C. M. D. This study was made six yards down the slope from the centre of the bank at the top. The bank has a very steep gradient of about 1 in 4 and faces east – there was no evidence of grazing.

Abundant: Ononis repens, Sanguisorba minor.

Frequent: Crepis capillaris, Festuca rubra, Galium verum, Helianthemum nummularium, Poa pratensis, Thymus pulegioides.

Occasional: Achillea millefolium, Carex muricata, Medicago lupulina, Myosotis arvensis, Salvia horminoides, Trisetum flavescens, Veronica arvensis.

Rare: Agrimonia eupatoria, Agrostis stolonifera, Aphanes arvensis, Anthoxanthum odoratum, Arenaria serpyllifolia, Arrhenatherum elatius, Bromus mollis, B. sterilis, Bryonia dioica (1), Carduus acanthoides, Carex divulsa, Catapodium rigidum, Centaurea nigra, Cerastium fontanum, Cirsium vulgare, Clematis vitalba, Crataegus monogyna < 2 ft., Dactylis glomerata, Galium aparine, Geranium molle, Geum urbanum, Hieracium pilosella, Lamium purpureum, Lotus corniculatus, Myosotis discolor, Phleum bertolonii, Plantago lanceolata, Potentilla argentea, P. reptans, Rosa canina < 2 ft., Rubus sp., Rumex acetosa, R. acetosella, R. pulcher, Sambucus nigra (1) 3 ft., Saxifraga granulata (M), Senecio jacobaea, Silene alba, S. vulgaris, Sonchus asper, Taraxacum officinale, Torilis nodosa, Trifolium dubium, T. repens, Ulmus sp (M) 3 ft., Urtica dioica, Veronica chamaedrys, V. hederifolia.

It is difficult to find established pasture on the Boulder Clay itself except when it is water-logged and becoming marshy. A reasonably good example of well drained meadow was found on the outskirts of Stevenage but as this now forms part of a recreation ground it has become subject to change.

Habitat Study 23   meadow, Aston End
TL/269 243 (22/S)   Alt. 325 ft.
      Soil: Boulder Clay overlying Upper Chalk (pH 6·5)
Surveyed: 26 June 1962, 2 Sept. 1962 with C. M. D. This study was made sixty yards along the fence on the north side of the recreation ground and five yards inside the ground from the fence.

Frequent: Agrostis tenuis, Anthoxanthum odoratum, Centaurea nigra, Leontodon taraxacoides, Trifolium pratense.

Occasional: Agrimonia eupatoria, Bellis perennis, Briza media, Chrysanthemum leucanthemum, Cynosurus cristatus, Festuca rubra, Holcus lanatus, Hypochoeris radicata, Lolium perenne, Lotus corniculatus, Plantago lanceolata, Prunella vulgaris, Ranunculus acris, R. bulbosus.

Rare: Carduus acanthoides (1), Cerastium fontanum, Cirsium vulgare, Crataegus monogyna (1) 3 ft., Dactylis glomerata, Leontodon autumnalis, L. hispidus (1), Luzula campestris, Pimpinella saxifraga, Plantago media, Rumex acetosa, Senecio jacobaea, Taraxacum officinale, Trisetum flavescens.

Roadside verges in the eastern part of the county have frequently a vegetation which closely resembles that of an established pasture. Sulphur clover (*Trifolium ochroleucon*) is often a feature of such habitats and a study was made of one.

Habitat Study 24 roadside, Little Hadham
TL/455 222 (42/L) Alt. 300 ft.
 Soil: Boulder Clay (pH 7·8)
Surveyed: 7 July 1962 with C. M. D., 15 Sept. 1962 with
C. M. D., 5 May 1963 with P. J. Ellison. This study was made
sixty-five yards to the east of last (i.e. most eastern) of a line
of planted poplars on the A120 road. The roadside verge is
nine yards wide in front of a closely-planted hawthorn hedge
six feet high.
Frequent: Achillea millefolium, Agrostis stolonifera,
 Convolvulus arvensis. Holcus lanatus, Plantago lanceo-
 lata, Ranunculus repens, Trifolium ochroleucon (L).
Occasional: Arrhenatherum elatius, Brachypodium sylvati-
 cum, Centaurea nigra, Chrysanthemum leucanthemum,
 Heracleum sphondylium, Lathyrus pratensis, Medicago
 lupulina, Poa pratensis (L), P. trivialis, Taraxacum offi-
 cinale, Trifolium pratense.
Rare: Acer campestre <1 ft., Agrimonia eupatoria,
 Agropyron repens, Anthriscus sylvestris, Bellis perennis,
 Clinopodium vulgare, Crataegus monogyna < 6 in.,
 Cynosurus cristatus, Dactylis glomerata, Festuca rubra,
 Galium mollugo, Geranium dissectum, Knautia arvensis,
 Lamium album, Leontodon autumnalis, Lolium perenne,
 Mercurialis perennis, Potentilla reptans, Primula veris,
 Prunella vulgaris, Prunus spinosa <6 in., Rosa canina,
 Rubus sp., Senecio erucifolius, Silene vulgaris, Swida
 sanguinea (1) 1 ft., Tragopogon pratensis, Trifolium
 repens, Trisetum flavescens, Ulmus sp. 6 in., Veronica
 chamaedrys, Vicia angustifolia, V. sepium, Viola sp.

Pastures on the Boulder Clay revert quickly to scrub if
they are not grazed or mown. The example given below
shows some acidity possibly caused by leaching.

Habitat Study 25 Wallington Common
TL/292 326 (23/W) Alt. 460 ft.
 Soil: Boulder Clay (pH 5·2)
Surveyed: 24 June 1962 with C. M. D., 25 Aug. 1962
with C. M. D. This study was approached from Wallington Church by proceeding along an overgrown lane to the
end of a rough piece of woodland and then ten yards beyond
From this point what was once the common is now
almost impenetrable scrub and the study was made in what
proved to be the only clearing.
Frequent: Achillea millefolium, Arrhenatherum elatius,
 Centaurea nigra, Cirsium arvense, Festuca rubra, Galium
 verum, Poa pratensis, Trisetum flavescens.
Occasional: Agrostis tenuis, Dactylis glomerata, Holcus
 lanatus, Lathyrus pratensis, Phleum bertolonii, Prunus
 spinosa <4 ft., Torilis japonica, Veronica chamaedrys.
Rare: Agrimonia eupatoria, Anthoxanthum odoratum,
 Anthriscus sylvestris, Bryonia dioica, Epilobium montanum, Galium aparine, Koeleria cristata, Lotus cornicu-
 latus, Luzula campestris, Myosotis arvensis, Poa trivialis,
 Primula veris, Quercus robur < 2 ft. Ranunculus
 repens, Rumex acetosa, R. crispus, Senecio erucifolius,
 Sonchus asper, Taraxacum officinale, Urtica dioica.

More heathy conditions still are produced at Patmore
Heath which is one of the areas of greatest botanical
interest in the county.

Habitat Study 26 Patmore Heath, Albury
TL/443 258 (42/M) Alt. 340 ft.
 Soil: Reading Beds (pH 4·4)
Surveyed: 5 May 1962 with P.C. and J. Hall and C. M. D.,
7 July 1962 with C. M. D. This study was made in the
centre of a bank above and to the west side of the large
pond at the top of the heath. The bank has a south aspect
with a slope of about 1 in 6. The Reading Beds here consist
mainly of sand with pebbles.
Frequent: Achillea millefolium, Agrostis tenuis, Anthoxanthum odoratum, Festuca rubra.

Occasional: Aira praecox (o-lf), Centaurea nigra, Crataegus
 monogyna (seedlings), Festuca tenuifolia, Hieracium
 pilosella (o-lf), Holcus lanatus, Hypochoeris radicata,
 Lotus corniculatus, Luzula campestris, Pimpinella saxifraga, Plantago lanceolata, Rumex acetosella, Sieglingia
 decumbens, Stellaria graminea.
Rare: Arrhenatherum elatius, Campanula rotundifolia,
 Carex ovalis (M), C. pilulifera, Crataegus monogyna (1)
 10 ft., Deschampsia cespitosa, Equisetum arvense, Fraxinus excelsior (1) 6 ft., Galium saxatile, G. verum, Hedera
 helix (M), Juncus effusus (M), Koeleria cristata, Leontodon hispidus, Lonicera periclymenum (M), Moehringia
 trinervia (M), Nardus stricta, Ornithopus perpusillus
 (r-o), Potentilla erecta (r-o), Quercus robur (2) 6 ft.,
 Rosa canina, Rubus sp., Rumex acetosa, Salix caprea (1),
 S. cinerea (1) 10 ft., Senecio erucifolius, Stellaria holostea,
 S. media, Thymus drucei, Trifolium dubium, T. pratense, Veronica officinalis.

Wet meadows are now few in the Region as there was
extensive drainage in previous times. Most of those that
remain have a fascinating flora and were made the subject
of studies. Bury Mead, a remote marshy area, repays close
examination.

Habitat Study 27 Bury Mead (first study), Ardeley
TL/329 266 (32/I) Alt. 410 ft.
 Soil: Boulder Clay (pH 7·5)
Surveyed: 15 July 1962 with L. and M. Ll-E. and C. M. D.,
15 Sept. 1962 with C. M. D. This study was made twenty-
five yards from the hedge at the top of the highest spring
feeding the stream to Wateringplace Green.
Frequent: Cirsium palustre, Holcus lanatus, Juncus inflexus
 (f-l.ab), Lysimachia nummularia, Mentha aquatica,
 Pulicaria dysenterica (f-l.ab), Ranunculus acris.
Occasional: Carex hirta, Epilobium parviflorum, Festuca
 rubra, Juncus subnodulosus, Lathyrus pratensis, Poa
 trivialis, Prunella vulgaris.
Rare: Bellis perennis, Cardamine pratensis, Carex flacca,
 C. otrubae, C. panicea, Centaurea nigra, Cerastium
 fontanum, Cynosurus cristatus, Dactylorhiza fuchsii,
 Deschampsia cespitosa, Epipactis palustris, Equisetum
 arvense, Festuca arundinacea, F. pratensis, Hypericum
 tetrapterum, Juncus articulatus, Leontodon taraxacoides,
 Lotus uliginosus, Rumex conglomeratus, Senecio
 erucifolius, Taraxacum officinale, Trifolium pratense,
 T. repens, Vicia cracca.

The second study was made a few yards away from the
first but in an adjoining meadow which was much drier.

Habitat Study 28 Bury Mead (second study), Ardeley
TL/329 266 (32/I) Alt. 410 ft.
 Soil: Boulder Clay (pH 6·7)
Surveyed: 15 July 1962 with L. and M. Ll.-E and
C. M. D., 15 Sept. 1962 with C. M. D. This study was made
twenty-five yards on the other side of the hedge forming
the field boundary of the site of the previous study.
Locally abundant: Juncus inflexus.
Frequent: Agrostis stolonifera, Cynosurus cristatus, Plantago
 lanceolata, Pulicaria dysenterica (L), Succisa pratensis (L),
 Trisetum flavescens.
Occasional: Achillea millefolium, Anthoxanthum odoratum,
 Betonica officinalis, Centaurea nigra (o-f), Cerastium
 fontanum, Filipendula ulmaria (L), Holcus lanatus,
 Lathyrus pratensis, Lotus corniculatus, Phleum bertolonii,
 Plantago media, Prunella vulgaris (o-f), Ranunculus
 acris, R. repens, Trifolium repens.
Rare: Agrimonia eupatoria, Ajuga reptans, Angelica sylves-
 tris, Arrhenatherum elatius, Briza media, Carex flacca,
 C. hirta, Cirsium palustre, Crataegus monogyna <2 ft.,
 Dactylis glomerata, Dactylorhiza fuchsii, Deschampsia

cespitosa, Equisetum arvense, Festuca arundinacea, F. rubra, Galium verum (r-o), Gymnadenia conopsea subsp, densiflora, Heracleum sphondylium, Hypochoeris radicata, Leontodon hispidus, L. taraxacoides, Lolium perenne, Lotus uliginosus, Pimpinella magna, Poa trivialis, Potentilla reptans, Primula veris, Quercus robur (1) 2 in., Rumex acetosa, Senecio erucifolius, Silaum silaus, Stellaria graminea, Taraxacum officinale, Trifolium pratense, Veronica chamaedrys, Vicia cracca.

A cattle-grazed meadow at Green End, Sandon, has numerous springs and a well-established pasture. It is one of the richest botanical sites in the county.

Habitat Study 29   Common Land, Green End, Sandon
TL/327 336 (33/G)   Alt. 440 ft.
            Soil: Glacial Gravel and Boulder Clay (pH 7·7)
Surveyed: 10 June 1962 with C. M. D., 9 Aug. 1962 with J. Russell and C. M. D. This study was made three feet above the right bank of the main stream after the confluence of the two main feeding streams. There are distinct vegetation zones each of limited extent and this accounts for the large number of species listed as local, that is appearing in only one part of the study.
Frequent: Apium nodiflorum (L), Caltha palustris (L), Carex flacca (L), Eleocharis palustris (L), E. quinqueflora (L), Juncus inflexus (L), Mentha aquatica (L), Ranunculus repens.
Occasional: Bellis perennis, Cardamine pratensis, Carex hirta (o-lf), Cerastium fontanum, Cirsium palustre, Cynosurus cristatus, Equisetum palustre, Festuca rubra, Leontodon taraxacoides, Nasturtium microphyllum (o-lf), Plantago lanceolata, Ranunculus acris, R. flammula, Trifolium pratense (L), Veronica beccabunga (L).
Rare: Achillea millefolium, Agrostis stolonifera, Anthoxanthum odoratum, Briza media, Carex nigra, C. otrubae, C. panicea, Centaurea nigra, Dactylorhiza incarnata, Epilobium parviflorum, Galium palustre, Glyceria sp., Holcus lanatus, Hypochoeris radicata, Juncus articulatus, Lolium perenne, Lotus corniculatus, L. uliginosus, Lychnis flos-cuculi, Luzula campestris, Phleum bertolonii, Plantago media, Poa trivialis, Prunella vulgaris (r-o), Ranunculus bulbosus, R. ficaria, Rumex acetosa (r-o), R. conglomeratus, Sagina procumbens, Scirpus setaceus, Senecio aquaticus, Taraxacum officinale, Trifolium fragiferum, T. repens.

Near to Green End, Sandon, is an undrained boggy depression with a flora that is unique in this part of Hertfordshire.

Habitat Study 30   The Moor, Sandon
TL/324 329 (33/G)   Alt. 450 ft.
            Soil: Boulder Clay (pH 7·5)
Surveyed: 10 June 1962 with C. M. D., 8 Aug. 1962 with C. M. D. This study was made in the lower part of the Moor in a wet hollow the location of which it would be difficult to define.
Co-dominant: Equisetum telmateia, Juncus subnodulosus.
Occasional: Angelica sylvestris (o-f), Caltha palustris, Cirsium palustre, Filipendula ulmaria, Galium uliginosum, Holcus lanatus, Lythrum salicaria, Mentha aquatica (o-f).
Rare: Cirsium arvense, Epilobium parviflorum, Equisetum arvense, Lathyrus pratensis, Lonicera periclymenum, Lychnis flos-cuculi, Poa pratensis, P. trivialis, Rubus sp., Scrophularia auriculata (r-o), Sonchus arvensis (r-o), Valeriana dioica, Vicia cracca.

A few miles further east is another small marsh known locally as Biggin Moor. This is possibly all that remains of Barkway Moor, a profitable station for nineteenth-century naturalists.

Habitat Study 31   Biggin Moor, Buckland
TL/380 336 (33/W) Alt. 370 ft. Soil: Alluvium (pH 7·5)
Surveyed: 5 May 1963 with P. C. and J. F. Hall and C. M. D., 15 July 1963 with L. and M. Ll.-E. and C. M. D. This study was made thirty five yards from the stream at the south side of the Moor and twelve yards from the wood on its eastern side.
Co-dominant: Hydrocotyle vulgaris, Juncus subnodulosus.
Frequent: Filipendula ulmaria.
Occasional: Angelica sylvestris (o-f), Arrhenatherum elatius, Cirsium palustre, Epilobium hirsutum, Equisetum palustre (o-f), Sonchus arvensis, Valeriana dioica.
Rare: Carex acutiformis, C. panicea, Crataegus monogyna (1) 3 in., Dactylorhiza fuchsii, D. fuchsii × praetermissa, Galium mollugo (r-o), G. uliginosum, Mentha aquatica, Rubus sp., Salix cinerea < 7 ft., Scrophularia auriculata.

The woods of the Boulder Clay Region are its crowning joy. They appear at first inspection to have great uniformity but they are in fact so variable that each merits a closer examination. Much of the Region was converted into airfields during the Second World War and a great deal of the woodland was used for the storage of ammunition. The metalled roads in the woods are still visible and the cleared portions of the woods have passed through some interesting stages of plant succession. A study was made of a wood previously used for military purposes.

Habitat Study 32   Scales Park, Nuthampstead
TL/419 337 (43/B) Alt. 440 ft. Soil: Boulder Clay (pH 7·0)
Surveyed: 5 May 1962 with P. C. Hall, 16 July 1962 with L. Ll.-E. This study was made behind the first bay on the left beyond a hut marked 'Lot 114'. The vegetation is still comparatively open.
Abundant: Filipendula ulmaria.
Frequent: Mercurialis perennis (L).
Occasional: Carex pendula, Deschampsia cespitosa, Festuca gigantea, Rubus sp., Rumex sanguineus.
Rare: Acer campestre < 3 ft., Ajuga reptans, Angelica sylvestris (M), Betula pendula < 10 ft., Bromus ramosus, Carex sylvatica, Circaea lutetiana, Cirsium arvense, Corylus avellana (2) < 3 ft., Crataegus monogyna (2) < 6 ft., Dactylorhiza fuchsii (M), Epilobium hirsutum, E. montanum, Fraxinus excelsior (2) < 6 ft., Geranium robertianum, Geum urbanum, Glechoma hederacea, Hypericum hirsutum (M), Lathyrus pratensis, Potentilla sterilis, Primula vulgaris, Quercus robur (2) 40 ft., Rosa arvensis, R. canina, Salix caprea < 20 ft., Tamus communis, Swida sanguinea (M) 15 ft., Veronica chamaedrys, Viola reichenbachiana.

Beeches Wood, which is near to Scales Park, has a flora more typical of the Boulder Clay woodland. Two studies were made to illustrate the change in flora to be found in one wood.

Habitat Study 33   Beeches Wood (first study), Brent Pelham
TL/446 309 (43/K) Alt. 410 ft. Soil: Boulder Clay (pH 6·4)
Surveyed: 1 July 1962 with J. C. Gardiner and C. M. D., 2 Sept. 1962 with C. M. D. This study was made thirty yards along a wide ride leaving the wood on the west side.
Frequent: Holcus lanatus.
Occasional: Carex otrubae (L), C. sylvatica, Deschampsia cespitosa (o-f), Juncus effusus, Lysimachia nummularia (o-f), P. trivialis (o-f), Prunus spinosa < 6 ft., Ranunculus repens, Rubus sp., Rumex sanguineus.
Rare: Agrimonia eupatoria, Agrostis stolonifera, Angelica sylvestris (1), Brachypodium sylvaticum, Bromus ramosus, Carex flacca, Carpinus betulus (1M) 6 ft., Centaurea nigra, Centaurium erythraea, Cerastium fontanum, Cirsium palustre, Corylus avellana (1) 7 ft., Crataegus monogyna (1) 6 ft., Dactylis glomerata,

Epilobium adenocaulon (r-o), E. montanum (1), Festuca arundinacea, F. pratensis, Fragaria vesca, Fraxinus excelsior (1) 4 ft., Geum urbanum, Glyceria plicata, Hypericum hirsutum, H. tetrapterum (r-o), Juncus bufonius, J. inflexus, Lathyrus pratensis, Ligustrum vulgare (r-o) < 8 ft., Listera ovata, Lonicera periclymenum, Lotus uliginosus, Mentha arvensis (r-o), Myosotis arvensis, Phleum bertolonii, Plantago major, Platanthera chlorantha, Poa annua, P. pratensis, Potentilla anserina, P. reptans, Prunella vulgaris (r-o), Quercus robur (1) 50 ft., Rosa canina, Rubus caesius, Rumex crispus, R. obtusifolius, Salix cinerea (1) 20 ft., Senecio erucifolius (1), Swida sanguinea < 6 ft., Trifolium repens, Veronica beccabunga, V. chamaedrys, V. serpyllifolia.

A remarkable contrast was found in the middle of the wood. The study made here has an added interest as among the plants recorded is *Carex strigosa*, a species of unusual distribution in the county.

Habitat Study 34   Beeches Wood (second study), Brent Pelham
TL/447 309 (43/K) Alt. 400 ft. Soil: Boulder Clay (pH 6·4) Surveyed: 1 July 1962 with J. C. Gardiner and C. M. D., 2 Sept. 1962 with C. M. D. This study was made at the crossing of the main rides of the wood and in line with the trees on the southern side of the ride going from east to west.
Frequent: Filipendula ulmaria, Glyceria plicata (L), Lotus uliginosus (L), Poa trivialis, Potentilla anserina.
Occasional: Festuca gigantea, Galium palustre, Lysimachia nummularia, Mentha arvensis (o-lf), Rubus sp., Rumex sanguineus (o-f).
Rare: Ajuga reptans, Alopecurus pratensis, Bromus ramosus, Carex pendula, C. remota (r-o), C. strigosa (r-o), C. sylvatica, Cerastium glomeratum, C. fontanum, Circaea lutetiana, Cirsium palustre, Corylus avellana (1) 20 ft., Dactylis glomerata, Dactylorhiza fuchsii (1), Deschampsia cespitosa, Epilobium adenocaulon, E. roseum, Fraxinus excelsior (1) 1 ft., Galeobdolon luteum, Geum urbanum, Holcus lanatus (r-o), Hypericum tetrapterum, Juncus bufonius, J. effusus, Potentilla reptans, Prunella vulgaris (r-o), Quercus robur (1 M) 50 ft., Ranunculus repens, Salix caprea (1) 30 ft., Scrophularia nodosa, Senecio vulgaris, Urtica dioica, Veronica beccabunga (M), V. chamaedrys, Vicia sepium.

A similar study was made in a nearby wood which has since been largely felled. The large number of species recorded arises from disturbed conditions brought about by the use of the ride by farm vehicles.

Habitat Study 35   Capons Wood, Buckland
TL/368 324 (33/R)   Alt. 430 ft.
Soil: Boulder Clay (pH 6·4)
Surveyed: 15 July 1962 with L. and M. Ll. E. and C. M. D., 5 May 1963 with C. M. D. This study was made at the last fork in the rides of the wood before the pond is reached and three yards in front of the large oak at the division of the ways.
Frequent: Epilobium hirsutum (f-ab), Festuca gigantea, Filipendula ulmaria (f-ab), Poa trivialis (L), Ranunculus ficaria, R. repens, Rubus sp.
Occasional: Carex pendula, C. strigosa, C. sylvatica, Cirsium palustre, Holcus lanatus, Hypericum tetrapterum, Juncus articulatus, Prunella vulgaris, Stachys sylvatica (L).
Rare: Agropyron repens, Ajuga reptans, Anagallis arvensis, Anemone nemorosa, Angelica sylvestris, Arctium sp., Atriplex patula, Bromus ramosus, Carex otrubae, C. remota, Circaea lutetiana, Cirsium arvense, C. vulgare, Crataegus monogyna (1) 4 ft., Deschampsia cespitosa,

Epilobium angustifolium, E. montanum, Fraxinus excelsior (2) < 3 ft., Galium aparine, Geranium robertianum, Geum urbanum, Glechoma hederacea, Hedera helix, Hypericum hirsutum, Juncus bufonius, J. subuliflorus, J. effusus, J. inflexus, Kickxia spuria, Lapsana communis, Lathyrus pratensis, Lychnis flos-cuculi, Lysimachia nummularia, Matricaria sp., Melilotus sp., Myosotis arvensis, Plantago major, Polygonum aviculare, P. convolvulus, Potentilla reptans, Primula vulgaris (1), Quercus robur, seedlings, (1) 50 ft., Rosa canina, Rumex crispus, R. sanguineus, Salix cinerea < 3 ft., Scrophularia nodosa, Senecio erucifolius, Sonchus asper, Taraxacum officinale, Tussilago farfara, Urtica dioica, Veronica chamaedrys, V. persica.

Great Hormead Park is a wood similar in many respects to those already described except that one corner, a little drier than the rest, provides the only known station in Hertfordshire for the true oxlip (*Primula elatior*).

Habitat Study 36   Great Hormead Park
TL/417 295 (42/E)   Alt. 410 ft.
Soil: Boulder Clay (pH 6·5)
Surveyed: 5 May 1962 with P. C. and J. F. Hall and C. M. D., 1 Aug. 1962 with J. Russell. This study was made ten yards within the wood at a point forty-five yards along the north face from the north-east corner.
Frequent: Anemone nemorosa (L), Carex pendula (L), Deschampsia cespitosa, Mercurialis perennis, Poa trivialis, Ranunculus ficaria, Rubus sp.
Occasional: Ajuga reptans, Carpinus betulus < 15 ft., Filipendula ulmaria, Rosa arvensis, Rumex obtusifolius.
Rare: Acer campestre (1) 3 ft., Arctium sp., Arum maculatum, Brachypodium sylvaticum, Carex sylvatica (1), Circaea lutetiana, Corylus avellana < 12 ft., Crataegus monogyna < 4 ft., C. laevigata < 8 ft., Endymion non-scriptus, Epilobium angustifolium, Festuca gigantea, Fragaria vesca, Fraxinus excelsior (2) 30 ft., Galium aparine, Geranium robertianum, Geum urbanum, Glechoma hederacea, Hypericum hirsutum, Juncus subuliflorus, Lonicera periclymenum, Orchis mascula (1), Paris quadrifolia, Platanthera chlorantha, Potentilla sterilis, Primula elatior, Prunella vulgaris, Prunus spinosa < 6 ft., Quercus robur (1) 2 ft., Ranunculus auricomus (r-o), R. repens, Rumex sanguineus, Solanum dulcamara, Stachys sylvatica, Urtica dioica, Vicia sepium, Viola reichenbachiana.

A study was made of one other wood in the north of the Region as its flora was different from the rest. At a place named New England on the Ordnance Survey Map there is a pond which appears to be artificial. The neighbouring woodland has some evidence of planting and arrangement but it is difficult to see for what purpose.

Habitat Study 37   New England, Nuthampstead
TL/419 358 (43/C)   Alt. 430 ft.
Soil: Boulder Clay (pH 4·6)
Surveyed: 1 July 1962 with J. C. Gardiner and C. M. D., 2 Sept. 1962 with C. M. D. This study was made twenty-five yards along a side track from the main ride on the north side of the pond. It is a comparatively open habitat.
Frequent: Rubus sp.
Occasional: Circaea lutetiana (L), Crataegus monogyna (seedlings), Epilobium hirsutum, E. montanum, Holcus lanatus, Juncus inflexus (o-f), Mentha aquatica, Poa nemoralis, P. trivialis, Rumex sanguineus.
Rare: Agrostis stolonifera, Alisma plantago-aquatica, Angelica sylvestris, Brachypodium sylvaticum, Bromus ramosus, Carex otrubae, C. pendula, C. remota, C. sylvatica, Cirsium arvense, C. palustre (1), Corylus

avellana (1) 7 ft., Crataegus monogyna < 2 ft., Dactylis glomerata, Deschampsia cespitosa, Epilobium angustifolium (r-o), E. obscurum, Festuca heterophylla, Fragaria vesca, Fraxinus excelsior (1) 5 ft., Galium aparine, Geum urbanum, Glechoma hederacea, Juncus subuliflorus, J. effusus, Myosotis arvensis, Poa pratensis, Potentilla reptans, Prunella vulgaris, Quercus robur (3) 40 ft., Ranunculus repens, Rosa canina, Rubus caesius, Salix caprea (2) 6 ft., Solanum dulcamara (M), Trisetum flavescens, Urtica dioica, Veronica serpyllifolia.

Two studies were made in Friar's Wood which is close to the Moor at Sandon. The first revealed a vegetation typical of recently cleared woodland on the Boulder Clay but the second, made in the middle of the wood, was not unlike a number which have been already considered.

Habitat Study 38 Friar's Wood (first study), Rushden
TL/323 327 (33/G) Alt. 470 ft.
Soil: Boulder Clay (pH 6·6)
Surveyed: 10 June 1962 with C. M. D., 8 Aug. 1962 with C. M. D. This study was made on the main ride into the wood at a position twenty yards from the uncleared portion and five yards to the right of the ride.
Frequent: Agrostis stolonifera, Carex flacca (lf-ab), Carex otrubae, Deschampsia cespitosa, Lotus uliginosus, Rubus sp.
Occasional: Angelica sylvestris, Carex pendula (o-f), C. sylvatica (o-f), Cirsium arvense, Filipendula ulmaria (o-f), Juncus inflexus, Mentha arvensis.
Rare: Ajuga reptans, Carex divulsa, C. remota, Cirsium palustre, C. vulgare (1), Crataegus monogyna (2) 2 ft., Dactylorhiza fuchsii (1), Epilobium hirsutum, Juncus articulatus, J. subuliflorus (r-o), Lathyrus pratensis (r-o), Lychnis flos-cuculi, Picris echioides, Plantago major, Poa annua, P. pratensis, P. trivialis, Polygonum aviculare, Potentilla reptans, Prunella vulgaris (r-o), Ranunculus repens, Rosa arvensis, R. canina, Rumex crispus, R. sanguineus, Salix caprea < 4 ft., Sonchus arvensis, Trifolium repens, Tripleurospermum maritimum (1), Vicia hirsuta, V. tetrasperma.

Habitat Study 39 Friar's Wood (second study), Rushden
TL/323 327 (33/G) Alt. 470 ft.
Soil: Boulder Clay (pH 7·0)
Surveyed: 10 June 1962 with C. M. D., 8 Aug. 1962 with C. M. D. This study was made on the same ride as the previous one but inside the wood – fifty yards beyond the cleared part.
Frequent: Juncus bufonius (L), Rosa arvensis (L), Rubus sp. (L).
Occasional: Agrostis stolonifera (L), Angelica sylvestris, Carex pendula, C. sylvatica (o-f), Festuca gigantea (o-f), Filipendula ulmaria (L), Rubus sp. (L).
Rare: Acer campestre (2) < 8 ft., Ajuga reptans, Anemone nemorosa, Bromus ramosus, Calamagrostis epigejos, Carex flacca, C. otrubae, C. ovalis, C. remota (r-o), Centaurium erythraea, Cerastium fontanum, Circaea lutetiana, Cirsium arvense, C. palustre, Corylus avellana (2) < 8 ft., Crataegus monogyna (1) 6 ft., Dactylis glomerata, Dactylorhiza fuchsii, Deschampsia cespitosa (r-o), Dipsacus fullonum, Endymion non-scriptus, Epilobium adenocaulon, E. angustifolium, E. hirsutum, E. montanum, E. parviflorum, Euphorbia exigua, Fragaria vesca, Fraxinus excelsior (3) < 25 ft., Geum urbanum, Glechoma hederacea (o-f), Glyceria plicata, Gnaphalium uliginosum, Heracleum sphondylium, Hypericum tetrapterum, Juncus articulatus (r-o), J. subuliflorus, J. effusus, Lonicera periclymenum, Lotus uliginosus, Lychnis flos-cuculi, Mentha arvensis, Milium effusum, Myosotis arvensis, Plantago major, Poa annua, P. trivialis (r-o), Polygonum aviculare, P. convolvulus, Populus tremula < 5 ft.,

Potentilla sterilis, Primula vulgaris, Prunus spinosa, Quercus robur (2) < 2 ft., Ranunculus ficaria, R. repens (r-o), Rumex crispus, R. sanguineus, Salix caprea (4) < 12 ft., Scrophularia nodosa, Senecio erucifolius, Sonchus arvensis, Swida sanguinea, Tamus communis (M), Taraxacum officinale, Veronica chamaedrys, Vicia sepium, V. tetrasperma, Viola sp.

The varied floras of the woods on the Boulder Clay in north Hertfordshire which have already been considered must be contrasted with the very limited flora of one additional wood which was studied. There is without doubt more of this type of woodland than that with a rich vegetation.

Habitat Study 40 wood, Wallington Common
TL/292 329 (23/W) Alt. 460 ft.
Soil: Boulder Clay (pH 6·2)
Surveyed: 24 June 1962 with C. M. D., 25 Aug. 1962. This study was reached by following an overgrown track from Wallington Church as far as a bend in the track at the side of the woodland. A dip in the wood was then followed for a distance of about seventy yards.
Locally dominant: Circaea lutetiana, Mercurialis perennis.
Occasional: Crataegus monogyna < 6 in., Endymion non-scriptus, Fraxinus excelsior (seedlings), Ulmus sp. (seedlings).
Rare: Acer campestre (1) 20 ft., Arum maculatum, Carex sylvatica, Fraxinus excelsior (1) 60 ft., Galium aparine, Poa trivialis, Ranunculus ficaria, Sambucus nigra < 12 ft., Tamus communis (2), Ulmus sp. (1) 60 ft., Urtica dioica.

To the south of the region the Boulder Clay gives rise to an even more varied woodland. Benington High Wood is on a steep slope above a chalk exposure and supports a flora of only a limited interest.

Habitat Study 41 Benington High Wood
TL/284 236 (22/W) Alt. 330 ft.
Soil: Boulder Clay (pH 7·4)
Surveyed: 13 May 1962, 20 July 1962 with P. M. Benoit. This study was made along the ride on the north side of the wood at a point about ninety yards after its junction with a narrow path from the scrub at the bottom of the wood. The ride here is about five yards wide.
Locally abundant: Endymion non-scriptus.
Frequent: Anemone nemorosa (L), Circaea lutetiana, Conopodium majus, Epilobium angustifolium, Mercurialis perennis, Poa trivialis.
Occasional: Deschampsia cespitosa, Galeobdolon luteum, Glechoma hederacea, Primula vulgaris, Prunella vulgaris (o-lf), Ranunculus repens, Rubus caesius, Viola riviniana.
Rare: Acer campestre < 2 ft., Agrostis sp., Ajuga reptans (r-o), Arctium sp.; Barbarea vulgaris, Bellis perennis, Brachypodium sylvaticum, Carpinus betulus < 3 ft., Cerastium glomeratum, Cirsium palustre (1), Crataegus monogyna (1) 3 ft., Epilobium adenocaulon, E. montanum, Fraxinus excelsior (1) 3 ft., Galium sp. (r-o), Geum urbanum, Hedera helix, Holcus lanatus, Hypericum hirsutum, H. perforatum, Juncus effusus, Lolium perenne, Moehringia trinervia, Myosotis arvensis, Plantago major, Poa annua, Potentilla sterilis, Ranunculus ficaria, Rosa arvensis, Rosa? micrantha, Rubus sp., Rumex crispus, R. sanguineus, Sambucus nigra < 7 ft., Scrophularia nodosa, Tussilago farfara, Urtica dioica, Veronica chamaedrys, V. officinalis, V. serpyllifolia, Vicia sepium, Viola hirta.

To the south-west of Standon is Plashes Wood which is undoubtedly the best wood left in the county. It is large and is partly on a gravelly soil which adds considerably to its total flora. Two studies were made here.

Habitat Study 42   Plashes Wood (first study), Standon
TL/379 204 (32/Q)   Alt. 350 ft.
                                Soil: Boulder Clay (pH 4·3)
Surveyed: 13 May 1962, 24 July 1962 with P. M. Benoit
and C. M. D. This study was made on the main ride of
the wood eight yards before the first ride on the left. The
main ride, which is heavily grazed by rabbits, is about
eight yards wide at this point.
Frequent: Agrostis tenuis, Holcus lanatus, Lotus uliginosus,
    Prunella vulgaris, Rubus sp. (L).
Occasional: Carex remota, C. sylvatica, Cirsium palustre,
    Fragaria vesca, Juncus effusus (o-f), Lysimachia nemorum,
    Mentha arvensis, Poa trivialis.
Rare: Agrimonia eupatoria, Agrostis canina, A. stolonifera,
    Ajuga reptans, Carex hirta, C. ovalis, Centaurium ery-
    thraea, Cerastium fontanum, Crataegus monogyna
    < 1 in., Deschampsia cespitosa, Epilobium adenocaulon,
    E. angustifolium, Festuca rubra, Fraxinus excelsior < 4 ft.,
    Galium aparine, G. palustre (r-o), Glechoma hederacea,
    Glyceria fluitans, Juncus subuliflorus, Lonicera pericyl-
    menum, Luzula multiflora, Lysimachia nummularia,
    Odontites verna, Phleum bertolonii, Plantago major,
    Poa annua, Populus tremula, Potentilla sterilis (r-o),
    Ranunculus repens (r-o), Rosa sp., Rubus caesius,
    Sagina procumbens, Salix caprea (1) 6 ft., Scrophularia
    nodosa, Stellaria graminea, Urtica dioica, Veronica
    chamaedrys, V. serpyllifolia, Viburnum opulus (1M)
    10 ft., Viola riviniana (r-o).

Habitat Study 43 Plashes Wood (second study), Standon
TL/385 210 (32/V)   Alt. 300 ft.
                                Soil: Boulder Clay (pH 6·0)
Surveyed: 13 May 1962, 24 July 1962 with P. M. Benoit
and C. M. D. It is difficult to give the exact location of this
study but it may suffice to say that it was in a dell on the
north-east side of the wood. The trees in this part of the
wood are mainly wild cherry (*Prunus avium* c. 60 ft.) but
none were growing within the area of the study.
Abundant: Chrysosplenium oppositifolium (L), Circaea
    lutetiana, Mercurialis perennis (L).
Occasional: Veronica montana.
Rare: Carex strigosa (2), Carpinus betulus (one fallen tree),
    Dryopteris dilatata, D. filix-mas, Fraxinus excelsior,
    seedlings, (1) 60 ft., Geum urbanum, Moehringia triner-
    via, Plantago major, Primula vulgaris (1), Prunella
    vulgaris, Ranunculus repens, Rubus sp., Rumex obtusi-
    folius (1), R. sanguineus, Sambucus nigra (1) 6 ft., Silene
    dioica, Ulmus sp. < 3 in., Urtica dioica.

Near to Plashes Wood is Kings Wood which has a
flora more reminiscent of the wetter woods in the north
of the Boulder Clay Region.

Habitat Study 44   Kings Wood, Standon
TL/372 233 (32/R)   Alt. 380 ft.
                                Soil: Boulder Clay (pH 5·3)
Surveyed: 13 May 1962, 24 July 1962 with P. M. Benoit
and C. M. D. This study was made fifty-five yards beyond
the hut on the main drive at a point just before where the
wood itself begins to narrow.
Frequent: Carex remota, C. sylvatica, Circaea lutetiana,
    Galium palustre, Holcus mollis (f-ab), Poa trivialis.
Occasional: Agrostis tenuis, Ajuga reptans, Carex strigosa,
    Deschampsia cespitosa (o-lf), Glechoma hederacea (o-f),
    Juncus subuliflorus, J. effusus, Mercurialis perennis,
    Prunella vulgaris, Ranunculus repens (L), Rumex
    sanguineus, Veronica chamaedrys.
Rare: Agrostis stolonifera, Carpinus betulus (M) < 6 ft.,
    Cerastium fontanum, Cirsium palustre, Epilobium
    adenocaulon, E. roseum, Fraxinus excelsior, seedlings,
    (1) 4 ft., Geum urbanum, Hypericum tetrapterum,

Lolium perenne, Lysimachia nemorum, L. nummularia,
    Plantago lanceolata, Potentilla reptans, P. sterilis (r-o),
    Primula vulgaris (r-o), Quercus robur, seedlings, (1M)
    40 ft., Ranunculus ficaria, Rubus sp., Rumex obtusifolius
    (r-o), Sagina procumbens, Urtica dioica, Veronica
    montana (r-o), V. serpyllifolia.

The woods in the valley of the River Ash are of special
interest for the abundance in them of *Myosotis sylvatica*,
a species of unusual distribution in the county. One of
these woods was chosen for a closer study.

Habitat Study 45   wood, Little Hadham
TL/444 222 (42/L)   Alt. 300 ft.
                                Soil: London Clay (pH 5·5)
Surveyed: 7 July 1962 with C. M. D., 8 Sept. 1962 with
C. M. D., 5 May 1963 with P. J. Ellison. This study was
made on the main path a hundred yards from the bottom
of the wood.
Frequent: Cirsium palustre (L), Myosotis sylvatica (L),
    Poa trivialis (f-l.ab), Rubus sp., Rumex conglomeratus.
Occasional: Betula pendula (seedlings), Carex sylvatica,
    Circaea lutetiana (o-f), Epilobium montanum, Galium
    aparine, Geum urbanum. Oxalis acetosella, Potentilla
    sterilis (o-lf), Rumex sanguineus, Salix caprea (seedlings),
    Viola riviniana.
Rare: Arctium minus, Betula pendula (1) 25 ft., Brachy-
    podium sylvaticum, Carex remota, Carpinus betulus (M)
    6 in., Corylus avellana (1) 3 ft., Crataegus monogyna
    (1) 3 in., Deschampsia cespitosa, Dryopteris filix-mas,
    Epilobium adenocaulon (r-o), E. angustifolium, E.
    parviflorum, Fraxinus excelsior, seedlings, (1) 20 ft., Hed-
    era helix, Hypericum perforatum, Juncus effusus (r-o),
    Listera ovata (2), Lonicera periclymenum, Luzula pilosa
    (r-o), Moehringia trinervia, Primula vulgaris, Ranun-
    culus repens (r-o), Rosa canina, Rubus idaeus, Salix
    caprea (1) 25 ft., Scrophularia nodosa, Stellaria media,
    Swida sanguinea (1) 3 in., Urtica dioica, Veronica cham-
    aedrys, V. serpyllifolia.

A wide ride in another nearby wood revealed a mixed
flora. It was, however, of added interest as it is most obviously cut at intervals of a year or so. The second visit
was made shortly after one of these periodic cuttings.

Habitat Study 46   Blakes Bushes, Ware Rural
TL/411 177 (41/D)   Alt. 285 ft.
                                Soil: Boulder Clay (pH 7·8)
Surveyed: 23 June 1962 with J. L. Fielding and C. M. D.,
30 Aug. 1962 with L. and M. Ll-E. and C. M. D. This
was made fifty yards along the ride to the north from the
intersection of rides in the western extension of the wood.
Frequent: Carex sylvatica, Dactylorhiza fuchsii, Festuca
    gigantea, Poa trivialis, Rubus caesius, Stachys sylvatica.
Occasional: Arrhenatherum elatius, Brachypodium sylva-
    ticum, Bromus ramosus, Carex divulsa, Circaea lutetiana,
    Deschampsia cespitosa, Hedera helix, Holcus lanatus,
    Potentilla sterilis, P. reptans, Primula vulgaris, Ranun-
    culus repens.
Rare: Acer campestre < 2 ft., Arum maculatum, Cirsium
    palustre, Corylus avellana < 2 ft., Crataegus monogyna
    < 1 ft., Dactylis glomerata (r-o), Endymion non-scriptus,
    Epilobium angustifolium, E. montanum, Filipendula ul-
    maria, Fraxinus excelsior < 1 ft., Galeobdolon luteum, Gal-
    ium aparine, Geum urbanum, Heracleum sphondylium,
    Hypericum hirsutum, Juncus subuliflorus, Lolium perenne,
    Lonicera periclymenum, Lysimachia nummularia, Mer-
    curialis perennis, Myosotis arvensis, Phleum bertolonii,
    Plantago major, Prunella vulgaris, Prunus spinosa < 2 ft.,
    Rosa arvensis, R. tomentosa, Rubus sp., Rumex crispus,
    R. sanguineus, Sanicula europaea, Stellaria media,

Tamus communis, Taraxacum officinale, Swida sanguinea < 5 ft., Tussilago farfara, Ulmus sp., seedlings, (1) 15 ft., Viburnum opulus < 6 ft., Vicia sepium, Viola riviniana.

To the south-east of Widford is one of the largest areas of woodland in the county. The study made so far for the woods here has failed to produce anything of outstanding interest but it is possible that they may merit still closer study.

Habitat Study 47   Marshland Wood, Widford
TL/426 154 (41/H)   Alt. 270 ft.
             Soil: Boulder Clay (pH 7·8)
Surveyed: 14 June 1962 with L. and M. Ll.-E. and C. M. D., 30 Aug. 1962 with L. and M. Ll.-E. and C. M. D. This study was made on the south side of the track on the north side of the wood. The centre of the study was eighteen yards after the bend in the track. There was evidence of rabbit grazing.
Frequent: Festuca gigantea, Geranium robertianum (L), Mercurialis perennis, Urtica dioica (L), Veronica chamaedrys, Viola riviniana (L).
Occasional: Brachypodium sylvaticum, Circaea lutetiana, Geum urbanum, Hedera helix (o-lf), Poa trivialis (o-f), Primula vulgaris (o-lf), Ranunculus ficaria (L).
Rare: Acer campestre < 2 ft. (1) 40 ft., Anthriscus sylvestris, Arum maculatum, Bromus ramosus, Carex remota, C. sylvatica, Carpinus betulus (seedlings), (2) 45 ft., Clematis vitalba, Crataegus monogyna < 2 ft. (1) 10 ft., Dactylis glomerata, Deschampsia cespitosa, Epilobium montanum, Euonymus europaeus < 1 ft., Fraxinus excelsior (1) 50 ft., Galium aparine, Heracleum sphondylium, Lonicera periclymenum, Lysimachia nummularia, Plantago major, Poa annua, Potentilla reptans, P. sterilis, Quercus robur (1) 6 in., Ranunculus repens, Rosa arvensis, Rubus sp., Rumex sanguineus, Stachys sylvatica, Stellaria holostea, Tamus communis, Taraxacum officinale, Torilis japonica (M), Ulmus sp. (1) 30 ft.

The weeds of arable land in the region are similar to those of the Chalk Region except that *Bunium bulbocastanum* is absent and *Euphorbia platyphyllos* more common. Rubbish dumps are few partly because of the sparse population but also because there are few disused pits.
There are no large ponds or lakes of note in the region.

C. THE CLAY-WITH-FLINTS REGION (Map 6)
This region lacks the comparative uniformity of the two regions already considered as chalk comes to the surface more frequently than it does in the Boulder Clay Region and there are many more small pockets of other deposits as well as more river gravel and alluvial deposits.
It may be helpful to deal with the Chalk first. This occurs mainly in exposures on the sides of river valleys. The largest of these is to the west of Boxmoor where Sheethanger and Roughdown Commons form an escarpment comparable in extent with the main range of the Chalk. The chief feature of these hills is the relative abundance of juniper (*Juniperus communis*) and frog orchid (*Coeloglossum viride*).

Habitat Study 48   Sheethanger Common, Hemel
                           Hempstead
TL/034 051 (00/H)   Alt. 400 ft.
             Soil: Upper Chalk (pH 7·7)
Surveyed: 8 July 1962 with C. M. D., 3 Sept. 1962 with B. Goater and C. M. D., 11 May 1963. This study was made on the unmown slope of the hill opposite a five-bar gate between two houses. The slope here is about 1 in 8 and north-facing – there was no evidence of grazing.
Frequent: Briza media, Centaurea nigra, Helictotrichon pratensis, Sanguisorba minor.

Occasional: Achillea millefolium, Festuca rubra, Helianthemum nummularium, Helictotrichon pubescens, Koeleria cristata (o-f), Leontodon hispidus (o-f), Plantago lanceolata, P. media, Poa pratensis, Pimpinella saxifraga, Trifolium pratense (o-f), Trisetum flavescens.
Rare: Acer pseudo-platanus (1) 3 in., Agrostis stolonifera, Arrhenatherum elatius, Betula pendula (1) 10 ft., Campanula rotundifolia, Carex caryophyllea, C. flacca, Carpinus betulus (1) 1 ft., Cirsium acaulon, Coeloglossum viride, Crataegus monogyna < 3 ft., Dactylis glomerata, Fraxinus excelsior (1) 1 ft., Galium verum (r-o), Holcus lanatus, Juniperus communis (2) < 4 ft., Linum catharticum, Lotus corniculatus (r-o), Medicago lupulina, Ophrys apifera (3), Poa angustifolia, Prunella vulgaris, Quercus robur (1) 6 in., Ranunculus repens, Rhinanthus minor, Rosa canina, Scabiosa columbaria, Senecio jacobaea, Taraxacum officinale, Swida sanguinea < 6 in., Thymus pulegioides, Tragopogon pratensis.

Habitat Study 49   Roughdown Common,
                       Hemel Hempstead
TL/046 057 (00/M)   Alt. 400 ft.
             Soil: Upper Chalk (pH 8·0)
Surveyed: 8 July 1962 with C. M. D., 9 Sept. 1962, 11 May 1963. This study was made at about the centre of the old chalk quarry. The site is north facing with a gradient of about 1 in 4 – there was no evidence of grazing although the grass was very short.
Frequent: Briza media, Euphrasia pseudo-kerneri, Gentianella amarella, Juniperus communis < 1 ft., Koeleria cristata, Linum catharticum.
Occasional: Bellis perennis (L), Campanula rotundifolia, Carex flacca, Cirsium acaulon, Cynosurus cristatus, Leontodon hispidus, L. taraxacoides, Lolium perenne, Medicago lupulina (o-f), Pimpinella saxifraga, Plantago lanceolata (o-f), P. media, Polygala vulgaris (L), Ranunculus bulbosus, R. repens, Sanguisorba minor (o-f), Thymus pulegioides, Trifolium pratense (o-f).
Rare: Anacamptis pyramidalis (1), Carex caryophyllea (r-o), Carlina vulgaris, Centaurea nigra, Chrysanthemum leucanthemum, Crataegus monogyna (1) 2 ft., Dactylis glomerata, Festuca rubra, Fraxinus excelsior (1) 1 ft., Helictotrichon pratensis (r-o), H. pubescens, Hieracium pilosella, Holcus lanatus, Lotus corniculatus (r-o), Prunella vulgaris, Prunus spinosa (1) 1 ft., Scabiosa columbaria (r-o), Swida sanguinea < 1 ft., Taraxacum officinale, Trifolium repens, Trisetum flavescens, Viburnum lantana (1) 1 ft.

The chalk exposures on the hillside slopes have often been disturbed by ploughing and so provide a habitat for *Gentianella germanica*, one of the more interesting Hertfordshire species.

Habitat Study 50   slope below Hoo Wood, Great
                         Gaddesden
TL/032 126 (01/G)   Alt. 475 ft.
             Soil: Upper Chalk (pH 8·0)
Surveyed: 8 July 1962 with C. M. D., 10 Sept. 1962 with C. M. D., 26 May 1963. This study was made six yards in front of the twenty-first concrete post in the fence from the end of the wood. There is a very slight gradient on the north-facing slope which was rabbit grazed.
Frequent: Agrostis stolonifera, Gentianella germanica, Leontodon hispidus, Lotus corniculatus, Medicago lupulina.
Occasional: Bellis perennis, Brachypodium sylvaticum (o-lf), Carex flacca (o-f), Daucus carota, Linum catharticum (o-f), Picris hieracioides, Prunella vulgaris (o-f), Ranunculus repens, Trifolium pratense.
Rare: Acer campestre (1) 4 in, Arrhenatherum elatius, Briza media, Bromus mollis, Carex sylvatica, Centaurea nigra,

Cerastium fontanum, Cirsium arvense, C. vulgare, Convolvulus arvensis, Crepis capillaris, Crataegus monogyna (2) 3 in., Cynosurus cristatus, Dactylis glomerata, Dactylorhiza fuchsii, Fragaria vesca, Galium mollugo, Geranium dissectum, Helianthemum nummularium (r-o), Holcus lanatus (r-o), Hypochoeris radicata, Knautia arvensis, Leontodon autumnalis, Lolium perenne, Medicago sativa, Ophrys apifera, Phleum bertolonii, Picris echioides, Plantago major (1), Poa pratensis, Polygala vulgaris (r-o), Potentilla reptans, Prunus sp. (1) 3 in., Quercus robur (1) 6 in., Ranunculus bulbosus, Rosa canina < 6 in., Sanguisorba minor, Sanicula europaea, Senecio jacobaea, Silene vulgaris, Sonchus arvensis, Taraxacum officinale, Trifolium repens, Tussilago farfara, Vicia angustifolia, Viola hirta.

In parts of the Ashridge Estate chalk is exposed not only on hill slopes but in places where it is close to the surface and has been worked for lime. A hill slope, the grid reference of which is given below misleadingly, was shown to me by Brigadier E. A. Glennie. It provides the only known present station in the county for *Spiranthes spiralis*.

Habitat Study 51 chalk slope near Berkhamsted
SP/990 110 (91/V) Alt. 500 ft. Common, Northchurch
Soil: Upper Chalk (pH 7·6)
Surveyed: 6 Sept 1962 with E. A. Glennie and C. M. D., 9 May 1963 with G. Elwell and C. M. D. The slope here is about 1 in 8 and south facing – there was some evidence of rabbit grazing.
Frequent: Centaurium erythraea, Festuca rubra (f-ab), Leontodon hispidus, Linum catharticum, Lotus corniculatus, Viola hirta.
Occasional: Brachypodium sylvaticum (o-f), Carex flacca (o-f), Clinopodium vulgare, Daucus carota (o-f), Hieracium pilosella, Luzula campestris, Origanum vulgare, Plantago lanceolata, Rosa canina <3 ft.
Rare: Acer campestre (1) 6 in., Agrimonia eupatoria, Bellis perennis, Betula sp. <2 ft. (1) 15 ft., Carex sylvatica, Centaurea scabiosa, Cirsium acaulon, Corylus avellana <5ft., Crataegus monogyna <2 ft., Cynosurus cristatus, Dactylorhiza fuchsii, Erigeron acer (r-o), Fagus sylvatica (1) 4 ft., Fragaria vesca, Galium mollugo, Hypericum perforatum, Knautia arvensis, Leontodon autumnalis, Medicago lupulina (r-o), Pastinaca sativa, Picris hieracioides, Poa angustifolia, Prunella vulgaris, Quercus robur (2) 1 ft., Ranunculus bulbosus, R. repens, Senecio jacobaea, Sorbus aria <2 ft., Spiranthes spiralis (7), Swida sanguinea (1) 2 ft., Taraxacum officinale, Tragopogon pratensis, Trifolium pratense (r-o).

A chalky bank on the edge of an arable field on the eastern side of the Region provided an unusual flora.

Habitat Study 52 chalk bank by Priors Wood, Kimpton
TL/185 172 (11/Y) Alt. 375 ft.
Soil: Upper Chalk (pH 7·7)
Surveyed: 17 June 1962 with H. B. Souster and C. M. D., 24 Aug. 1962 with J. Lovell. This study was made fifty yards from the north-west corner of the wood on the bank above the arable field on the west side of the wood. The species shown * were found in the arable field but most of them were also present on the lower and more disturbed part of the bank.
Frequent: Agrostis stolonifera, Sanguisorba minor.
Occasional: *Alopecurus myosuroides (L), *Anagallis arvensis, Centaurea nigra, Clinopodium vulgare, Crataegus monogyna, seedlings, (1) 3 ft., *Euphorbia exigua (L), Festuca rubra, Hedera helix, *Iberis amara (o-lf), *Kickxia elatine (L), *K. spuria (L), Knautia arvensis, Linum cathar-

ticum, *Lolium multiflorum, *Medicago lupulina, *Myosotis arvensis, Poa pratensis, P. trivialis, Trifolium campestre (L), *Tripleurospermum maritimum (o-lf), *Veronica persica, Viola hirta.
Rare: Acer campestre <6 ft., Achillea millefolium, *Aethusa cynapium, Agrimonia eupatoria, Bellis perennis, Brachypodium sylvaticum, *Capsella bursa-pastoris, Carex flacca, Carpinus betulus <4 ft., Centaurea scabiosa, Centaurium erythraea, Cerastium fontanum, *Chaenorhinum minus, Cirsium acaulon, *C. arvense, Corylus avellana <10 ft., Crepis capillaris, Dactylis glomerata, Daucus carota, Fagus sylvatica (1) 12 ft., Fragaria vesca (r-o), Galium mollugo, Helianthemum nummularium, Helictotrichon pubescens, Heracleum sphondylium (1), Hieracium pilosella, Leontodon autumnalis, L. hispidus, Lolium perenne, Pastinaca sativa, Phleum bertolonii, Plantago lanceolata (r-o), *Polygonum convolvulus, Prunella vulgaris, Quercus robur <2 ft., *Ranunculus repens, Rosa canina, Rubus sp., Sanicula europaea, Senecio erucifolius, *Sherardia arvensis, *Sonchus arvensis, *Stellaria media (r-o), Swida sanguinea <5 ft., Tamus communis, Taraxacum officinale, *Torilis arvensis, Trisetum flavescens, Veronica arvensis, V. chamaedrys, *Viola arvensis.

The outcrops of chalk in the Region so far considered have been isolated ones but in the area to the south-west of Hitchin the clay-with-flints cover is generally shallow and the chalk is exposed much more frequently. A study was made of a chalk bank which is representative of what is seen often in this part of the county.

Habitat Study 53 chalk bank near Westbury Wood, Offley
TL/137 258 (12/H) Alt. 510 ft.
Soil: Middle Chalk (pH 7·8)
Surveyed: 10 May 1962 with L. Ll.-E., 12 July 1962 with L. Ll.-E. This study was made eighty yards along the footpath going north from the detached portion of the wood. The bank, which has a west aspect, was grazed heavily by rabbits. The study was limited to about twelve yards of the bank itself and the margin of the adjoining arable field to give an area approximately equal to that of the other studies. As in the previous study species shown * were weeds in the arable field but most were present also on the disturbed part of the bank.
Frequent: Fragaria vesca, Linum catharticum, Medicago lupulina, Sanguisorba minor, Viola hirta.
Occasional: Agrostis stolonifera, Brachypodium sylvaticum (o-lf), Centaurea scabiosa, Clinopodium vulgare, Festuca rubra, Glechoma hederacea (o-f), Hieracium pilosella, Lolium perenne, Phleum bertolonii, Plantago lanceolata (o-f), *Poa annua, Potentilla reptans, Veronica chamaedrys, *Veronica polita (L).
Rare: Agrimonia eupatoria (r-o), *Anagallis arvensis, Arrhenatherum elatius, Bellis perennis, Bryonia dioica, *Capsella bursa-pastoris, Carpinus betulus (1) 8 ft., Centaurea nigra, *Chaenorhinum minus, *Cirsium arvense (M), Crataegus monogyna <8 ft., Dactylis glomerata, *Euphorbia exigua, *Galium aparine, G. mollugo, *Kickxia spuria, Knautia arvensis, Lapsana communis, Legousia hybrida, Mercurialis perennis (r-o), Origanum vulgare, Pastinaca sativa, Plantago major, *Polygonum aviculare, *P. convolvulus, Prunella vulgaris (r-o), Prunus spinosa (M) 10 ft., Ranunculus acris, R. repens, Reseda lutea, Rhamnus catharticus <3 ft., Rosa sp. <3 ft., Rubus sp. <6 ft., Sambucus nigra <6 ft., Senecio erucifolius, S. jacobaea, *Sherardia arvensis, *Sinapis arvensis, Taraxacum officinale, Tripleurospermum maritimum, Trisetum flavescens, Tussilago farfara, *Viola arvensis, *Veronica persica.

In the neighbourhood of Offley a great deal of chalk is exposed and there is a limited amount of beech woodland. A small but excellent example of this was studied in a wood between Offley and Hitchin.

Habitat Study 54 wood at foot of Pinnacle Hill, Preston TL/168 267 (12/T) Alt. 320 ft.
Soil: Middle Chalk (pH 7·8)
Surveyed: 27 May 1962 with J. Lovell, 12 July 1962 with L. Ll.-E. This study was reached by proceeding thirty yards along the main path in the wood from the bridle way and then following a minor track to the left for six yards.
Locally abundant: Hedera helix.
Frequent: Galium odoratum (L), Sanicula europaea, Veronica chamaedrys (L).
Occasional: Bromus ramosus (o-f).
Rare: Acer campestre < 8 ft., Acer pseudo-platanus (2) < 10 ft., Arrhenatherum elatius, Cirsium arvense, Clinopodium vulgare, Crataegus monogyna < 6 ft., Dactylis glomerata, Daphne laureola (1) 1 ft., Epilobium montanum, Fagus sylvatica (2) < 50 ft., Fragaria vesca, Fraxinus excelsior (1) 1 ft., Galium mollugo (r-o), Geranium robertianum, Heracleum sphondylium, Hypericum hirsutum, Leontodon hispidus, Ophrys insectifera, Poa nemoralis, Potentilla sterilis, Quercus robur (1) 1 ft., Rhamnus catharticus < 1 ft., Rosa sp., Silene vulgaris, Sonchus sp. (1), Stachys sylvatica, Swida sanguinea < 4 ft., Tamus communis, Taxus baccata (1) 1 ft., Viburnum lantana (2) 3 ft., Viola reichenbachiana.

To the west of the Lea Valley the flora is influenced by glacial deposits which usually overlie the Clay-with-Flints. At Pepperstock these produced heathy conditions for it was here that James Saunders found *Lycopodium clavatum*. The flora has now changed but unusual plant associations were found on the edge of what was probably at one time a brick field.

Habitat Study 55 meadow, Pepperstock, Flamstead TL/081 177 (01/Y) Alt. 530 ft.
Soil: Pebbly Clay and Sand (pH 4·7)
Surveyed: 17 June 1962 with H. B. Souster, 26 Aug. 1962 with H. B. Souster and C. M. D. This study was made on the west-facing slope of the first dell in the meadow. The gradient is about 1 in 6. There was no evidence of grazing.
Frequent: Agrostis tenuis, Anthoxanthum odoratum, Festuca rubra (f-ab), Succisa pratensis.
Occasional: Agrostis stolonifera, Centaurea nigra, Conopodium majus, Holcus lanatus, Hypochoeris radicata, Lolium perenne, Lotus corniculatus, Luzula campestris, Plantago lanceolata, Potentilla erecta (o-lf), Ranunculus acris, R. bulbosus, Trifolium pratense, T. repens.
Rare: Achillea millefolium, Betonica officinalis, Briza media, Campanula rotundifolia, Cerastium fontanum (r-o), Cirsium acaulon, Crataegus monogyna < 1 ft., Cynosurus cristatus (r-o), Dactylis glomerata (r-o), Galeopsis tetrahit, Hieracium pilosella (r-o), Juncus subuliflorus, Leontodon hispidus, Polygala vulgaris (r-o), Prunus avium < 2 ft., Quercus robur < 6 in., Ranunculus repens, Rosa sp. (1) 1 ft., Rubus sp., Rumex acetosa, Sambucus nigra (M), Sieglingia decumbens (r-o), Stellaria graminea, Taraxacum officinale, Trifolium medium, Trisetum flavescens, Veronica chamaedrys.

The Clay-with-Flints makes a shallow covering at Hudnall Common leaving exposures of the Upper Chalk on the higher ground and by the roadside. A study was made at the highest part of the Common.

Habitat Study 56 Hudnall Common, Little Gaddesden TL/008 132 (01/B) Alt. 500 ft.
Soil: Upper Chalk (pH 7·7)
Surveyed: 26 April 1962 with L. and M. Ll.-E. and C. M. D., 14 July 1962 with H. B. Souster. This study was

made on the east side of a very prominent dell on the upper part of the Common. The gradient is about 1 in 3 and there was evidence of intensive grazing by rabbits.
Frequent: Agrostis stolonifera, Asperula cynanchica (L), Festuca ovina, Hieracium pilosella, Holcus lanatus (L), Leontodon hispidus, Linum catharticum, Trisetum flavescens.
Occasional: Achillea millefolium, Crataegus monogyna (seedlings), Cynosurus cristatus (o-f), Festuca rubra, Gentianella amarella, Koeleria cristata (o-f), Lotus corniculatus (o-f), Medicago lupulina, Plantago lanceolata, Polygala vulgaris, Senecio jacobaea, Viola hirta.
Rare: Agrimonia eupatoria, Agrostis tenuis, Arrhenatherum elatius, Bellis perennis, Brachypodium sylvaticum, Briza media, Bromus erectus, Campanula rotundifolia, Carex flacca, Carlina vulgaris (1), Cerastium fontanum, Cirsium acaulon (r-o), C. arvense, Crataegus monogyna < 6 ft., Crepis capillaris, Dactylis glomerata, Epilobium angustifolium, Euphrasia sp., Fraxinus excelsior (1) 1 ft., Galium verum, Leontodon taraxacoides (r-o), Lolium perenne, Luzula campestris, Mercurialis perennis, Myosotis arvensis (1), Plantago media (M), Poa annua, Potentilla sterilis, Prunella vulgaris (r-o), Pteridium aquilinum, Quercus robur (1) 6 in., Ranunculus repens, Rosa sp. (r-o), Rubus sp. (r-o), Swida sanguinea (1) 2 ft., Taraxacum officinale, Thymus pulegioides, Trifolium pratense, T. repens, Tussilago farfara, Urtica dioica, Veronica chamaedrys.

In the west of the Region the Clay-with-Flints is generally deeper and covers larger areas. The greater part of the Ashridge Estate is on the Clay-with-Flints but apart from the chalk exposures already considered its flora is limited and disappointing. This large National Trust property forms the biggest open space in the county and is much enjoyed by the general public. A study made at Berkhamsted Common is typical of much of Ashridge.

Habitat Study 57 Berkhamsted Common, Northchurch SP/988 114 (91/V) Alt. 590 ft.
Soil: Clay with Flints (pH 4·9)
Surveyed: 2 July 1962, 6 Sept. 1962 with C. M. D., 9 May 1963. This study was made on the right-hand side of the wide ride on the west side of the common at a point one hundred yards north of the road to Coldharbour Farm.
Abundant: Agrostis canina.
Frequent: Agrostis tenuis, Calluna vulgaris (L), Festuca rubra, Holcus lanatus, Hypochoeris radicata, Sieglingia decumbens (L).
Occasional: Achillea millefolium (o-f), Anthoxanthum odoratum, Conopodium majus, Galium saxatile (o-f), Luzula campestris, Polygala serpyllifolia (L), Potentilla erecta, Rumex acetosella (o-f).
Rare: Aira praecox, Cerastium fontanum, Leontodon autumnalis, Plantago lanceolata, Poa annua, Prunella vulgaris, Pteridium aquilinum (M), Quercus petraea (1) 6 ft., Q. robur (3) 3 ft., Rubus sp., Trifolium repens, Ulex europaeus < 4 ft.

The Clay-with-Flints in the extreme west of the county had apparently an interesting flora in the mid-nineteenth century but close searching has failed to reveal any survival of this. An isolated site still having a native flora was considered to be worthy of study.

Habitat Study 58 Geary's Hill, Wigginton SP/941 097 (90/P) Alt. 625 ft.
Soil: Clay with Flints (pH 4·7)
Surveyed: 8 June 1962 with C. M. D., 11 Aug. 1962 with D. E. Allen and C. M. D. This study was made on the left-hand side of the rough road to Lower Wood at a point two hundred yards from the metalled road.

Abundant: Agrostis tenuis.

Frequent: Festuca rubra (f-ab), Galium saxatile (f-ab), Luzula campestris, Poa pratensis (L), Potentilla erecta (L).

Occasional: Aira praecox (o-f), Anthoxanthum odoratum (o-f), Calluna vulgaris (o-f), Hieracium pilosella, Holcus lanatus, Hypochoeris radicata, Prunus spinosa < 6 in., Rumex acetosella (o-f), Trifolium repens.

Rare: Agrostis stolonifera, Arrhenatherum elatius, Campanula rotundifolia, Centaurea nigra (r-o), Conopodium majus, Dactylis glomerata, Galeopsis tetrahit, Galium verum, Hypericum perforatum, Leontodon autumnalis, Lolium perenne, Lonicera periclymenum, Lotus corniculatus, Plantago lanceolata (r-o), Poa annua, Quercus robur < 6 in., Ranunculus bulbosus (1), Rumex acetosa, Sieglingia decumbens, Stellaria holostea, Trifolium dubium.

The weeds of the arable fields in the Clay-with-Flints Region are generally worthy of study only in those areas most influenced by the Chalk. On the Clay-with-Flints itself *Spergula arvensis* and *Scleranthus annuus* are worth noting as weeds. A roadside verge was studied to illustrate the species most likely to colonise disturbed habitats. The soil here was Upper Chalk but the Clay-with-Flints was a short distance away on the hill slopes.

Habitat Study 59 roadside, Great Gaddesden
TL/018 129 (01/B) Alt. 380 ft.
Soil: Middle Chalk (pH 5·9)
Surveyed: 14 July 1962 with H. B. Souster, 10 Sept. 1962 with C. M. D. This study was made on the west side of the B486 road mid-way between the 4th and 5th telegraph posts north of the Egg Packing Station.
Frequent: Arrhenatherum elatius (f-ab), Convolvulus arvensis (L), Poa trivialis (L).
Occasional: Achillea millefolium, Agrostis stolonifera, A. tenuis (o-f), Centaurea nigra, Heracleum sphondylium (o-f), Holcus lanatus (o-f), Hypericum perforatum (o-f), Lotus corniculatus, Plantago lanceolata (o-f), Prunella vulgaris, Trisetum flavescens, Vicia hirsuta (o-f).
Rare: Agropyron repens, Allium vineale, Anthriscus sylvestris, Crataegus monogyna < 1 ft., Crepis capillaris, Cynosurus cristatus (r-o), Dactylis glomerata, Hypochoeris radicata, Lapsana communis, Lathyrus pratensis, Leontodon autumnalis (r-o), Lolium perenne, Malva moschata, Phleum bertolonii, Poa annua, Plantago major, Polygonum aviculare, Prunus sp. (1) 1 ft., Quercus robur < 1 ft., Ranunculus acris, Raphanus raphanistrum, Rosa sp., Rubus sp., Rumex acetosa (r-o), Silene alba, Stellaria holostea, Taraxacum officinale, Trifolium repens, Tripleurospermum maritimum, Veronica chamaedrys, Vicia angustifolia.

The woods of the Region are varied in their floras depending mainly on differences in soils. To the east of the Lea Valley it is generally better wooded than to the west and it is here that the influence of the Chalk is most visible. A study was made of a wood to the south-west of Hitchin.

Habitat Study 60 Wain Wood, Preston
TL/180 256 (12/X) Alt. 420 ft.
Soil: Middle Chalk (pH 5·1)
Surveyed: 17 May 1962 with J. Lovell, 12 July 1962 with L. Ll.-E. This study was made at the intersection of the path at the back of the gamekeeper's cottage with the main ride of the wood. In this part of the wood the trees are mainly oak and hornbeam growing to a height of about 30 ft.
Frequent: Aphanes microcarpa (L on ride only), Deschampsia cespitosa, Endymion non-scriptus (L), Luzula pilosa (L), Lysimachia nemorum, Oxalis acetosella (L).

Occasional: Brachypodium sylvaticum, Cerastium fontanum, Dryopteris filix-mas, Fragaria vesca, Galeobdolon luteum, Glechoma hederacea, Milium effusum, Moehringia trinervia, Potentilla sterilis, Prunella vulgaris, Ranunculus repens, Viola reichenbachiana.

Rare: Ajuga reptans (r-o), Anemone nemorosa, Anthoxanthum odoratum, Callitriche stagnalis, Carpinus betulus, seedlings, (1) 30 ft., Cerastium glomeratum, Circaea lutetiana, Conopodium majus, Crataegus monogyna < 6 in., Dryopteris dilatata, Fraxinus excelsior < 1 ft., Juncus effusus (1), Plantago major, Poa annua (r-o), Quercus robur (seedlings), Ranunculus ficaria, Rubus sp. (r-o), Rumex sanguineus (r-o), Stachys sylvatica, Stellaria media, Trifolium repens (r-o), Urtica dioica, Veronica chamaedrys (r-o).

To the west of the Lea Valley the woodland changes as the Chalk has less influence. A number of studies in woods were made here, the first in a small wood little affected by human interference.

Habitat Study 61 Upper Sawpit Wood, Flamstead
TL/088 138 (01/W) Alt. 450 ft.
Soil: Clay-with-Flints overlying Upper Chalk (pH 5·4)
Surveyed: 14 July 1962 with H. B. Souster, 10 Sept. 1962 with C. M. D. This study was made fifty-five yards along the path into the wood from the road.
Frequent: Galeobdolon luteum, Hedera helix (f-ab), Oxalis acetosella.
Occasional: Melica uniflora (o-lf), Milium effusum, Rubus sp.
Rare: Acer campestre (2) < 5 ft., Anthriscus sylvestris, Corylus avellana < 20 ft., Crataegus monogyna < 12 ft., Endymion non-scriptus, Fagus sylvatica (2) 50 ft., Fraxinus excelsior (1) 4 in., Galeopsis tetrahit, Galium odoratum, Geranium robertianum, Geum urbanum, Lapsana communis, Lonicera periclymenum, Mercurialis perennis (r-o), Populus tremula (suckers), Prunus avium (5) 50 ft. P. spinosa < 2 ft., Pteridium aquilinum (1), Quercus robur (1) 4 ft., Rosa arvensis, R. canina, Sanicula europaea, Stellaria media, Tamus communis, Viburnum opulus < 2 ft., Vicia sepium.

The next study was made in the wide ride of a wood recently felled and planted with conifers. It had a mixed flora.

Habitat Study 62 Newlands Wood, Flamstead
TL/052 135 (01/L) Alt. 525 ft.
Soil: Clay with Flints (pH 5·6)
Surveyed: 26 April 1962 with L. and M. Ll.-E. and C. M. D., 21 July 1962 with P. M. Benoit and C. M. D. This study was made on the path through the wood about thirty-four yards inside the planted part. The wood had been planted with larch which had grown to a height of about six feet at the time of the study. There was no evidence of grazing.
Frequent: Agrostis tenuis, Anthoxanthum odoratum, Deschampsia cespitosa, Epilobium angustifolium (L), Holcus lanatus.
Occasional: Ajuga reptans, Brachypodium sylvaticum (o-lf), Carex sylvatica, Cynosurus cristatus, Glechoma hederacea (o-f), Holcus mollis (L), Hypericum perforatum, Juncus effusus, Lotus uliginosus, Mercurialis perennis (o-lf), Plantago lanceolata, Veronica chamaedrys (o-lf).
Rare: Achillea millefolium, Agrimonia eupatoria, Arctium minus, Betula pendula < 8 ft. Carex pallescens (M), C. spicata, Centaurium erythraea, Cirsium arvense, C. palustre, Corylus avellana < 2 ft., Crataegus monogyna < 2 ft., Crepis capillaris, Dactylis glomerata, Dactylorhiza fuchsii, Fagus sylvatica < 8 ft., Fragaria vesca (r-o),

Galeopsis tetrahit, Geum urbanum, Hieracium pilosella, Hypochoeris radicata, Juncus subuliflorus (r-o), Lolium perenne, Lysimachia nemorum (M), Poa trivialis, Potentilla anserina, P. reptans, P. sterilis (r-o), Prunella vulgaris, Quercus robur <3 ft., Ranunculus repens, Rosa canina (M), Rubus sp., Rumex acetosella, R. sanguineus, Sagina procumbens, Salix caprea <3 ft., Senecio jacobaea, Taraxacum officinale (1), Trifolium dubium, T. repens, Ulmus glabra <3 ft., Veronica officinalis, Viola riviniana.

The influence of the Chalk was still evident in the next study.

Habitat Study 63   High Park Wood, Great Gaddesden
TL/028 105 (01/F)   Alt. 450 ft.
                         Soil: Upper Chalk (pH 7·5)
Surveyed: 26 April 1962 with L. and M. Ll.E. and C. M. D., 14 July 1962 with H. B. Souster. This study was made ten yards from the main path and five yards from a big dell in the higher part of the wood. It was comparatively open woodland with little ground flora.
Frequent: Allium ursinum (lf – l.ab), Mercurialis perennis (lf – l. ab), Ranunculus auricomus, R. ficaria.
Occasional: Arum maculatum, Bromus ramosus, Endymion nonscriptus (o-f), Galeobdolon luteum (o-f), Galium aparine (o-f), G. odoratum (o-f), Hedera helix, Milium effusum.
Rare: Acer campestre (1) 60 ft., Anthriscus sylvestris (r-o), Arctium sp., Carex sylvatica, Circaea lutetiana, Corylus avellana (2) 15 ft., Crataegus monogyna (1) 6 in., Fraxinus excelsior, seedlings, (1) 60 ft., Geum urbanum (r-o), Glechoma hederacea (M), Poa trivialis, Ribes rubrum (1) 2 ft., Rosa sp. (1), Sanicula europaea (r-o), Stachys sylvatica, Taraxacum officinale, Ulmus sp. (1) 40 ft., Urtica dioica, Veronica chamaedrys, Vicia sepium, Viola reichenbachiana.

The largest wood on the Clay-with-Flints is High Scrubs. The woodland itself has a limited flora but clearings produce many interesting species. It is a wood that no doubt merits further study.

Habitat Study 64   High Scrubs, Tring Urban
SP/933 079 (90/I)   Alt:. 610 ft.
                         Soil: Clay with Flints (pH 4·0)
Surveyed: 6 May 1962 with P. C. and J. Hall and C. M. D., 21 July 1962 with P. M. Benoit. This study was reached by following the main track through the wood from the road for a distance of seventy yards and then proceeding at right angles with the track and to the right for a distance of fifty yards.
Abundant: Agrostis tenuis, Deschampsia flexuosa, Holcus mollis.
Frequent: Rubus sp.
Occasional: Betula pubescens < 12 ft., Calluna vulgaris (o-lf), Epilobium angustifolium, Quercus robur (seedlings).
Rare: Betula pendula (2) <2 ft., Carex pilulifera, Carpinus betulus (1) 6 ft., Corylus avellana (1) 2 ft., Crataegus monogyna <2 ft., Galium saxatile, Hypericum pulchrum, Juncus subuliflorus, Luzula pilosa, Pteridium aquilinum, Quercus cerris (1) 6 ft., Q. petraea (1) 3 ft., Q. robur (1) 4 ft., Ulex europaeus (r-o).

The Clay-with-Flints Region is well served with streams and rivers. Springs near to the river courses as at Whitwell, by the River Mimram, and at a number of places by the River Gade are used to provide water-cress beds. The Gade is the largest river in the region and below Great Gaddesden it flows through some good water meadows.

Habitat Study 65   meadow, Water End, Great Gaddesden
TL/036 106 (01/F)   Alt. 340 ft.
                         Soil: Alluvium overlying Valley Gravel (pH 7·4)
Surveyed: 24 April 1962 with L. and M. Ll.-E. and C. M. D., 14 July 1962 with H. B. Souster. This study was made on the left-hand bank of the stream ten yards above the weir. A number of aquatic species in the stream came in the area of study and these are given as local (L) in the list below. The meadow was heavily grazed by cattle.
Frequent: Achillea millefolium, Bellis perennis, Catabrosa aquatica (L), Galium palustre, Nasturtium officinale (L), Plantago lanceolata, Ranunculus repens, Stellaria alsine (L), Trifolium dubium, T. repens, Veronica beccabunga (L).
Occasional: Carex hirta, Cerastium fontanum, Crepis capillaris, Cynosurus cristatus, Epilobium hirsutum, Hieracium pilosella, Holcus lanatus, Juncus inflexus, Lemna minor (L), Leontodon autumnalis, Lolium perenne, Poa trivialis, Ranunculus ficaria, Rumex hydrolapathum (L), Scrophularia auriculata (L), Trifolium pratense, Trisetum flavescens, Typha latifolia (L).
Rare: Agrimonia eupatoria, Apium nodiflorum (L), Cirsium arvense, Conopodium majus, Erophila verna, Geranium molle, Glyceria sp., Lotus corniculatus, Mentha aquatica, Poa annua, Ranunculus acris, Rumex acetosa (M), R. conglomeratus, Senecio aquaticus, S. jacobaea (r-o), S. vulgaris, Taraxacum officinale (r-o), Urtica dioica, Veronica arvensis, V. chamaedrys.

A meadow by the River Ver below Redbourn provided a similar study.

Habitat Study 66   meadow, south of Redbourn
TL/113 113 (11/A)   Alt. 290 ft.
                         Soil: Alluvium overlying Valley Gravel (pH 6·5)
Surveyed: 17 June 1962 with H. B. Souster and C. M. D., 26 Aug. 1962 with H. B. Souster and C. M. D. This study was made on the left bank of the northerly branch of the stream forty-five yards from the main A5 road. The meadow which was grazed by cattle had been sprayed a short time before the first visit but it had made a remarkable recovery by the time of the second.
Frequent: Apium nodiflorum (L), Cynosurus cristatus, Festuca rubra, Glyceria plicata (L), Plantago lanceolata, Ranunculus penicillatus (L).
Occasional: Achillea millefolium (o-f), Agrostis stolonifera, Cerastium fontanum (o-f), Equisetum arvense, Holcus lanatus (o-f), Leontodon autumnalis (o-f), Myosotis scorpioides (L), Nasturtium officinale (L), Poa trivialis, Ranunculus acris, R. repens (o-f), Rumex conglomeratus, Trifolium repens (o-f), Veronica beccabunga.
Rare: Alopecurus pratensis, Bellis perennis (r-o), Bidens cernua, Carex hirta (r-o), Catabrosa aquatica (L), Cirsium palustre, Crepis capillaris, Dactylis glomerata, Epilobium parviflorum, Festuca pratensis, Juncus articulatus, J. bufonius, J. inflexus, Lemna minor (L), Lolium perenne, Luzula campestris, Lychnis flos-cuculi, Medicago lupulina, Mentha aquatica, Phleum bertolonii, Plantago major (r-o), Poa annua, Polygonum aviculare, P. persicaria, Rumex acetosa, R. crispus, R. obtusifolius, Scrophularia auriculata, Senecio aquaticus, S. erucifolius, Stellaria alsine, Taraxacum officinale, Trifolium pratense, Veronica anagallis-aquatica (L), V. chamaedrys.

D. THE LEA GRAVELS REGION (Map 7)
      The large area of river gravels associated with the River Lea and its tributaries is very difficult to interpret as it includes outliers of all the deposits which have already been considered. It is in addition the part of the county most affected by human interference. Chalk outcrops still appear as on the spoil heaps of the Welwyn tunnels (21/MN) and at Dawley Warren.

Habitat Study 67   scrub below Dawley Warren, Tewin
TL/262 156 (21/S)   Alt. 300 ft.
Soil:Upper Chalk (pH 7·9)
Surveyed: 20 May 1962 with L. and M. Ll.-E., 30 July 1962 with C. M. D. Dawley Warren is a large disused firing range and chalk has been brought to the surface to provide the firing platforms, etc. The study was made to the right of the path out of the wood at a point less given over to scrub than the woodland margin.
Frequent: Leontodon hispidus, Linum catharticum, Sanguisorba minor (f-ab), Thymus sp. (f-l.ab).
Occasional: Agrimonia eupatoria (o-f), Brachypodium sylvaticum, Carex flacca, Clinopodium vulgare, Crataegus monogyna < 4 ft., Festuca rubra, Fragaria vesca, Helianthemum nummularium (o-lf), Lotus corniculatus, Medicago lupulina, Poa angustifolia, Trisetum flavescens, Viola hirta.
Rare: Acer campestre (1) 6 in., Agrostis stolonifera, Arrhenatherum elatius, Bellis perennis, Betula pendula (1) 4 ft., B. pubescens (1) 2 ft., Blackstonia perfoliata, Briza media, Carlina vulgaris, Carpinus betulus < 5 ft., Centaurea nigra, Centaurium erythraea, Cirsium vulgare, Convolvulus arvensis, Corylus avellana (1) 2 ft., Dactylis glomerata, Festuca ovina, Fraxinus excelsior (1) 1 ft., Helictotrichon pubescens, Hieracium pilosella, Holcus lanatus, Hypericum perforatum, Knautia arvensis, Koeleria cristata (r-o), Origanum vulgare, Picris hieracioides (r-o), Plantago lanceolata (r-o), Potentilla reptans, Primula veris, Prunella vulgaris, Prunus spinosa < 2 ft., Quercus robur < 2 ft., Ranunculus bulbosus (1), R. repens, Rosa canina < 4 ft., Rubus sp., Scabiosa columbaria, (r-o), Senecio erucifolius, Tamus communis, Taraxacum officinale, Tragopogon pratensis, Trifolium pratense, Veronica chamaedrys (r-o).

The pastures of the Region are varied because of its complex geological basis and a number were chosen for closer study. Gustard Wood Common is of considerable interest for its abundance of juniper and its wide range of other species. It is kept comparatively clear from scrub largely by the efforts of the Mid Herts Golf Club which exercises special care to preserve the beauty and amenities of the Common. Bower Heath (11/N) provides a similar habitat.

Habitat Study 68   Gustard Wood Common,
Wheathampstead
TL/174 163 (11/T)   Alt. 418 ft.
Soil: Clay-with-Flints (pH 4·0)
Surveyed: 26th April 1962 with L. and M. Ll.-E. and C. M. D., 5 July 1962 with C. M. D. This study was made ten yards from the road to Wheathampstead at about thirty yards from the cross-roads on the Common.
Abundant: Festuca tenuifolia.
Frequent: Calluna vulgaris (L), Galium saxatile, Luzula campestris, Stellaria graminea.
Occasional: Agrostis tenuis (o-f.), Campanula rotundifolia, Festuca rubra, Potentilla erecta, Quercus robur (seedlings).
Rare: Achillea millefolium, Galeopsis tetrahit, Helictotrichon pratense (M), Holcus lanatus, Juniperus communis < 6 ft., Quercus robur (1) 8 ft., Rubus sp., R. idaeus (1), Rumex acetosa.

A slope above the River Ash at Easneye provided a poor pasture but an interesting list of species.

Habitat Study 69   hill slope, Easneye, Stanstead Abbots
TL/376 136 (31/R)   Alt. 175 ft.
Soil: Sand and Gravel (pH 6·3)
Surveyed: 26 May 1962 with H. B. and G. Souster and C. M. D., 26 July 1962 with P. M. Benoit and C. M. D. This study was made about half way up the slope at a

position which it would be difficult to define. The slope had a steep gradient of about 1 in 3, a west aspect, and was rabbit grazed.
Frequent: Agrostis tenuis (f-ab), Cerastium fontanum, Leontodon taraxacoides, Veronica arvensis.
Occasional: Achillea millefolium (o-f), Festuca ovina, F. rubra (o-f), Hypochoeris radicata, Luzula campestris (o-f), Poa pratensis, Potentilla erecta, P. reptans, Rumex acetosella, Taraxacum laevigatum, Trifolium micranthum, T. repens, Veronica chamaedrys, Vicia angustifolia.
Rare: Agrostis canina, Aphanes microcarpa, Bellis perennis, Betonica officinalis, Bromus mollis, B. thominii, Centaurium erythraea, Cerastium arvense, C. glomeratum, Cirsium arvense, C. vulgare (1), Crataegus monogyna < 3 ft., Crepis capillaris, Cynosurus cristatus (r-o), Dactylis glomerata, Glechoma hederacea, Hieracium pilosella (r-o), Holcus lanatus, H. mollis, Hypericum perforatum, Lathyrus pratensis, Linum catharticum, Lolium perenne, Lotus corniculatus, Myosotis discolor, Nardus stricta (r-o), Plantago lanceolata, P. major, Poa annua, P. trivialis, Potentilla sterilis, Prunella vulgaris (r-o), Quercus cerris < 1 ft., Rosa canina < 2 ft., Rubus sp. < 2 ft., Rumex acetosa, Sieglingia decumbens, Trifolium dubium (r-o), T. pratense, Trisetum flavescens, Veronica officinalis (r-o), V. serpyllifolia (r-o), Viola sp., Vulpia bromoides.

Codicote High Heath had at one time an interesting acid heathland flora. It is now unfortunately quarried away but in what little remains a useful study was made.

Habitat Study 70   Codicote High Heath
TL/209 185 (21/E)   Alt. 325 ft.
Soil: Glacial Gravel (pH 4·4)
Surveyed: 27 May 1962 with J. Lovell, 20 July 1962 with P. M. Benoit. This study was made on the lower slope of the hill, which forms the only remaining part of the heath, at its furthest point from the village. The slope here is slight and west facing. At the time of the study there was evidence of rabbit grazing.
Frequent: Calluna vulgaris (L), Festuca ovina (f-ab)., F. rubra, Galium saxatile, Hypochoeris radicata (f-ab), Lotus corniculatus, Potentilla erecta.
Occasional: Achillea millefolium (o-f), Agrostis canina, Hieracium pilosella (o-f), Luzula campestris, Rumex acetosella, Sieglingia decumbens (o-lf), Trifolium dubium.
Rare: Acer pseudo-platanus (1), Anthoxanthum odoratum (r-o), Betula pendula < 4 ft., Conopodium majus (r-o), Crataegus monogyna < 1 ft., Holcus lanatus, Narcissus sp. (1, probably planted) Plantago lanceolata (r-o), Prunella vulgaris, Quercus robur < 4 ft., Rubus sp., Rumex acetosa (1), Sarothamnus scoparius < 4 ft., Trifolium pratense, T. repens, Veronica chamaedrys, V. officinalis, Viola canina.

Wet pastures in the Region are likewise varied and differences between them depend not only on minor soil changes but on the waterlogged state of the ground. Two meadows very close to each other have rich but contrasting vegetations.

Habitat Study 71   meadow, Langley
TL/222 229 (22/G)   Alt. 325 ft.
Soil: Glacial Gravel (pH 6·2)
Surveyed: 2 June 1962 with H. and D. Meyer and C. M. D., 31 July 1962 with C. M. D. This study was made in the lower part of the meadow forty-five yards from the fourth group of trees from the corner of the field. There was a close cattle-grazed turf.
Frequent: Anthoxanthum odoratum, Cynosurus cristatus, Hypochoeris radicata, Leontodon taraxacoides, Lotus corniculatus, Prunella vulgaris, Trifolium pratense.

Occasional: Agrimonia eupatoria (o-f), Agrostis tenuis, Bellis perennis, Carex flacca (o-f), Centaurea nigra (o-f), Cirsium arvense, Genista tinctoria, Holcus lanatus, Leontodon autumnalis, Linum catharticum, Orchis morio, Plantago lanceolata, Poa pratensis, Ranunculus bulbosus.

Rare: Centaurium erythraea, Cerastium fontanum, Crataegus monogyna (2) 6 in., Dactylis glomerata, Festuca pratensis, F. rubra, Lathyrus pratensis, Lolium perenne (r-o), Luzula campestris (r-o), Odontites verna, Plantago media, Potentilla reptans, Ranunculus acris, R. repens (r-o), Rosa canina (2) 6 in., Rumex acetosa, Taraxacum officinale, Trifolium repens (r-o), Trisetum flavescens.

Burleigh Meadow is only a short distance from the previous study but is an excellent example of wet heathland pasture. The meadow, which has been known to Hertfordshire naturalists for many years, was ploughed during the Second World War. When the farmer decided in 1955 to allow it to return to pasture the first species to colonise the lower part of the meadow was *Scirpus setaceus* which formed an attractive natural lawn.

Habitat Study 72   Burleigh Meadow, Knebworth
TL/225 228 (22/G)   Alt. 325 ft.
                      Soil: Glacial Gravel (pH 4·9)
Surveyed: 2 June 1962 with H. and D. Meyer and C. M. D., 31 July 1962 with C. M. D. This study was made a distance of seventy yards in a line from the oak on the right hand side of the cottage to the tree by the side of the pond. The meadow had been cut for hay shortly before the second visit.

Frequent: Agrostis tenuis (f-ab), Juncus effusus (f-ab), J. subuliflorus, Luzula campestris.

Occasional: Achillea millefolium (o-f), Agrostis canina, Holcus lanatus (o-f), Hypochoeris radicata, Lotus uliginosus, Potentilla erecta (o-f), Stellaria graminea.

Rare: Achillea ptarmica, Agrostis stolonifera, Anthoxanthum odoratum (1), Centaurea nigra, Cerastium fontanum, Conopodium majus (r-o), Genista anglica, G. tinctoria, Hypericum pulchrum, Leontodon autumnalis, Pedicularis sylvatica, Plantago lanceolata (r-o), Poa annua, Prunella vulgaris, Ranunculus repens (r-o), Rumex acetosa, R. acetosella, Sieglingia decumbens, Silaum silaus, Taraxacum officinale, Veronica officinalis, Viola canina.

Water meadows are a feature of the lower reaches of most of the rivers but remnants of natural vegetation in them are rare. By the Stort Navigation there are small portions of meadow land which well repay study.

Habitat Study 73   Hunsdon Mead
TL/420 110 (41/F)   Alt. 110 ft.   Soil: Alluvium (pH 5·9)
Surveyed: 24 June 1962 with J. L. Fielding, 30 Aug. 1962 with L. and M. Ll.-E. and C. M. D. This study was made six yards from the river bank in the middle of the bend in the river. At the time of the second visit the meadow was being grazed by a flock of sheep.

Frequent: Briza media, Bromus commutatus, Cerastium fontanum, Festuca pratensis.

Occasional: Anthoxanthum odoratum, Carex hirta, Cynosurus cristatus (o-f), Equisetum arvense (o-f), Holcus lanatus, Lathyrus pratensis (o-f), Ophioglossum vulgatum, Ranunculus acris, Rhinanthus minor, Trifolium pratense.

Rare: Achillea millefolium, Ajuga reptans, Bellis perennis, Carex flacca, Centaurea nigra, Chrysanthemum leucanthemum, Cirsium arvense, C. palustre (r-o), C. vulgare, Dactylis glomerata, Deschampsia cespitosa, Filipendula ulmaria, Heracleum sphondylium, Leontodon autumnalis (r-o), L. hispidus, Linum catharticum (r-o), Lolium

perenne (r-o), Lotus corniculatus (r-o), Luzula campestris, Lychnis flos-cuculi, Orchis morio, Plantago lanceolata (r-o), Polygonum amphibium (terrestrial form), Primula veris, Prunella vulgaris, Ranunculus repens, Rosa canina (1) 2 in., Rumex acetosa, Silaum silaus, Taraxacum officinale, Trifolium dubium, T. repens.

A meadow by the River Lea below Wheathampstead is of interest as the river is now maintained principally by Luton's very considerable sewage outfall. In periods of high rainfall the river floods the meadow but this seems to have had little harmful effect on the vegetation.

Habitat Study 74   meadow above Water End,
                              Wheathampstead
TL/196 139 (11/W)   Alt. 230 ft.   Soil: Alluvium (pH 7·8)
Surveyed: 20 May 1962 with L. and M. Ll.-E. and C. M. D., 30 July 1962 with C. M. D. This study was made about twenty yards from the river in the meadow in the long bend of the river opposite Gray's Wood.

Locally abundant: Agrostis stolonifera, Carex acutiformis, Glyceria plicata.

Frequent: Eleocharis palustris, Juncus articulatus, J. inflexus (L), Mentha aquatica (L), Myosoton aquaticum, Ranunculus repens (L).

Occasional: Carex hirta (o-f), Cerastium fontanum (o-f), Glyceria fluitans, Holcus lanatus, Poa trivialis, Polygonum amphibium (o-lf).

Rare: Alopecurus geniculatus, Cardamine pratensis, Cirsium palustre, Epilobium hirsutum (r-o), E. parviflorum, Lysimachia nummularia, Myosotis sp., Nasturtium microphyllum, Plantago major, Ranunculus acris, Rumex conglomeratus, R. crispus, Scrophularia auriculata, Trifolium pratense, T. repens (r-o), Urtica dioica, Veronica beccabunga (r-o).

A marshy meadow at Rye Meads provided a useful study. It adjoins a large sewage works which is the headquarters of the Rye Meads Ringing Group, well known for its pioneer ornithological research. The meadow itself is not directly affected by the sewage effluent. It is an interesting site as it is almost the only remnant of a long series of marshy meadows that at one time skirted the Lower Lea Valley.

Habitat Study 75   meadow, Rye Meads,
                              Stanstead Abbots
TL/391 108 (31/V)   Alt. 95 ft.   Soil: Alluvium (pH 5·7)
Surveyed: 14th June 1962 with L. and M. Ll.-E. and C. M. D., 8 Sept. 1962 with C. M. D. This study was made fifteen yards from the hedge in the last field towards Ryegate Farm from the Sewage Works.

Frequent: Bromus commutatus, Centaurea nigra, Thalictrum flavum (L).

Occasional: Ajuga reptans, Anthoxanthum odoratum, Festuca pratensis, F. rubra, Filipendula ulmaria (o-f), Holcus lanatus (o-f), Juncus effusus (o-lf), Plantago lanceolata, Rumex acetosa, Sisymbrium officinale, Taraxacum officinale.

Rare: Alopecurus pratensis, Angelica sylvestris (r-o), Arrhenatherum elatius, Briza media, Carex acutiformis (r-o), C. hirta, Cerastium fontanum, Cirsium palustre, Crataegus monogyna (1) 3 in., Dactylis glomerata, Deschampsia cespitosa, Juncus subuliflorus, Lathyrus pratensis, Lysimachia nummularia, Ophioglossum vulgatum, Phleum pratense, Poa pratensis, Prunella vulgaris, Ranunculus acris (r-o), R. repens, Salix caprea (1) 6 in., Succisa pratensis, Trifolium repens, Valeriana officinalis, Vicia cracca (r-o).

The remaining marsh to be studied in the Lea Gravels Region is in the valley of the River Stort and must rank as one of the finest marshes in the county.

Habitat Study 76   Sawbridgeworth Marsh
TL/493 157 (41/X) Alt. 160 ft.   Soil: Alluvium (pH 7·5)
Surveyed: 24 June 1962 with J. L. Fielding and C. M. D.,
30 Aug. 1962 with L. and M. Ll.-E. and C. M. D. This
study was made by the side of the ditch which forms the
boundary of the lower part of the marsh at a point about a
hundred yards north of the hedge crossing the upper part
of the marsh.
Frequent: Berula erecta (L), Equisetum fluviatile (L),
Juncus subnodulosus, Mentha aquatica.
Occasional: Carex acutiformis (o-lf), Equisetum palustre
(o-lf), Festuca rubra, Filipendula ulmaria, Holcus lanatus
(o-f), Lotus uliginosus, Nasturtium microphyllum,
Poa trivialis, Sparganium erectum, Valeriana dioica.
Rare: Agrostis stolonifera, Angelica sylvestris, Bidens
cernua, Caltha palustris, Cardamine pratensis, Carex
disticha, C. nigra, C. panicea, Catabrosa aquatica,
Cerastium fontanum, Cirsium palustre, Dactylorhiza
praetermissa, Epilobium parviflorum (r-o), E. palustre
(r-o), Festuca arundinacea, F. pratensis, Galium palustre,
G. uliginosum (r-o), Glyceria plicata, Hypericum tetrapterum, Juncus acutiflorus, J. inflexus, Lathyrus pratensis,
Lemna minor, Lychnis flos-cuculi, Lycopus europaeus,
Lysimachia nummularia, Lythrum salicaria, Myosotis
scorpioides, Phalaris arundinacea, Polygonum amphibium (1), Ranunculus acris, Rhinanthus minor, Rumex
acetosa, R. conglomeratus, Scrophularia auriculata,
Sonchus arvensis, Stellaria alsine, Triglochin palustre,
Valeriana officinalis, Veronica beccabunga (r-o), Vicia
cracca.

Natural woodland is not a feature of the river gravels
but there is sufficient Boulder Clay in the region to com-
pensate for this. The result is that it is better wooded than
might have been expected but close inspection shows that
many of the woods are planted and much of the old woodland has been subject to comparatively recent replanting.
One of the largest wooded areas in the region forms part
of the Knebworth Estate where the Boulder Clay is less in
evidence.

Habitat Study 77   Newton Wood, Knebworth
TL/224 222 (22/G)   Alt. 340 ft.
Soil: Clay-with-Flints overlying Upper Chalk (pH 4·5)
Surveyed: 2 June 1962 with H. and D. Meyer and C. M. D.,
31 July 1962 with C. M. D. This study was made on the
main ride through the wood from Burleigh Meadow
(H.S.72) at a point thirty-five yards beyond the track on
the left marked 'Private'. The wood here is open which
contributes to the large number of species recorded.
Frequent: Glechoma hederacea.
Occasional: Carex sylvatica (o-f), Circaea lutetiana, Cir-
sium palustre, Endymion non-scriptus (L), Holcus
lanatus (o-f), Juncus bufonius (L), Mentha arvensis (L),
Poa annua (L), P. trivialis (o-f), Rubus sp.
Rare: Agrostis tenuis (r-o), A stolonifera, Ajuga reptans,
Anagallis arvensis, Angelica sylvestris, Aphanes arvensis,
Arenaria serpyllifolia, Betula pubescens (2) 6 in., Callitriche stagnalis, Capsella bursa-pastoris, Carex otrubae,
C. pallescens, C. remota (r-o), Carpinus betulus < 6 ft.,
Centaurium erythraea, Cerastium fontanum, C. glomeratum, Cirsium arvense, C. vulgare, Deschampsia cespitosa,   Epilobium adenocaulon, E. angustifolium, E.
montanum, Fragaria vesca, Galeopsis tetrahit, Galium
aparine, G. palustre, Geranium robertianum, Geum
urbanum, Gnaphalium uliginosum, Hypericum pulchrum, H. tetrapterum, Juncus effusus, J. inflexus (1),
J. subuliflorus, Lolium perenne, Lonicera periclymenum,
Luzula pilosa (r-o), Lychnis flos-cuculi, Lycopus europaeus, Lysimachia nemorum, L. nummularia, Moehringia
trinervia, Myosotis arvensis, Plantago major (r-o),
Polygonum aviculare, Potentilla reptans (r-o), Potentilla

sterilis, Prunella vulgaris (r-o), Quercus robur (1) 50 ft.,
Ranunculus repens, Rosa sp., Rumex obtusifolius,
R. sanguineus, Sagina procumbens (r-o), Salix caprea
(2) <2 ft., Sanicula europaea, Scirpus setaceus, Senecio
jacobaea, Solanum dulcamara, Stachys sylvatica, Stellaria
alsine, S. graminea, Taraxacum officinale, Trifolium
repens, Tripleurospermum maritimum, Veronica beccabunga, V. chamaedrys, V. montana, V. serpyllifolia,
Viola riviniana.

The Boulder Clay is more in evidence in the following
four studies which were made in woods managed by the
Forestry Commission. In the vicinity of the first study
there had been a great deal of re-planting.

Habitat Study 78   Bramfield Park Wood (first study)
TL/285 157 (21/X)   Alt. 300 ft.
                         Soil: Boulder Clay (pH 5·8)
Surveyed: 20 May 1962 with L. and M. Ll.-E. and
C. M. D., 24 July 1962 with P. M. Benoit and C. M. D.
This study was made fifteen yards along the ride to the
north-east from the main intersection of rides in the wood.
Frequent: Agrostis tenuis, Anthoxanthum odoratum,
Holcus lanatus, Populus tremula <3 ft.
Occasional: Bromus ramosus, Carex remota, C. sylvatica,
Carpinus betulus (seedlings), Deschampsia cespitosa,
Festuca rubra, Glyceria fluitans (L), Hedera helix,
Juncus effusus, Lonicera periclymenum, Lysimachia
nummularia, Potentilla reptans (o-lf), Stellaria graminea,
S. holostea.
Rare: Agrostis canina, A stolonifera, Ajuga reptans (r-o),
Angelica sylvestris, Betonica officinalis, Betula pendula
(1) 30 ft., Callitriche stagnalis, Cardamine pratensis,
Carex demissa, C. flacca, C. ovalis, C. pallescens, Carpinus betulus < 15 ft., Cerastium fontanum, Crataegus
monogyna < 6 ft., Dactylis glomerata, Dryopteris
filix-mas, Epilobium montanum, Fragaria vesca, Fraxinus
excelsior <20 ft., Galium aparine, G. palustre (r-o),
Geranium robertianum, Geum urbanum, Gnaphalium
uliginosum, Holcus mollis, Juncus articulatus (r-o),
J. bufonius, J. subuliflorus, Listera ovata (1), Lotus
uliginosus, Luzula multiflora, L. pilosa, Lychnis flos-
cuculi, Mentha arvensis (r-o), Milium effusum, Odontites
verna, Phleum bertolonii, Plantago major, Poa annua
(r-o), P. trivialis, Potentilla erecta (r-o), P. sterilis,
Prunella vulgaris (r-o), Quercus robur (1) 2 in., Ranunculus acris, R. auricomus, R. repens (r-o), Rosa arvensis,
Rubus sp., Rumex sanguineus, Sagina procumbens,
Scirpus setaceus, Swida sanguinea, Tamus communis,
Trifolium dubium, T. repens, Veronica chamaedrys,
Viburnum opulus (3) <2 ft., Vicia angustifolia, Viola
riviniana.

The second study was made a short distance from the
first but in a part of the wood free from interference.

Habitat Study 79 Bramfield Park Wood (second study)
TL/285 159 (21/X)   Alt. 300 ft.
                         Soil: Boulder Clay (pH 6·1)
Surveyed: 20 May 1962 with L. and M. Ll.-E. and
C. M. D., 24 July 1962 with P. M. Benoit and C. M. D.
This study was reached by continuing along the ride in
which the previous study was made and then taking the
first ride on the left. The second study was made on this
ride fifty-five yards before its exit from the wood.
Frequent: Centaurea nigra, Prunella vulgaris.
Occasional: Brachypodium sylvaticum, Chrysanthemum
leucanthemum, Crataegus monogyna < 8 ft., Epilobium
angustifolium, Holcus lanatus, Plantago lanceolata
(o-f), Rosa arvensis (o-lf), R. canina, Rubus sp. (o-f),
Senecio erucifolius.

43

Rare: Acer pseudo-platanus < 6 ft., Agrimonia eupatoria, Agrostis stolonifera, A. tenuis, Arrhenatherum elatius, Bellis perennis, Betula pendula (1) 25 ft., Cerastium fontanum, Cirsium arvense, C. palustre, C. vulgare, Cynosurus cristatus (r-o), Dactylis glomerata, Festuca rubra, Fragaria vesca, Fraxinus excelsior < 12 ft., Galium mollugo, Geum urbanum, Hedera helix, Heracleum sphondylium, Hypericum hirsutum, Odontites verna, Plantago major, P. trivialis, Potentilla reptans (r-o), Quercus robur < 12 ft., Ranunculus repens, Rubus idaeus, Rumex acetosa, R. sanguineus, Sarothamnus scoparius < 8 ft., Swida sanguinea, Tamus communis, Vicia angustifolia, V. tetrasperma, Viola riviniana.

The next study showed a considerable variation in the flora resulting from a change within the area of the study.

Habitat Study 80   Wren's Wood, Watton-at-Stone
TL/285 175   (21/Y)   Alt. 375 ft.
                                    Soil: Boulder Clay (pH 6·7)
Surveyed: 20 May 1962 with L. and M. Ll.-E. and C. M. D., 22 July 1962 with A. Lowe. This study was made at the western end of a gravel drive and at the base of an ash tree. The vegetation fell into three distinct zones: (1) the bare side of the drive (2) a bank (3) a portion of rough woodland. This accounts for the large number of species in the list being given as 'local'.
Frequent: Agrostis canina (L), A. tenuis, Galium mollugo (lf-l.ab), Holcus lanatus (f-ab), Mercurialis perennis (L), Sagina procumbens (L).
Occasional: Agrostis stolonifera, Brachypodium sylvaticum (L), Clinopodium vulgare (L), Epilobium angustifolium (L), E. montanum, Glechoma hederacea, Moehringia trinervia (L), Stellaria holostea, Viburnum opulus < 4 ft.
Rare: Acer pseudo-platanus < 4 ft., Achillea millefolium, Alopecurus myosuroides, Arctium minus, Arrhenatherum elatius, Bromus ramosus, Carpinus betulus < 5 ft., Cerastium fontanum, C. glomeratum, Cirsium arvense, C. palustre, C. vulgare, Circaea lutetiana, Corylus avellana < 1 ft., Crataegus monogyna < 6 in., Crepis capillaris, Dactylis glomerata, Endymion non-scriptus, Epilobium adenocaulon, Euphorbia amygdaloides, Fagus sylvatica < 2 ft., Fragaria vesca (r-o), Fraxinus excelsior, seedlings, (1) 30 ft., Geranium robertianum, Hedera helix, Heracleum sphondylium (r-o), Holcus mollis, Hypericum hirsutum (r-o), H. perforatum, Juncus effusus, J. subuliflorus, Lonicera periclymenum, Lychnis flos-cuculi, Mentha arvensis, Myosotis arvensis, Odontites verna, Phleum bertolonii, Plantago major, Poa annua, P. nemoralis, Polygonum aviculare, Potentilla reptans, P. sterilis, Prunella vulgaris, Ranunculus repens (r-o), Rubus sp. (r-o), Rumex crispus (1), R. sanguineus (1), Sanicula europaea (r-o), Scrophularia nodosa (1), Senecio jacobaea, Silene vulgaris, Stachys sylvatica (r-o), Stellaria media, Swida sanguinea, Tamus communis, Tussilago farfara, Urtica dioica, Veronica chamaedrys (r-o), V. officinalis, V. serpyllifolia, Viola riviniana.

The last study made in the Forestry Commission woodland illustrates the somewhat variable nature of the Boulder Clay in this part of the county.

Habitat Study 81   Nicholson's Wood, Watton-at-Stone
TL/281 171 (21/Y)   Alt. 400 ft.
                                    Soil: Boulder Clay (pH 4·2)
Surveyed: 20 May 1962 with L. and M. Ll.-E. and C. M. D., 28 July 1962 with A. Lowe. This study was made in a clearing six yards from the main path.
Abundant: Aira praecox.
Frequent: Carex pilulifera (f-ab), Galium saxatile, Holcus mollis, Juncus effusus (L), Rumex acetosella.

Occasional: Agrostis canina (o-f), A. tenuis (o-f), Anthoxanthum odoratum, Holcus lanatus, Hypochoeris radicata, Luzula campestris (o-f), Pteridium aquilinum.
Rare: Betula pubescens (2) 5 ft., Calluna vulgaris (r-o), Carpinus betulus (1) 4 ft., Epilobium angustifolium (r-o), Juncus subuliflorus (r-o), Lonicera periclymenum, Luzula multiflora, L. pilosa, Polygala serpyllifolia (r-o), Potentilla erecta (r-o), Quercus sp. (1 planted), 4 ft., Rubus sp. (r-o).

The Boulder Clay becomes less evident in the southern part of the Region and the last woodland study was made on yet another geological formation.

Habitat Study 82   Easneye Wood, Stanstead Abbots
TL/386 136 (31/W)   Alt. 200 ft.
Soil: Sand and Gravel overlying Reading Beds (pH 7·2)
Surveyed: 26 May 1962 with H.B. and G. Souster and C. M. D., 22 July 1962 with P. M. Benoit and C. M. D. This study was made on the east side of the main ride into the wood at a point ninety-five yards from the fence at the top of this ride. The shade was only moderate but the interior of the wood at this point was completely denuded of ground vegetation.
Locally abundant: Mercurialis perennis, Poa trivialis, Ranunculus ficaria.
Frequent: Carex pendula (L), Ulmus sp., < 30 ft., Urtica dioica (L).
Occasional: Galeobdolon luteum (L), Glechoma hederacea (o-lf).
Rare: Agrimonia eupatoria, Ajuga reptans, Arum maculatum, Circaea lutetiana, Cirsium arvense, Corylus avellana (1) 4 ft., Crataegus monogyna (1) 2 ft., Dipsacus pilosus, Endymion non-scriptus, Festuca gigantea, Galium aparine, Geum urbanum, Heracleum sphondylium (r-o), Moehringia trinervia, Plantago major, Poa annua, Polygonum aviculare, Potentilla reptans (r-o), P. sterilis (r-o), Ranunculus repens, Rubus sp., Rumex sanguineus, Sambucus nigra, Silene dioica, Sorbus aucuparia (1) 30 ft., Stachys sylvatica, Taraxacum officinale, Veronica chamaedrys, Vicia sepium, Viola riviniana.

The Lea Gravels Region has a wide assortment of soils which gives a great variety to the weeds of arable land. The colonist flora is not, however, as interesting as it is in the neighbouring Boulder Clay Region. A study was made of a railway embankment in the hope that it would reveal some of the elements in the colonist flora of at least one part of the Region.

Habitat Study 83   railway bank, Nine Springs, Hitchin
                                                              Urban
TL/203 287 (22/E)   Alt. 200 ft.
                                    Soil: Chalk (pH 7·7)
Surveyed: 9 June 1962 with J. Lovell, 8 Aug. 1962 with C. M. D. This study was made on the west aspect of the embankment at a point twenty yards north of the platelayer's hut and five yards down the bank.
Frequent: Bromus erectus, Centaurea scabiosa (f-ab).
Occasional: Achillea millefolium, Arrhenatherum elatius, Cerastium arvense (L), Convolvulus arvensis, Daucus carota, Festuca rubra, Hypericum perforatum (o-f), Plantago lanceolata (o-f), Poa angustifolia, Potentilla reptans, Silene alba, S. vulgaris, Valerianella locusta.
Rare: Anthriscus sylvestris, Arabidopsis thaliana, Arenaria leptoclados, Artemisia vulgaris (r-o), Centaurea nigra, Chrysanthemum leucanthemum, Dactylis glomerata (r-o), Fumaria officinalis, Hieracium pilosella, Lamium purpureum, Lathyrus pratensis, Linaria vulgaris, Origanum vulgare, Picris hieracioides (r-o), Rumex acetosa (r-o), R. crispus, Senecio jacobaea, S. vulgaris, Taraxacum officinale, Veronica arvensis, Vicia angustifolia (r-o), V. hirsuta (r-o).

The gravels are quarried throughout the Region and the holes that are left in the ground are almost invariably soon filled with rubbish with the result that the incidence of refuse tips is no doubt greater here than anywhere else in Britain and probably in the whole world. This adds continuously to an alien flora in the county that has interested botanists for half a century. As the source of most of the rubbish are the dustbins of North London many species have their origin in bird-seed mixtures and these are features of all the rubbish dumps. Near to Wymondley a few farmers use wool manure (shoddy) on the light gravelly soils. Some wool-adventive species have been recorded but many fewer than from Bedfordshire where a greater amount of shoddy is used on the sandy fields in the middle of that county.

The Region is well served with water. At Hertford the River Lea is joined by the Mimram, Beane and Rib and below the town the river is navigable for the rest of its course. At Chadwell, between Hertford and Ware, the New River begins. This was constructed by Sir Hugh Myddleton in 1631 and it still carries water to London. Below Ware the Lea is joined by the Ash and the Stort, the latter having been made navigable as far as Bishop's Stortford.

From the confluence of the Stort and the Lea to the county boundary there is a continuous chain of flooded gravel pits that is soon to be transformed into the Lea Valley National Park. The lower stretches of the Lea and the Stort are subject to periodic dredging but still contain an interesting aquatic flora in which *Myriophyllum verticillatum*, *Sagittaria sagittifolia*, *Sparganium emersum* and *Potamogeton lucens* are prominent. The flooded gravel pits are subject to constant change and while they give rise to interesting plant associations these were not considered to be stable enough to merit special study.

The River Lea finally leaves the county near to Waltham Abbey at a height of only sixty-nine feet above sea level.

E. THE COLNE GRAVELS REGION (Map 8)

This is closely comparable with the Lea Gravels Region from which it has been separated only for convenience. The River Colne which rises near Colney Heath is joined by the River Ver to the south of St. Albans and by the River Gade at Rickmansworth. The Gade, with its tributary, the River Bulbourne, determines the route of the Grand Union Canal from Tring to Watford. Also at Rickmansworth the Colne is joined by the River Chess, the cleanest and most delightful of all the chalk streams of the county.

The gravels are the most distinguishing feature of the Region but all geological formations which have been so far considered still appear to complicate what would otherwise be a simple structure. There are chalk exposures on the sides of the river valleys and they are especially evident in the extreme south of the Region.

To the north of Sarratt is an interesting site called Commonwood Common. The higher part, affected by the Clay-with-Flints, is very acid but the lower part is pure chalk showing signs of previous excavation. A study was made there and it will be the last time that we shall need to study the Chalk in detail.

Habitat Study 84   Commonwood Common, Sarratt
TL/046 001 (00/F)   Alt. 325 ft.
    Soil: Upper Chalk (pH 7·9)
Surveyed: 19 May 1962 with C. M. D., 23 July 1962 with P. M. Benoit and C. M. D. This study was made four yards below the division in the paths on the lower slope of the large pit. The gradient here is about 1 in 10 and the aspect south-east.
Frequent: Bromus erectus, Trisetum flavescens.

Occasional: Bellis perennis, Brachypodium sylvaticum, Briza media, Carex flacca (o-f), Crataegus monogyna (seedlings), Festuca ovina, F. rubra (o-f), Helictotrichon pubescens (L), Leontodon hispidus, Plantago lanceolata (o-f), Sanguisorba minor (o-f), Swida sanguinea < 5 ft., Vicia angustifolia.
Rare: Acer campestre (1) 3 ft., Achillea millefolium (r-o), Agrimonia eupatoria (r-o), Agrostis stolonifera, A. tenuis, Arrhenatherum elatius, Carex caryophyllea, Catapodium rigidum, Centaurea nigra (r-o), Chrysanthemum leucanthemum, Cirsium acaulon (r-o), Clematis vitalba, Crataegus monogyna < 3 ft., Cynosurus cristatus (r-o), Dactylis glomerata, Daucus carota, Fraxinus excelsior (1) 15 ft., Galium aparine, G. mollugo, G. verum (r-o), Hedera helix (r-o), Heracleum sphondylium, Hieracium pilosella, Holcus lanatus, Ilex aquifolium (1) 6 in., Juniperus communis (4) < 2 ft., Koeleria cristata, Leontodon autumnalis, Linum catharticum (r-o), Lolium perenne, Lotus corniculatus (r-o), Malus sylvestris (1) 4 ft., Medicago lupulina (r-o), Picris hieracioides, Plantago major, P. media (r-o), Poa annua, P. pratensis (r-o), Potentilla sterilis, Prunella vulgaris (r-o), Prunus avium (1) 2 ft., P. spinosa < 2 ft., Ranunculus acris, R. bulbosus, R. repens, Rosa canina (r-o), Rubus sp., Salix caprea (1) 6 ft., Sanicula europaea, Senecio jacobaea, Sieglingia decumbens, Stachys sylvatica, Taraxacum laevigata, T. officinale, Tamus communis, Thymus pulegioides, Torilis japonica, Tragopogon pratensis, Trifolium pratense (r-o), T. repens (r-o), Ulex europaeus (1) 2 ft.

Dry pastures within the Region are few but they are generally worthy of study. Nomansland, an open space suffering from a great deal of human pressure, is a good example of the survival of unusual species in adverse conditions.

Habitat Study 85   Nomansland, Sandridge
TL/166 125 (11/R)   Alt. 300 ft.
    Soil: Valley Gravel (pH 4·1)
Surveyed: 26 April 1962 with L. and M. Ll.-E. and C. M. D., 5 July 1962. This study was made one hundred yards to the west of a path crossing the common and five yards below a shallow depression about twenty yards from the metalled road.
Abundant: Calluna vulgaris, Festuca ovina, Luzula campestris.
Frequent: Agrostis tenuis, Aira praecox (f-l.ab), Galium saxatile, Rumex acetosella.
Occasional: Ulex minor < 6 in.
Rare: Genista anglica (r-o), Hieracium pilosella (r-o), Hypochoeris radicata (r-o), Sieglingia decumbens, Ulex europaeus < 2 ft.

A similar study made at Chorleywood Common produced as small a list but with no redeeming features of unusual species.

Habitat Study 86   Chorleywood Common
TQ/030 965 (09/I)   Alt. 350 ft.
    Soil: Glacial Gravel (pH 4·0)
Surveyed: 12 June 1962 with C. M. D., 23 Aug. 1962 with C. M. D. This study was made on the side of a major ride on the west side of the Common.
Frequent: Agrostis tenuis, Festuca ovina, F. rubra, Rumex acetosella.
Occasional: Calluna vulgaris (o-lf), Galium saxatile (o-f), Luzula campestris (o-f), Sieglingia decumbens (o-f).
Rare: Campanula rotundifolia, Hypochoeris radicata, Potentilla erecta, Pteridium aquilinum, Quercus robur (2) < 2 ft., Rubus sp., Ulex europaeus (1) 6 in.

The wet pastures of the Region are worthy of close study and the best example is Bricketwood Common. This was at one time wet heath, remnants of which may still be seen, but it is now mainly scrub in an advanced stage of development. It has, with every justification, attracted the attention of Hertfordshire naturalists more than any other site and it has still much to commend it for further study. It was considered to merit three separate studies.

Habitat Study 87   Bricketwood Common, St. Stephen
(first study)
TL/130 008 (10/F) Alt. 250 ft. Soil: Boulder Clay (pH 4·9)
Surveyed: 4 July 1962 with C. M. D., 3 Sept. 1962 with B. Goater and C. M. D., 11 May 1963. This study was reached by entering the Common by the track opposite the road to Munden House and proceeding about 250 yards to the pond marked on the Ordnance Survey Map. The study itself was made on the side of the track thirty yards short of the track leaving it on the right.
Locally abundant: Molinia caerulea.
Frequent: Agrostis canina, Juncus subuliflorus.
Occasional: Agrostis stolonifera, Carex ovalis (o-lf), Endymion non-scriptus, Galium saxatile (L), Juncus acutiflorus (o-f).
Rare: Agrostis tenuis (r-o), Anthoxanthum odoratum, Betula pendula (3) < 20 ft., Carex demissa, C. nigra (r-o), C. panicea, Cirsium palustre (1), Corylus avellana (1) 1 ft., Dactylorhiza fuchsii, Deschampsia cespitosa, Glyceria fluitans (r-o), Gnaphalium uliginosum, Holcus lanatus, Juncus bufonius, J. bulbosus, J. effusus (r-o), J. kochii, Lotus uliginosus, Luzula multiflora, Peplis portula, Populus tremula (1) 4 ft., Potentilla erecta, Quercus robur < 1 ft., Ranunculus flammula (r-o), Salix cinerea < 10 ft., Sieglingia decumbens, Succisa pratensis, Viola riviniana.

Habitat Study 88   Bricketwood Common, St. Stephen
(second study)
TL/127 010 (10/F) Alt. 250 ft. Soil: Boulder Clay (pH 5·8)
Surveyed: 4 July 1962 with C. M. D., 3 Sept. 1962 with B. Goater and C. M. D. This study was reached by proceeding further along the trackway on which the previous study was made to the bridge over the railway. The study itself was made a further eighty yards along track from the manhole cover on the bridge.
Frequent: Callitriche stagnalis (L), Glyceria fluitans (L), Holcus mollis, Poa trivialis.
Occasional: Cerastium glomeratum, Corylus avellana (o-lf) < 18 ft., Festuca gigantea (o-f), Polygonum hydropiper, Quercus robur (seedlings), Rubus sp.
Rare: Agrostis stolonifera, Ajuga reptans (r-o), Betula pendula (1) 30 ft., Bidens cernua, Brachypodium sylvaticum, Cardamine flexuosa (r-o), Carex remota, C. sylvatica, Circaea lutetiana (r-o), Crataegus monogyna < 6 ft., Deschampsia cespitosa, Epilobium adenocaulon, E. montanum, E. roseum, Fragaria vesca, Fraxinus excelsior (2) 3 ft., Geum urbanum, Gnaphalium uliginosum, Holcus lanatus, Juncus bufonius, J. effusus, J. subuliflorus, Lapsana communis, Lonicera periclymenum (r-o), Lysimachia nemorum, L. nummularia, Plantago major, Poa annua (r-o), Potentilla anserina, P. reptans (r-o), P. sterilis, Pteridium aquilinum, Quercus robur (1) 40 ft., R. sceleratus, Rosa arvensis, Rumex conglomeratus, R. sanguineus, Salix caprea (1) 2 ft., Scrophularia nodosa, Trifolium repens, Veronica chamaedrys, Viola riviniana.

Habitat Study 89   Bricketwood Common, St. Stephen
(third study)
TL/131 007 (10/F) Alt. 250 ft. Soil: Boulder Clay (pH 4·8)
Surveyed: 4 July 1962 with C. M. D., 3 Sept. 1962 with

B. Goater and C. M. D. This study was made on the track used to approach H.S. 87 at a distance of two hundred yards from the metalled road.
Locally dominant: Pteridium aquilinum.
Frequent: Holcus lanatus (L), Juncus bufonius.
Occasional: Agrostis canina (o-f), Frangula alnus < 4 ft., Gnaphalium uliginosum, Juncus acutiflorus, Lonicera periclymenum, Populus tremula (suckers), Potentilla erecta, Quercus robur (seedlings).
Rare: Anthoxanthum odoratum, Betula pubescens (1) 20 ft., B. pendula (r-o) < 20 ft., Bidens cernua (1), Callitriche stagnalis, Carex pallescens, Cirsium palustre, Crataegus monogyna < 6 ft., Deschampsia cespitosa, Endymion non-scriptus, Epilobium angustifolium, Glyceria fluitans, Hieracium perpropinquum, Juncus bulbosus, J. subuliflorus, Lotus uliginosus, Luzula multiflora, Molinia caerulea (r-o), Populus tremula (1) 15 ft., Quercus robur (1) 20 ft., Rubus sp., Salix aurita < 3 ft., S. cinerea < 4 ft., Sieglingia decumbens, Succisa pratensis, Teucrium scorodonia (r-o), Trifolium sp. (1), Viburnum opulus (2) < 4 ft., Viola riviniana.

Without doubt the best water meadows in the county are those beside the River Chess at Sarratt Bottom. In addition they contain some Hertfordshire rarities in *Geum rivale, Pedicularis palustris* and *Blysmus compressus*.

Habitat Study 90   Sarratt Bottom (first study)
TQ/031 989 (09/J)   Alt. 220 ft.
          Soil: Alluvium overlying Middle Chalk (pH 5·2)
Surveyed: 12 June 1962 with C. M. D., 23 Aug. 1962 with C. M. D. This study was made ten yards to the north-west of the western end of the ditch crossing the meadows.
Frequent: Juncus effusus (f-ab.), Lychnis flos-cuculi, Senecio aquaticus.
Occasional: Anthoxanthum odoratum (o-f), Carex disticha, C. hirta, C. panicea, Equisetum palustre, Filipendula ulmaria, Galium palustre, Holcus lanatus, Juncus articulatus, Lotus uliginosus, Phleum bertolonii, Ranunculus repens (o-f), Rumex acetosa, R. conglomeratus.
Rare: Agrostis stolonifera, Ajuga reptans, Cardamine pratensis (r-o), Carex demissa, C. nigra, C. ovalis, Centaurea nigra, Cerastium fontanum, Cirsium palustre, Deschampsia cespitosa, Epilobium parviflorum, Festuca pratensis, F. rubra, Galium uliginosum (r-o), Glyceria fluitans, Hypericum tetrapterum, Hypochoeris radicata, Juncus inflexus, Lathyrus pratensis, Leontodon autumnalis, Luzula campestris, Lysimachia nummularia, Plantago lanceolata, P. major, Poa pratensis, P. trivialis, Potentilla anserina, P. erecta, Prunella vulgaris (r-o), Ranunculus acris, R. flammula (r-o), Rumex obtusifolius, Salix cinerea (1) 1 ft., Stellaria graminea (r-o), Taraxacum officinale, Trifolium pratense, T. repens, Valeriana dioica.

Habitat Study 91   Sarratt Bottom (second study)
TQ/0315 9880 (09/J)   Alt. 220 ft.
          Soil: Alluvium overlying Middle Chalk (pH 5·5)
Surveyed: 12 June 1962 with C. M. D., 23 Aug. 1962 with C. M. D. This study was made one hundred yards beyond the ditch and twenty yards inside the meadow from the river.
Frequent: Anthoxanthum odoratum, Carex hirta, Cynosurus cristatus, Poa trivialis (L), Ranunculus flammula.
Occasional: Agrostis stolonifera, Alopecurus geniculatus (o-f), Cardamine pratensis (o-f), Carex nigra, C. panicea (o-f), Holcus lanatus (o-f), Juncus articulatus (o-f), J. effusus, Leontodon autumnalis, Lychnis flos-cuculi, Ranunculus acris, R. repens, Senecio aquaticus, Stellaria alsine.
Rare: Bellis perennis, Caltha palustris (r-o), Carex disticha, C. ovalis, Centaurea nigra, Cerastium fontanum, Cir-

sium palustre, Eleocharis palustris (r-o), Equisetum arvense, Festuca pratensis, F. rubra, Galium palustre (r-o), G. uliginosum, Glyceria fluitans, Juncus inflexus, Lotus uliginosus, Luzula campestris, Myosotis scorpioides, Odontites verna, Plantago lanceolata, Poa pratensis, Polygonum persicaria, Potentilla erecta, Prunella vulgaris, Rumex acetosa (r-o), R. conglomeratus (r-o), Sagina procumbens, Succisa pratensis, Trifolium pratense (r-o), T. repens (r-o), Veronica beccabunga.

Croxley Common Moor is similar in origin to Sarratt Bottom but is larger in extent and more dried out. Notwithstanding its proximity to recent industrial development it must still rank as one of the more important botanical sites in the county.

Habitat Study 92 Croxley Common Moor,
Rickmansworth
TQ 082 948 (09/X) Alt. 170 ft.
Soil: Alluvium (pH 4·6)
Surveyed: 16 June 1962 with C. M. D., 4 Aug. 1962 with E. B. Bangerter, A. C. Jermy and C. M. D. This study was made two hundred yards beyond the pylon on the path across the Moor from the industrial estate and then twenty yards to the east. There is here a very slight slope with a west aspect.
Frequent: Agrostis tenuis, Aira praecox (f-l.ab.), Festuca ovina (f-ab.), Hieracium pilosella (f-ab.), Rumex acetosella.
Occasional: Achillea millefolium (o-f), Festuca rubra (o-f), Galium verum, Genista anglica, G. tinctoria, Hypochoeris radicata, Lotus corniculatus, Luzula campestris (o-f), Poa pratensis, Ranunculus bulbosus.
Rare: Crataegus monogyna (2) 3 in., Koeleria cristata, Leontodon autumnalis, Nardus stricta, Plantago lanceolata (r-o), Sarothamnus scoparius (1) 3 ft., Trifolium dubium, T. pratense, T. repens.

As so much of the Colne Gravels Region is either built-up or given over to gravel pits it is the least wooded part of the county. The few woods are on various soils and studies were made in two adjoining woods on the Boulder Clay in the north of the Region.

Habitat Study 93. Titnols Wood, Hatfield
TL/194 115 (11/V). Alt. 350 ft.
Soil: Boulder Clay (pH 5·0)
Surveyed: 17 June 1962 with H. B. Souster, 24 Aug. 1962 with J. Lovell. This study was made in the main ride of the wood thirty-five yards beyond the barrier at the entrance to the wood.
Locally dominant: Rubus sp.
Frequent: Epilobium angustifolium.
Occasional: Circaea lutetiana, Fragaria vesca, Fraxinus excelsior (seedlings), Poa annua, P. trivialis.
Rare: Carex pendula, C. sylvatica (r-o), Carpinus betulus <6 in., Corylus avellana (1) 8 ft., Deschampsia cespitosa (r-o), Dryopteris filix-mas (1), Epilobium montanum, Fraxinus excelsior (1) 50 ft., Geranium robertianum (r-o), Geum urbanum, Glechoma hederacea, Lonicera periclymenum, Lysimachia nemorum, Potentilla sterilis, Prunella vulgaris (r-o), Prunus avium <6 ft., Pteridium aquilinum (r-o), Quercus robur (1) 12 ft., Ranunculus repens, Rosa arvensis, Rumex obtusifolius (1), R. sanguineus, Sanicula europaea, Stachys sylvatica, Tamus communis, Viola riviniana.

Habitat Study 94 Symondshyde Great Wood, Hatfield
TL/193 112 (11/V) Alt. 360 ft.
Soil: Boulder Clay (pH 4·8)
Surveyed: 17 June 1962 with H. B. Souster, 24 Aug. 1962

with J. Lovell. This study was made at the division of the paths separating Chalkdell Wood and Symondshyde Great Wood – there is here an open habitat.
Frequent: Agrostis stolonifera, Poa trivialis, Rubus sp.
Occasional: Ajuga reptans (o-f), Brachypodium sylvaticum (o-f), Fragaria vesca, Galium palustre, Holcus lanatus, Potentilla sterilis, Viola riviniana.
Rare: Acer pseudo–platanus < 4 ft., Agrimonia eupatoria, Atriplex hastata (1), Carpinus betulus (1) 8 ft., Circaea lutetiana (r-o), Dactylis glomerata, Fraxinus excelsior (seedlings) (1) 50 ft., Galium aparine, Geum urbanum, Lonicera periclymenum (r-o), Lysimachia nemorum, Mentha arvensis, Mercurialis perennis, Plantago major, Poa annua, P. nemoralis, Polygonum hydropiper, Potentilla reptans (r-o), Prunella vulgaris (r-o), Pteridium aquilinum, Quercus robur (seedlings) (1) 50 ft., Ranunculus repens (r-o), Rosa arvensis, Stachys sylvatica, Swida sanguinea (1) 10 ft., Veronica montana.

In the large Whippendell Wood (09/T), near Watford, and in neighbouring woods *Cardamine bulbifera* is frequent. To the south-west of Rickmansworth there are a few woods such as Bottom Wood (09/G) and Pollardshill Wood (09/G) which are influenced by the Chalk. A wooded area similar to this lies on the slope above the River Chess between Sarratt Bottom and Sarratt. A small wood here was chosen for closer study.

Habitat Study 95 wood, Dawes Lane, Sarratt
TQ/036 993 (09/J) Alt. 405 ft.
Soil: Reading Beds overlying Upper Chalk (pH 5·3)
Surveyed: 19 May 1962 with C. M. D., 23 July 1962 with P. M. Benoit and C. M. D. This study was made seventy yards along a track into the wood from the road and then six yards to the east of the track.
Frequent: Mercurialis perennis, Oxalis acetosella, Ranunculus ficaria.
Occasional: Ajuga reptans, Circaea lutetiana, Corylus avellana < 25 ft., Endymion non-scriptus (o-lf), Fraxinus excelsior (seedlings), Galium odoratum.
Rare: Acer pseudo–platanus (1) 9 in., Arum maculatum (r-o), Brachypodium sylvaticum, Cardamine sp., Carex sylvatica, Crataegus monogyna < 3 in., Dryopteris dilatata, D. filix-mas, Epilobium montanum, Fagus sylvatica (1) 6 in., Festuca gigantea, Fraxinus excelsior (2) 40 ft., Galium aparine, Geranium robertianum, Geum urbanum, Hedera helix, Heracleum sphondylium, Listera ovata (1), Lonicera periclymenum, Moehringia trinervia, Poa trivialis, Prunella vulgaris, Prunus sp. (1) 20 ft., Ranunculus repens, Rosa canina, Rubus sp. (r-o), Rumex sanguineus, Sanicula europaea, Solanum dulcamara, Stachys sylvatica, Tamus communis (r-o), Ulmus glabra (1) 50 ft., Veronica chamaedrys, V. montana, Viola riviniana (r-o).

The weeds of arable land are, as in the Lea Gravels Region, of greatest interest on the more chalky soils. The gravels are extensively quarried and in the neighbourhood of Hatfield and St. Albans many of the disused pits are used as rubbish dumps. The flooded pits below Rickmansworth occupy the once botanically rich Harefield Moor (mainly in Middlesex) and similar wet meadow land of which only fragments now remain. The most northerly pit, Batchworth Lake, with the land adjoining it, is now owned as a pleasure ground by Rickmansworth U.D.C.
The aquatic flora of the lower reaches of the River Colne and the associated canal system is similar to that of the Lea Navigation with the addition of two locally abundant species, *Lepidium latifolium* and *Impatiens capensis*.
The River Colne leaves the county at an altitude of 125 feet above sea level.

F. THE LONDON CLAY REGION (Map 9)

The various deposits grouped together to form this Region include not only the London Clay itself but Reading Beds and various gravels superimposed on the clay. There are some chalk exposures but the London Clay itself covers large enough areas to give the Region a uniformity equalled in the county only in the Chalk Region. No part of the London Clay Region is more than twenty-five miles from Central London.

There is here very little arable farming but a large amount of grazing. Most of the pasture is on badly drained land and it was difficult to find well-drained grassland to study. An examination of a railway cutting was, however, of some value.

Habitat Study 96 railway, north of Goffs Oak, Cheshunt
TL/306 040 (30/C)   Alt. 225 ft.
                          Soil: London Clay (pH 6·2)
Surveyed: 3 June 1962 with C. M. D., 4 Sept. 1962 with C. M. D. This study was made on the west-facing side of the cutting thirty yards south of the 14th mile-post.
Frequent: Achillea millefolium, Agrostis tenuis, Festuca rubra (f-ab.), Lathyrus pratensis (f-ab.), Potentilla reptans.
Occasional: Arrhenatherum elatius (o-f), Daucus carota, Heracleum sphondylium (o-f), Holcus lanatus (o-f), Lathyrus nissolia, Lotus corniculatus, Rumex acetosa, Vicia angustifolia, V. hirsuta (o-f).
Rare: Agropyron repens, Alopecurus pratensis, Anthoxanthum odoratum, Arabidopsis thaliana, Cerastium glomeratum, Cirsium arvense, Crataegus mongyna <6 in., Crepis capillaris, C. taraxacifolia, Dactylis glomerata, Geranium dissectum, Hieracium pilosella, H. sp., Hypericum perforatum, Hypochoeris radicata, Luzula campestris, Medicago lupulina, Myosotis discolor, Plantago lanceolata, Poa pratensis (r-o), Ranunculus acris, R. repens (r-o), Rosa canina <2 ft., Rubus sp., Rumex crispus, Senecio erucifolius (r-o), Stellaria graminea, Taraxacum officinale (1), Tragopogon pratensis, Trifolium dubium, T. pratense, Trisetum flavescens.

The greatest botanical interest in the Region lies in its wet heathy pastures and the finest of these is Hertford Heath.

Habitat Study 97   Hertford Heath (east side),
                                  Great Amwell
TL/353 111 (31K)   Alt. 310 ft.
     Soil: Pebble Gravel overlying London Clay (pH 3·7)
Surveyed: 26 May 1962 with H. B. Souster and C. M. D., 22 July 1962 with P. M. Benoit and C. M. D. This study was reached by proceeding 150 yards along the path skirting the Heath from the road below Little Amwell and by then following the fork in the path on the left for another 200 yards.
Abundant: Carex pilulifera.
Frequent: Carex ovalis, Festuca rubra, Holcus mollis (L), Juncus effusus, Potentilla erecta, Pteridium aquilinum (L).
Occasional: Agrostis canina, A. tenuis (o-f), Carex nigra, Juncus articulatus, Luzula campestris, Melampyrum pratense (o-lf), Quercus robur <3 ft., Sieglingia decumbens (o-f).
Rare: Anthoxanthum odoratum (r-o), Betula pendula (1) 8 ft., Calluna vulgaris (r-o), Deschampsia cespitosa, Galium saxatile, Genista anglica, Juncus subuliflorus, Molinia caerulea (r-o), Nardus stricta, Populus tremula, Salix cinerea (1) 6 in.

Habitat Study 98   The Roundings, Hertford Heath
                                (west side), Great Amwell
TL/350 107 (31/K)   Alt. 310 ft.
     Soil: Pebble Gravel overlying London Clay (pH 4·2)
Surveyed: 26 May 1962 with H. B. Souster and C. M. D.,

26 July 1962 with P. M. Benoit and C. M. D. This study was reached from the private road skirting the Roundings by taking the first major trackway on the right and proceeding a hundred yards along this and then a further 75 yards along a minor track on the right. The study was made in a clearing on the right at a point ten yards from the track.
Frequent: Agrostis canina, A. tenuis, Festuca rubra, Nardus stricta, Potentilla erecta, Sieglingia decumbens.
Occasional: Anthoxanthum odoratum (o-f), Carex nigra (o-f), C. ovalis (o-f), C. pilulifera (o-lf), Galium saxatile, Holcus lanatus, Juncus subuliflorus (o-lf), Rumex acetosella.
Rare: Achillea ptarmica, Betula pendula (1) 10 ft., Calluna vulgaris (r-o), Crataegus mongyna (1) 3 in., Deschampsia cespitosa, Epilobium angustifolium, Genista anglica, Juncus effusus (r-o), Luzula campestris (r-o), Molinia caerulea (r-o), Pedicularis sylvatica (r-o), Potentilla reptans, Quercus robur <1 ft., Rubus sp., Rumex acetosa, Salix repens <1 ft., Succisa pratensis, Ulex europaeus (2) 4 ft.

The same geological conditions prevail at Foulwells but the gradual silting up of a natural spring has given the site a calcareous nature. Foulwells, which was well known to earlier botanists, was unfortunately drained in 1963 and it will lose, at least for the time being, its unique flora.

Habitat Study 99   Foulwells (first study), Brickendon
                                  Liberty
TL/322 066 (30/I)   Alt. 325 ft.
Soil: Pebble Gravel overlying London Clay (pH not known)
Surveyed: 3 June 1962 with C. M. D., 2 Aug. 1962 with D. K. Kent, J. Russell and C. M. D. This study was made in the wettest part of the small boggy area.
Frequent: Carex panicea (f-ab.), Eleocharis quinqueflora (f-l.ab.), Equisetum telmateia (L), Eupatorium cannabinum (L), Juncus acutiflorus (L), J. inflexus (L).
Occasional: Ajuga reptans, Angelica sylvestris, Carex acutiformis (o-lf), Festuca arundinacea, Gymnadenia conopsea subsp. densiflora, Pulicaria dysenterica (o-lf), Valeriana dioica (o-lf).
Rare: Arrhenatherum elatius, Betula sp. <2 in., Briza media, Carex flacca, C. hirta, Carpinus betulus <2 in., Centaurium erythraea, Cerastium glomeratum (1), Cirsium arvense, C. palustre, Dactylorhiza fuchsii, Epilobium hirsutum, Epipactis palustris (12), Equisetum palustre, Eriophorum angustifolium, Filipendula ulmaria, Holcus lanatus, Juncus articulatus, J. effusus, J. subuliflorus, Lathyrus pratensis, Lotus uliginosus, Lychnis flos-cuculi, Mentha aquatica, Potentilla erecta, P. reptans, Prunella vulgaris, Pteridium aquilinum, Quercus robur (1) 4 in., Rosa arvensis, R. sp., Rubus sp., Salix cinerea (1) 6 ft., Solanum dulcamara, Succisa pratensis (r-o), Taraxacum officinale, Triglochin palustre, Tussilago farfara, Vicia cracca.

A study was made in another part of the site not immediately affected by the dainage operation.

Habitat Study 100   Foulwells (second study),
                                  Brickendon Liberty
TL/322 066 (30/I)   Alt. 325 ft.
Soil: Pebble Gravel overlying London Clay (pH 5.9)
Surveyed: 3 June 1962 with C. M. D., 2 Aug. 1962 with D. H. Kent, J. Russell and C. M. D. This study was made in a dried out portion above the previous site. It was situated below a rough thicket which had developed naturally on the north side of the marsh.
Frequent: Agrostis tenuis, Carex flacca.
Occasional: Fragaria vesca, Holcus lanatus (o-f), Lotus corniculatus, Potentilla erecta, Pulicaria dysenterica (o-f), Trifolium pratense, Ulmus sp. <2 ft., Veronica officinalis, Vicia tetrasperma.

Mr. W. H. Fordham (right), President of Letchworth Naturalists' Society, handing the deeds of Fox Covert to Baron Dimsdale, Chairman of the Executive Committee of the Hertfordshire and Middlesex Trust for Nature Conservation, 17 April 1966. Fox Covert was the first nature reserve to be owned by the Trust.

HERTS. PICTORIAL

▲ Therfield Heath. Habitat Study 1

▼ Church Hill. Habitat Study 2

▲ Wilbury Hill.   Habitat Study 7

▼ Purwell Meadow.   Habitat Study 8

▲ Chalk bank, Aldbury Nowers.   Habitat Study 14   JEAN BOWDEN
▼ Oddy Hill.   Habitat Study 15   JEAN BOWDEN

▲ Wood, Aldbury Nowers. Habitat Study 16   JEAN BOWDEN

Stubbings Wood. ►
Habitat Study 17

JEAN BOWDEN

▲ Wilstone Reservoir. Rushy Meadow (Habitat Studies 18 and 19) is on the extreme right in the middle of the view
J. K. ST JOSEPH, CAMBRIDGE UNIVERSITY COLLECTION

▼ Startops End Reservoir. Habitat Study 20
JEAN BOWDEN

▲ Patmore Heath.   Habitat Study 26   JEAN BOWDEN

▼ Sheethanger Common.   Habitat Study 48   JEAN BOWDEN

▲ Roughdown Common.   Habitat Study 49   JEAN BOWDEN

▼ Ashridge   AEROFILMS

▲ Dawley Warren. Habitat Study 67   JEAN BOWDEN

▼ Meadow, Redbourn. Habitat Study 66   JEAN BOWDEN

▲ Watery Grove. Burleigh Meadow (Habitat Study 72) is in the centre foreground of the view   AEROFILMS

▼ Newton Wood.   Habitat Study 77   JEAN BOWDEN

▲ Nomansland

▼ Nomansland.   Habitat Study 85

AEROFILMS

JEAN BOWDEN

▲ Chorleywood Common.   Habitat Study 86   JEAN BOWDEN
▼ Bricketwood Common.   Habitat Study 88   JEAN BOWDEN

▲ Hertford Heath. Habitat 97 is in the small clearing in the centre of the wooded area   AEROFILMS
▼ The Roundings, Hertford Heath. Habitat Study 98   JEAN BOWDEN

▲ Grand Union Canal, Dudswell   JEAN BOWDEN
▼ Batchworth Lake, Rickmansworth   AEROFILMS

▲ Arkley Manorial Lands.   Habitat Study 101   PHYLLIS WHITE
▼ Hadley Green.   Habitat Study 102   PHYLLIS WHITE

▲ Northaw Great Wood   PHYLLIS WHITE

▲ Long Pond, Totteridge.   Habitat Study 109   PHYLLIS WHITE

Rare: Achillea millefolium, Ajuga reptans, Alopecurus pratensis, Angelica sylvestris, Anthriscus sylvestris, Anthoxanthum odoratum, Arrhenatherum elatius, Bellis perennis, Bromus mollis, Carex distans, C. sylvatica (1), Centaurea nigra, Centaurium erythraea, Cerastium fontanum, Cirsium arvense, C. palustre, Crataegus monogyna < 2 in., Cynosurus cristatus, Dactylis glomerata (r-o), Epilobium angustifolium, Equisetum telmateia (r-o), Eupatorium cannabinum (r-o), Festuca rubra, Filipendula ulmaria, Fraxinus excelsior < 3 in., Geranium dissectum, G. molle, Holcus mollis, Hypericum tetrapterum, Juncus inflexus (r-o), J. subuliflorus, Lathyrus pratensis (r-o), Leontodon hispidus (1), L. taraxacoides (r-o), Linum catharticum, Lotus uliginosus, Luzula campestris, Lychnis flos-cuculi, Medicago lupulina, Mentha aquatica, Myosotis arvensis, Phleum bertolonii, Plantago major, P. lanceolata, Polygala vulgaris, Prunella vulgaris (r-o), Quercus robur < 6 in., Ranunculus acris, R. repens, Rubus sp., Rumex acetosa, R. obtusifolius, R. sanguineus, Scrophularia auriculata, Senecio jacobaea, Stachys sylvatica, Taraxacum officinale, Torilis japonica, Trifolium dubium, T. medium, Tussilago farfara, Veronica serpyllifolia, Vicia angustifolia, Viola hirta.

The two following studies were made of heathy pastures in places that were in Hertfordshire but are now incorporated into Greater London. The Arkley Manorial Lands are sometimes known locally as Rowley Bank.

Habitat Study 101   Arkley Manorial Lands,
TQ/215 960 (29/D)   Alt. 420 ft.   Barnet
    Soil: Pebble Gravel overlying London Clay (pH 4·0)
Surveyed: 16 June 1962 with C. M. D., 4 Aug. 1962 with E. B. Bangerter, A. C. Jermy and C. M. D. This study was made in a depression about forty yards from the road.
Frequent: Agrostis tenuis (f-l. ab.), Festuca rubra (f-l. ab.), Holcus lanatus, Juncus acutiflorus, Rumex acetosella.
Occasional: Epilobium angustifolium, Holcus mollis (o-lf), Nardus stricta (o-lf), Rubus sp., Ulex europaeus < 3 ft.
Rare: Achillea ptarmica, Anthoxanthum odoratum, Betula pendula < 3 ft., B. pubescens < 3 ft., Campanula rotundifolia, Carex nigra, C. ovalis, C. pilulifera (1), Crataegus monogyna < 4 ft., Galium saxatile (r-o), Genista anglica, Hypochoeris radicata, Juncus effusus, Luzula campestris, Potentilla erecta (r-o), Quercus robur < 5 ft., Ranunculus flammula, Rumex acetosa, Salix cinerea < 6 ft., Ulex minor < 2 ft.

Hadley Green is now completely urbanised but the ponds and rough grass support an unusual flora which well repaid study.

Habitat Study 102   Hadley Green, Barnet
TQ/245 975   (29/N)   Alt. 420 ft.
    Soil: Pebble Gravel overlying London Clay (pH 4·3)
Surveyed: 16 June 1962 with C. M. D., 4 Aug. 1962 with E. B. Bangerter, A. C. Jermy and C. M. D. This study was made by a ditch draining from the road to the pond on the west side of the road. The centre chosen for the study was five yards east of a horse-chestnut tree.
Abundant: Carex nigra, Festuca rubra, Nardus stricta (L).
Frequent: Agrostis canina, A. tenuis, Glyceria fluitans (L), Juncus bulbosus (L).
Occasional: Holcus lanatus (o-f), Juncus articulatus (o-f), Potentilla erecta (o-f), Rumex acetosella, Sieglingia decumbens.
Rare: Achillea millefolium (r-o), Bidens sp., Cirsium arvense, Dactylis glomerata, Deschampsia cespitosa, Juncus effusus, Leontodon autumnalis, Lolium perenne, Luzula campestris, Ranunculus repens, Taraxacum officinale.

The woods of the London Clay Region were the subject of pioneer ecological studies by Sir Edward Salisbury.

Wormley Wood (30/CDHI) was singled out by Sir Edward as representative of these woods and for a time it was hoped that it would become a National Nature Reserve. The plans for this did not succeed but an examination of the wood was made for the Nature Conservancy.
    The other woods in this part of the county are no less interesting than Wormley Wood and especially those bordering the Spital Brook.

Habitat Study 103   Spital Brook, Hoddesdon
TL/348 081 (30/P)   Alt. 175 ft.
    Soil: Alluvium overlying London Clay (pH 4·0)
Surveyed: 3 June 1962 with C. M. D., 2 Aug. 1962 with D. H. Kent, J. Russell and C. M. D. This study was made by the path at the side of the Spital Brook twenty yards to the east of the ford at Elbow Lane. It is an open habitat with little ground vegetation.
Frequent: Melampyrum pratense (L).
Occasional: Anemone nemorosa, Carpinus betulus < 40 ft., Lonicera periclymenum, Luzula pilosa, Poa nemoralis.
Rare: Angelica sylvestris, Anthoxanthum odoratum, Betonica officinalis, Brachypodium sylvaticum, Cardamine flexuosa, Carex pendula, C. remota, C. sylvatica (1), Circaea lutetiana, Cirsium palustre, Conopodium majus, Corylus avellana (1) 10 ft., Crataegus monogyna (1) 1 ft., Deschampsia cespitosa, Epilobium montanum, Festuca gigantea, F. tenuifolia, Galium palustre, Geum urbanum, Heracleum sphondylium (1), Holcus lanatus (1), Hypericum tetrapterum (1), Lathyrus montanus, Milium effusum, Oxalis acetosella (r-o), Poa trivialis, Potentilla erecta, P. sterilis, Quercus petraea (1) 50 ft., Q. robur (1) 50 ft., Ranunculus ficaria, R. repens, Rosa arvensis, Rubus sp., Rumex sanguineus, Senecio vulgaris (1), Stachys sylvatica, Teucrium scorodonia, Veronica chamaedrys.

Bishop's Wood, in the extreme west of the Region, is on a mixture of soils. It has as a result of this a rich and varied flora which makes it one of the most interesting woods in the county.

Habitat Study 104   Bishop's Wood (first study),
TQ/066 921 (09/R)   Alt. 320 ft.   Rickmansworth Urban
Surveyed: 12 June 1962 with C. M. D., 23 Aug. 1962.
          Soil: Reading Beds (pH 4·6)
This study was made thirty-five yards along a very wet path beyond a bridge over the woodland stream in the north-west side of the wood.
Locally abundant: Holcus mollis.
Frequent: Epilobium angustifolium, Lonicera periclymenum (f-ab).
Occasional: Agrostis tenuis (o-f), Betula pendula (o-lf) < 20 ft., Juncus effusus, Poa trivialis, Potentilla erecta (o-f), P. reptans, Quercus robur < 1 ft., Rubus sp. (o-f), Teucrium scorodonia.
Rare: Ajuga reptans, Anthoxanthum odoratum, Carex flacca, C. pallescens, C. sylvatica (1), Cirsium palustre, Corylus avellana (1) 5 ft., Crataegus monogyna (1) 3 ft., Epilobium montanum, Euphorbia amygdaloides, Fragaria vesca (r-o), Fraxinus excelsior (1) 1 ft., Ilex aquifolium (1) 1 ft., Juncus subuliflorus (r-o), Lotus uliginosus, Luzula multiflora, L. pilosa, Lysimachia nemorum, Poa annua, Populus tremula (suckers) < 6 ft., Quercus robur (2) 40 ft., Salix caprea (1) 6 ft., Sonchus oleraceus, Veronica chamaedrys, Viola riviniana.

Habitat Study 105   Bishop's Wood (second study)
          Rickmansworth Urban
TQ/0693 9160 (09/Q)   Alt. 320 ft.
    Soil: Glacial Gravel overlying London Clay (pH 4·7)
Surveyed: 12 June 1962 with C. M. D. This study was made thirty yards inside the first gate into the wood from

49

the road to the east of a reservoir and then two yards to the right of the ride. This was a somewhat disturbed habitat with a very mixed flora.

Frequent: Holcus lanatus (L), Holcus mollis (L), Hypochoeris radicata (L), Vulpia bromoides.

Occasional: Agrostis canina, A. tenuis, Brachypodium sylvaticum, Betula pendula < 6 ft., Carpinus betulus (L) < 10 ft., Epilobium angustifolium, Juncus effusus, Luzula multiflora, L. pilosa, Poa trivialis, Potentilla erecta (o-lf), Rubus sp., Sagina procumbens, Teucrium scorodonia.

Rare: Aira caryophyllea (r-o), Ajuga reptans, Betula pubescens < 6 in., Carex ovalis (r-o), C. pallescens, C. pendula, C. pilulifera, Centaurium erythraea, Cerastium fontanum, C. glomeratum, Cirsium arvense, C. palustre, C. vulgare, Crataegus monogyna (2) 1 ft., Dactylis glomerata, Deschampsia cespitosa, Epilobium hirsutum, E. montanum, Fragaria vesca (r-o), Fraxinus excelsior (1) 4 ft., Galium saxatile (r-o), Gnaphalium uliginosum, Hypericum pulchrum, Juncus acutiflorus (1), J. subuliflorus, Lolium perenne, Lysimachia nemorum, Mentha arvensis (r-o), Myosotis arvensis, Plantago lanceolata (r-o), P. major, Poa annua, P. nemoralis, Polygonum aviculare, Populus tremula, Potentilla reptans, Pteridium aquilinum (M), Prunella vulgaris (r-o), Quercus robur (2) 2 ft., Ranunculus acris, R. repens, Rumex acetosa, R. sanguineus, Salix caprea (2) < 10 ft., S. cinerea (1) 3 ft., Scrophularia nodosa, Scutellaria minor (r-o), Sonchus arvensis, Taraxacum officinale, Trifolium dubium, T. pratense, T. repens (r-o), Tripleurospermum maritimum, Trisetum flavescens, Urtica dioica, Veronica chamaedrys (1), V. officinalis, Vicia angustifolia, Viola riviniana.

Hadley Wood, which is close to Hadley Green, had formerly a rich flora but it now suffers from too much interference. Some of the original flora is preserved in a woodland margin at the top of a large railway cutting through the wood.

Habitat Study 106   Hadley Wood, Barnet
TQ/261 973 (29/T)   Alt. 250 ft.
                Soil: London Clay (pH 4·7)
Surveyed: 16 June 1962 with C. M. D., 4 Aug. 1962 with E. B. Bangerter, A. C. Jermy and C. M. D. This study was made by the side of a ditch on the north side of the wood. The place chosen for examination was 200 yards from the last major track crossing the wood on the west side of the railway.

Frequent: Cardamine flexuosa, Holcus lanatus, Rubus sp., Urtica dioica (L).

Occasional: Carpinus betulus (seedlings), Fraxinus excelsior (seedlings), Rumex sanguineus.

Rare: Acer pseudo-platanus (1) 1 ft., Agrostis tenuis, Arrhenatherum elatius, Carex remota (1), Circaea lutetiana, Crataegus monogyna (2) 3 in., Deschampsia cespitosa, Dryopteris dilatata (r-o), Epilobium angustifolium, E. montanum, Fagus sylvatica (1) 6 in., Festuca gigantea, Geranium robertianum, Glechoma hederacea (r-o), Glyceria fluitans, Ilex aquifolium < 3 in., Juncus effusus, Lonicera periclymenum, Oxalis acetosella, Poa annua, Polygonum hydropiper, Ranunculus repens (r-o), Rosa arvensis, R. canina, Rumex obtusifolius, Salix caprea (1) 2 ft., Sambucus nigra (seedlings), (1) 15 ft., Sorbus aucuparia < 3 in., Stachys sylvatica, Tamus communis.

To the north-east of Potters Bar is Great Wood (20/SWX) which is one of the largest woods in the county. The Hertfordshire and North Middlesex Branch of British Naturalists' Association has made a detailed study of the natural history of the wood which will soon be published.

This should assist greatly the natural-history studies directed from Hertfordshire County Council's School Camp at Carbone Hill in the eastern part of the wood.

More woodland to the west of Potters Bar would repay closer attention. A study was made in one wood here.

Habitat Study 107   Redwell Wood, Ridge
TL/218 022 (20/B)   Alt. 400 ft.
                Soil: London Clay (pH 7·8)
Surveyed: 16 June 1962 with C. M. D., 26 Aug, 1962 with H. B. Souster and C. M. D. This study was made two hundred yards along the main ride from the lodge gate and five yards inside the wood to the left.

Frequent: Circaea lutetiana, Festuca gigantea, Poa trivialis.

Occasional: Carex remota, C. sylvatica, Epilobium montanum, Geum urbanum, Holcus lanatus, Juncus effusus, Lysimachia nemorum, Rubus sp., Solanum dulcamara (o-f).

Rare: Arctium minus (1), Bromus ramosus, Carex divulsa, Corylus avellana (2) 10 ft., Crataegus monogyna < 1 ft., Epilobium angustifolium, E. hirsutum, E. obscurum, Fragaria vesca, Fraxinus excelsior < 6 ft., Galium aparine (r-o), Geranium robertianum (r-o), Lysimachia nummularia, Moehringia trinervia, Potentilla reptans, Prunus spinosa < 6 ft., Quercus robur (seedlings), (2) 50 ft., Rosa arvensis (2), R. canina, Rubus caesius (r-o), Rumex sanguineus, Swida sanguinea (2) < 5 ft., Taraxacum officinale, Urtica dioica, Veronica chamaedrys, Viola riviniana.

The only large pieces of water in the Region are the reservoirs near to Elstree. Aldenham Reservoir is of similar age to the Tring Reservoirs as it was constructed for the same purpose, namely that of serving the needs of the Grand Union Canal system. Less than a kilometre away a new reservoir, the Hilfield Reservoir, was opened in 1957 by the Colne Valley Water Company to provide drinking water. It has already established a shore vegetation which includes most of the species for which botanists have visited the older reservoir.

Habitat Study 108   Aldenham Reservoir, Elstree
TQ/171 955 (19/S)   Alt. 325 ft.
                Soil: London Clay (pH 6·7)
Surveyed: 16 June 1962 with C. M. D. when the water level was high and the site almost submerged, 4 Aug. 1962 with E. B. Bangerter, A. C. Jermy and C. M. D. when there was a dry shore about ten yards wide. The study was made twenty yards to the south of the fence around the boat house and a distance of five yards from the last *Salix fragilis* tree in a direct line to the water's edge.

Abundant: Eleocharis palustris (l. dom.), Glyceria maxima (l. dom.), Mentha arvensis, Veronica scutellata.

Frequent: Bidens sp. (L).

Occasional: Juncus articulatus, Lycopus europaeus (o-f), Myosotis scorpioides, Polygonum amphibium, Ranunculus peltatus, R. flammula, Salix cinerea < 6 ft.

Rare: Alisma plantago-aquatica, Galium palustre (r-o), Juncus effusus, Plantago major, Rorippa islandica, Rumex crispus, Salix fragilis (1) 4 ft., Solanum dulcamara.

A number of parks in the London Clay Region have artificial lakes and there are many ponds in open spaces. Most of the lakes and ponds were at some time ornamental and introduced species still survive. Native plants ultimately gain control in these habitats but otherwise there are few brooks to provide an aquatic flora.

The ponds at Totteridge repaid examination until about fifty years ago but their more limited flora now was illustrated by one remaining study.

Habitat Study 109   Long Pond, Totteridge,
TQ/232 941 (29/H)   Alt. 410 ft.   Barnet
Soil: Pebble Gravel overlying London Clay (pH 5·4)
Surveyed: 16 June 1962 with C. M. D., 4 Sept. 1962 with
C. M. D. This study was made in the middle of the grass
verge opposite the last post but two by the roadside and
also opposite the lamp post No. 102.
Frequent: Agrostis tenuis, Alopecurus geniculatus (f-ab.),
Carex hirta (f-ab), C. ovalis, Holcus lanatus.
Occasional: Anthoxanthum odoratum (o-f), Deschampsia
cespitosa, Festuca rubra (o-f), Juncus effusus, Ranunculus
acris (o-f), R. repens (o-f), Rumex acetosa (o-f).
Rare: Alopecurus pratensis, Centaurea nigra, Glyceria

fluitans, Poa pratensis, P. trivialis.

There is little arable farming and almost no quarrying
in the Region and a correspondingly limited adventive
flora.

The population pressure in this part of the county may be
expected to continue and it will lose some of its botanical
interest. On the other hand the region contains a considerable Green Belt which contains within it some of the most
unspoiled countryside in the county. This was the part of
Hertfordshire best known to W. H. Coleman and his
contemporaries and it is probably the part which would
most repay a continued study.

THE PLAN OF THE FLORA

Sequence. This follows that of *List of Vascular Plants*, Dandy (1968).

Nomenclature. The first name given is that adopted in *List of Vascular Plants* except for a few changes suggested by Mr. Dandy to bring the Flora into line with modern nomenclatural practice. Plants the names of which are printed in **bold type** are those which the author considers to have appeared in the county. The names of plants regarding which there is doubt as to their appearance in the county are printed in ordinary (i.e. Roman) type. Synonyms are printed in *italics*. The full synonymy is not given but all names used in Pryor's Flora, if they differ from those now used, are given. Pryor accounted for all the names used by Webb and Coleman.

Map references. These refer to a map of the distribution of the species which may be found in the Map Section following the Flora.

English names. These are names in italics which the author considers to be in general use and no attempt has been made to account for those used in limited circles in Hertfordshire.

First records. These appear at the end of the first line and follow the name of the plant. Herbarium specimens have been taken to establish first records equally with those established in print and in manuscript lists. The first records given in Pryor's Flora are in some cases misleading and in a few cases when a first record given by Pryor pre-dates that given in the present Flora it means that the basis for Pryor's record has not been found.

Habitat. The notes on the habitat of the species refer to the type of habitat in which the author has found the species growing in Hertfordshire.

Status. This follows the habitat and is the opinion of the author as to whether the species is a native, a colonist, a casual, etc. in Hertfordshire. The habitat and status of a species may be different in Hertfordshire from that elsewhere in the British Isles e.g. *Cerastium diffusum* is a native of sandy seashores in coastal counties but in Hertfordshire it is a colonist on railway tracks.

Distribution and abundancy. The notes which follow account for the present distribution and relative abundance of the species in the county. Native species and colonists which have been found since 1951 in more than six tetrads have their present distribution shown in maps in the Map Section and those found in six or fewer tetrads have their present distribution, related to the tetrad system, fully accounted for. Most casuals recorded since 1951 are similarly treated but less account has been taken of some species of garden origin of which there are many in the county. Any known changes in distribution are noted but in few cases are the stations in which earlier botanists found the plants given. Extinct species, or those feared to be extinct, are noted and the last known record for these is given or indicated in some other way.

Habitat Studies. A cross reference is given to the Habitat Studies, if any, in which the species is mentioned.

Map Section. The distribution maps of the 696 species which appear in this section are based on field records made from 1951 to 1966 inclusive. The tetrad to which they are related is reduced to 0.87 of the size of the reduction of the 10 kilometre grid squares in the maps in the *Atlas of the British Flora.*

A summary of the records is shown on Map 56g. There are 335 complete tetrads in the area covered by the Flora and parts of 172. For the complete tetrads an average of 261 species was recorded compared with an average expectation of 335 species – see Dony (1963), and this represents a cover of 78% of the complete flora having been achieved in the preparation of the Flora. Of the partial tetrads 29 had more species recorded from them than the average returned for the complete tetrads and 5 had more than the average expectation for a complete tetrad. A total of 117,703 records related to the tetrad system were made during the survey and 23 tetrads had at the end of the survey above the average expectation of records for a complete tetrad.

70 species were recorded for all the complete, or nearly complete, tetrads and close search failed to reveal three species (*Convolvulus arvensis, Euphorbia peplus* and *Ranunculus ficaria*) each in one tetrad only and the following nine species were still awaiting record in fewer than six tetrads: *Acer campestre, Brachypodium sylvaticum, Corylus avellana, Lathyrus pratensis, Papaver rhoeas, Ranunculus acris, Sinapis arvensis, Tussilago farfara* and *Veronica chamaedrys.*

ABBREVIATIONS USED IN THE FLORA

! used after a station means that the author has seen the plant there; used after a person's name means that it is a joint record with the author.

(34/K) etc. is a tetrad reference and for the identification of these see the inset maps on Maps 4, 5, 7, 8.

Webb and Coleman Flora Hertfordiensis, Webb and Coleman, 1849.

Pryor Flora of Hertfordshire, Pryor, 1887.

Kent and Lousley A handlist of plants of the London area. Kent, D. H. and Lousley, J. E., 1951–57.

Hb. H.M. Hitchin Museum Herbarium.

Hb. Ph. Phillips Herbarium.

Hb. Gr. A. W. Graveson Herbarium.

Hb. B.M. British Museum (Natural History) Herbarium.

Hb. or Herb. Herbarium, used to show other collections e.g. Hb. Druce (Druce Herbarium), Hb. Cambridge (Botany School, Cambridge Herbarium).

B.E.C. 1910 *Rep.* etc. Report of the Botanical Society and Exchange Club of the British Isles for 1910 etc.

W.E.C. 1911–12 *Rep.* etc. Report of Watson Botanical Exchange Club for 1911–12 etc.

J. Bot. Journal of Botany.

Trans. Herts. N.H.S. Transactions, Hertfordshire Natural History Society.

Proc. Herts. N.H.S. Proceedings, Hertfordshire Natural History Society.

v.c. 20   Watsonian vice-county 20, Herts. (see Map 1b).

v.c. 21   Watsonian vice-county 21, Middlesex.

v.c. 24   Watsonian vice-county 24, Bucks.

v.c. 30   Watsonian vice-county 30, Bedford.

v.c. 20 [Beds.]   a part of the Watsonian vice-county 20 now in the administrative county of Bedfordshire.

v.c. 20 [G.L.]   a part of the Watsonian vice-county 20 now in the administrative area of Greater London.

v.c. 21 [Herts. 1904–65, G.L.]   a part of the Watsonian vice-county 21 which was in the administrative county of Hertfordshire from 1904 to 1965 and is now in the administrative area of Greater London.

The Flora

PTERIDOPHYTA

LYCOPSIDA

LYCOPODIACEAE
Lycopodium L.
L. clavatum L.   *Stagshorn Clubmoss* Pamplin (see Pryor, 496), 1837
Heathy places   Native
Very rare and recorded by nineteenth-century botanists

only from Broxbourne Wood and a few places in the neighbourhood of Tring. In all of these it is now extinct. It was found in 1963 by B. F. C. Sennitt in a gravel pit south of St. Albans!, *Hb. H.M.* It appears to be well established here and is growing in association with various species of *Sphagnum*.

SPHENOPSIDA

EQUISETACEAE
Equisetum L.
E. fluviatile L.   (Map 10a)   *Water Horsetail*
E. limosum L.   Coleman, 1838
Wet and marshy places   Native
Locally frequent and showing no distribution pattern. H.S. 76.

E. palustre L. (Map 10b) *Marsh Horsetail* Blake, c. 1820
Marshy places   Native
More common than the preceding. H.S. 9, 10, 18, 29, 31, 76, 90.

E. sylvaticum L.   *Wood Horsetail*   Coleman, 1838
Damp places, usually in woods   Native
Very rare and mainly on the London Clay. Recent records are: railway bank, Hitchin, 1932, *E. Macalister Hall*,

Hb. Ph.; side of Bayford Wood, confirming an earlier record by Coleman, 1954 (30/D)!, *R. M. Payne in Kent and Lousley*, 325; hedgerow, Watling Street, near Elstree, (19/X)!, *C. S. Nicholson in Kent and Lousley*, 325, *Hb. H.M.*

E. arvense L. (Map 10c) *Common Horsetail, Ironweed*
                                                Coleman, 1838
Roadside verges, railway banks, waste places, etc. Native
Common throughout the county. H.S. 8, 19, 26–28, 30, 66, 73, 91.

E. telmateia Ehrh.   (Map 10d)   *Great Horsetail*
E. maximum auct.   Coleman, 1838
Wet places   Native
Common in woods on the London Clay and appearing less frequently in wet habitats elsewhere. H.S. 30, 99, 100.

FILICOPSIDA

Osmunda regalis L. (OSMUNDACEAE) *Royal Fern.* 'By a hedge-side in a medow on the left hand of the way that goes from St. Albans to Windridge', W. Coles, 1657.

POLYPODIACEAE
Pteridium Scop.
P. aquilinum (L.) Kuhn (Map 10e) *Bracken* Kalm, 1748
Pteris aquilina L.
Heaths and commons, wood borders, etc.   Native
Locally abundant and occurring on all but the most calcareous soils. H.S. 56, 57, 61, 64, 81, 86, 88, 89, 93, 94, 97, 99, 105.

Adiantum capillus-veneris L., *Maidenhair Fern*, occurs on a wall by the side of the Lea Navigation, Ware, 1956 (31/M)!, *Lloyd-Evans, Hb. H.M.* It is apparently maintained by the sheltered position of the wall.

Blechnum L.
B. spicant (L.) Roth   *Hard Fern*   Woodward, 1787
Heaths and heathy woods   Native
Recorded by earlier workers from a very few stations scattered over the county. It is still rare and the only recent records are: Hertford Heath, *E. J. Salisbury, Trans. Herts. N.H.S.* 17 (1918), 60; Sherrards Wood (21/G)!, *E. G. Kellett*; Well Wood, 1952 (20/R), *R. M. Payne in Kent and Lousley*, 327; High Scrubs, 1957 (90/J)!, *R. A. Boniface and F. Rose.*

Phyllitis Hill
P. scolopendrium (L.) Newm.   (Map 10f)   *Hart's-Scolopendrium vulgare* Sm.   *tongue Fern* Gerard, 1597
Old walls, brickwork and shady places near walls. Denizen
Considered to be rare by earlier workers but it appears to have increased in frequency.

Asplenium L.
A. adiantum-nigrum L. (Map 10g) *Black Spleenwort*
                                                Coleman, 1838
This was considered by Coleman to be 'not very rare' on dry banks of hollow lanes. It is now found only on walls and is occasional as a wall denizen throughout the county.

A. trichomanes L.   (Map 10h)   *Maidenhair Spleenwort*
                                                Coles, 1657
Old walls, brickwork, etc.   Denizen
The least common of the spleenworts to be found in the county.

A. ruta-muraria L.   (Map 10i)   *Wall-Rue* Webb and
                                                Coleman, 1843
Old walls   Denizen
A species which has apparently increased as it was thought to be rare in the 19th century. It is now to be found frequently on old walls throughout the county.

Ceterach DC.
C. officinarum DC.   (Map 10j)   *Rusty-back Fern*
                                                Woodward, 1787

Old walls   Denizen
In common with other ferns to be found on walls in the
county this species has at least held its own and may have
increased.

Athyrium Roth
A. filix-femina (L.) Roth   (Map 10k)   *Lady Fern*
                                             Coleman, 1839
Damp woods and shady places   Native
Scattered in suitable habitats throughout the county but
never common.

Cystopteris Bernh.
C. fragilis (L.) Bernh., *Brittle Bladder Fern*, was recorded
from Berry Grove by Ada Selby (1883) but it was not
permanent. The only current record is from a garden wall
at Barley, 1963 (33/Z) where it was apparently growing
spontaneously.

Dryopteris Adans.
D. filix-mas (L.) Schott   (Map 10 l)   *Male Fern*
Aspidium filix-mas (L.) Sw.   H. D. Henslow, 1833
Woods, hedgerows and occasionally on walls   Native
Generally common but becoming scarce on calcareous
soils. H.S. 43, 45, 60, 78, 93, 95.

D. borreri Newm.   (Map 10m)   *Golden-scaled Male Fern*
                                             Edwards, 1860
A scarce native of woodland and generally found only in
those woods in which *D. filix-mas* is very abundant.
The two ferns are superficially alike and it is possible that
D. borreri has been overlooked.

D. carthusiana (Vill.) H. P. Fuchs   (Map 10n)   *Narrow*
D. spinulosa Watt, *Aspidium spinulosum* Sw.   *Buckler Fern*
                                             Coleman, 1838
Heathy places in woods, wet heaths, etc.   Native
Uncommon probably through lack of suitable habitats.
It occurs at Patmore Heath (42/M) with hybrids with
D. dilatata, Hb H.M.

D. dilatata (Hoffm.) A. Gray   (Map 10o)   *Broad Buckler*
Aspidium dilatatum (Hoffm.) Sm.   *Fern*
                                             Blake, c. 1820
Woods and shady places   Native
Frequent and scarcely less common and well distributed
than *D. filix-mas*. H.S. 43, 60, 95, 106.

Polystichum Roth
P. setiferum (Forsk.) Woynar   *Soft Shield Fern*
Aspidium angulare Kit. ex Willd.   Coleman, 1838
Hedgerows, ditches, etc.   Native
Rare. Both Coleman and Pryor appeared to be uncertain
regarding the identity of this and the following species.
During the period of the present survey *P. setiferum* has
been found only in the Devil's Dyke, near Marford, from
where it had previously been recorded by Edwards 'in
boundless profusion' (11/W), *T. D. V. Swinscow; near to
Bayford Wood, 1953 (30/E), R. M. Payne, Hb. R. M. Payne;*
Langton's Lane (32/K), *Lloyd-Evans.*

P. aculeatum (L.) Roth   *Hard Shield Fern* Blake, c. 1820
Aspidium aculeatum (L.) Sw., *A. lobatum* (Huds.) Sw.
Hedgerows, ditches, etc.   Native
Rare. Roman Road, Hare Street, 1962 (32/E)!, *H. Bowry,
Hb. H.M.;* Nimney Brook (31/Y), *J. Hopkins;* bourn
between Sacombe Green and High Cross where it is
abundant, 1960 (31/P)!, *P. C. and J. Hall;* Ballingdon
Bottom (01/M)!, *P. Taylor, Hb. H.M.;* near Cross Farm,
Bovingdon, 1961 (00/G), *Hb. H.M.*

Thelypteris Schmidel
T. limbosperma (All.) H. P. Fuchs   *Mountain Fern*
T. oreopteris (Ehrh.) Slosson, *Aspidium oreopteris* (Ehrh.) Sw.
                                             Coleman, 1839
Woods   Native
Very rare. Found by 19th-century botanists in a few places
mainly on the Clay-with-Flints and London Clay but seen
recently only at Wormley Wood, 1955 (30/I)!, one of
Pryor's stations, *F. Rose and T. D. V. Swinscow.*

T. dryopteris (L.) Slosson was recorded as *Phegopteris
dryopteris* (L.) Fée from Broxbourne by J. W. Higgens
in *B.E.C.* 1916 Rep. 511, where it is suggested that Pryor's
record of *Phegopteris calcarea* (Sm.) Fée (*T. robertiana*
(Hoffm.) Slosson) may be in error. Higgens's record is also
a very doubtful one.

Polypodium L.
P. vulgare L. sensu lato (Map 11a)   *Polypody* Blake, 1819
Old walls, tree stumps, etc.   Native
Occasional. The following specimens have been referred
by A.C. Jermy to **P. interjectum** Shivas: 'Fern Lane',
near Hertford, 1835, *L. Manser, Hb. H.M.;* wall, Norton
Bury, 1960 (23/H)!, *H. and D. Meyer, Hb. H.M.;* tree
stump, Stubbings Wood, 1963 (91/A), *L. H. Pinkess,
Hb. H.M.;* wall, Pirton Hall, 1963 (13/G), *Hb. H.M.;* wall,
Hamels, 1965 (32/S), *Hb. H.M.;* wall, Cold Hall, 1965
(30/N), *Hb. H.M.;* wall, Cheshunt College, 1966 (30/Q),
Hb. H.M. A specimen collected from brickwork, Aldenham Park, 1965 (19/T), by B. Goater was considered by Mr.
Jermy to be **P. interjectum** × **P. vulgare** sensu stricto.

MARSILEACEAE
Pilularia L.
P. globulifera L.   *Pillwort*   Webb and Coleman, 1843
Sides of ponds   Native
Extinct and seen by Coleman only at Northaw.

AZOLLACEAE
Azolla Lam.
A. filiculoides Lam.   *Water Fern*   Peirson, 1915
Ponds and slow flowing rivers   Colonist
Rare but often abundant for a few years when it does
appear: ditches south of Redbourn, 1955 (11/A)!, *T. G.
Skinner, Hb. H.M.;* Pré Mill, 1959 (10/J), *J. Lovell!;* Dobbs
Weir (30/Z), where it appeared for a number of years, *H.
Peirson, J. Bot. 1915,* 308; Long Pond, Totteridge Lane,
1957 (29/H), *J. D. J. Hinson;* Hertford Heath, 1937
(31/K), *D. McClintock;* Hoddesdon Bury, 1964 (30/N);
Home Farm, Wrotham Park, 1965 (29/P), v.c. 21 [Herts.],
Hb. H.M.

OPHIOGLOSSACEAE
Ophioglossum L.
O. vulgatum L.   (Map 11b)   *Adder's Tongue*
                                             Coleman, 1838
Damp pastures   Native
Frequent and well distributed in the county but easily
overlooked. H.S. 10, 73, 75.

Botrychium lunaria (L.) Sw. 'We went with Professor and
Mrs. Cowell to Mr. Pollard's at High Down, near Hitchin.
We found *Botrychium Lunaria* for the first time in Herts.'
June 7, 1882. *Memorials, Journal and Botanical correspondence of C.C. Babington,* 1897, p. 234. High Down is a most
unlikely place for moonwort to have grown and it seems
strange that neither Babington nor Pollard took a voucher
specimen or reported their record to Baker and Newbould
for inclusion in *Topographical Botany* and to Daydon Jackson
for the *Flora of Hertfordshire.*

SPERMATOPHYTA

GYMNOSPERMAE

Coniferous trees are planted throughout the county. Yew (**Taxus baccata** L.), H.S. 54, as well as being a frequent churchyard tree is to be found in woodland especially when this has been developed around old houses or gardens. Scots Pine (**Pinus sylvestris** L.), Corsican Pine (**P. nigra** Arnold), Norway Spruce (**Picea abies** (L.) Karst.) and Larch (**Larix decidua** Mill.) are the principal conifers which are planted either to form whole plantations or as protection for sapling deciduous trees. They often survive especially in beech woods. Clumps of pines are sometimes planted at road junctions with pleasing scenic effect as at Wilbury Hill (23/B).

CUPRESSACEAE
Juniperus L.
J. communis L.   (Map 11c)   *Juniper*   Steele MS., c. 1730
Chalk hills, sandy heaths, etc.   Native
Rare but often locally abundant in the places in which it grows. H.S. 48, 49, 68, 84. Juniper has been known for a long time in the county and it is supposed that Gustard Wood, where it is especially common, has its name derived from an old name for juniper (*Place Names in Hertfordshire* p. 56). It has become extinct on the slopes of Ravensburgh Castle (02/Z and 12/E) and in the adjoining part of Bedfordshire and on Royston Heath (34/F K and 33/J P) where Little observed a great many stunted plants between 1908 and 1913 (*J. Bot. 1917*, 75). In the south-west of the county the juniper is holding its own and is often regenerating contrary to its reported fate elsewhere in south-east England. It is faring especially well on Roughdown Common immediately above the gas works and Boxmoor railway station. On Gustard Wood Common there are some very fine trees up to 20 ft. high but it is protected here to some extent by the staff of the Mid-Herts Golf Club. At Chipperfield Common (00/K), Commonwood Common (00/K and 09/P) and on the chalk above Aldbury (91/R) it is being crowded out by scrub and is fighting a losing battle for survival.

ANGIOSPERMAE : DICOTYLEDONES

RANUNCULACEAE
Caltha L.
C. palustris L.   (Map 11d)   *Marsh Marigold, Mayblobs*
Franks, 1821
Marshes and wet meadows   Native
Frequent and well distributed. H.S. 19, 29, 30, 76, 91.

Helleborus L.
H. foetidus L.   *Setterwort*   H. Fordham, 1836
Wood verges, ditches, etc.   Naturalized
Rare as it has always been. Tingley Wood (13/F)!, *J. Pollard, Hb. H.M.*; The Bury, Ashwell (24/Q), *W. H. Fordham*; Easneye Wood, *D. McClintock*; High Wych, *D. McClintock*; Weston Hill, 1966 (23/L), *H. Bowry*; spontaneously in garden, Hitchin, 1966 (12/Z).

H. viridis L. subsp. **occidentalis** (Reut.) Schiffn. (Map 11e)
Green Hellebore   Steele MS., c. 1730
Woods and meadows   Native
Rare and apparently less common than it was a century ago.

Anemone L.
A. nemorosa L. (Map 11f)   *Wood Anemone*   Blake, 1820
Woods and occasionally on heathy commons   Native
Common in woods on the Boulder Clay, occasional elsewhere but becoming rare on the Clay-with-Flints. A paper by Salisbury (1916) was based largely on Hertfordshire material. H.S. 12, 16, 17, 35, 36, 39, 41, 60, 103.

A. ranunculoides L. and **A. apennina** L. There are early records of both of these species as garden escapes (see *Pryor*, 3). I know of no recent records.

Pulsatilla Mill.
P. vulgaris Mill.   *Pasque Flower*   Dickson, 1815
Anemone pulsatilla L.
Chalk downs   Native
A very rare and attractive species which, because it flowers in spring, is probably the best known of all our more rare Hertfordshire plants. H.S. 2. Aldbury Nowers, where it is decreasing (91/L)!, *Dickson*; Therfield Heath, especially abundant on Church Hill (33/J)!, *Fordham* (see *Pryor*, 2); slope below Tingley Wood where G. L. Evans has found it sparingly (13/F), *Pollard* (see *Pryor*, 2). There are no recent records from the other stations given by Pryor i.e. Arbury Banks and Ravensburgh Castle.

Clematis L.
C. vitalba L. (Map 11g)   *Old Man's Beard, Traveller's Joy*
Turner, 1548
Hedges and wood borders   Native
Common except on the London Clay. H.S. 17, 22, 47, 84.

Ranunculus L.
R. acris L.   (Map 11h)   *Upright or Meadow Buttercup*
Blake, 1820
Meadows and pastures   Native
Abundant. H.S. 8, 9, 13, 17–19, 23, 27–29, 53, 55, 59, 65, 66, 71, 73–76, 78, 84, 90, 91, 96, 100, 105, 109.

R. repens L.   (Map 11i)   *Creeping Buttercup*   Blake, 1820
Roadside verges, arable land, waste places, etc.   Native
Ubiquitous. H.S. 8, 9, 11, 14, 15, 18–21, 24, 25, 28, 29, 33–39, 41–53, 55, 56, 60, 62, 65–67, 71–75, 77–80, 82, 84, 88, 90, 91, 93–96, 100, 102, 105, 106, 109.

R. bulbosus L. (Map 11j) *Bulbous or Common Buttercup*
Franks, 1823
Pastures   Native
Abundant. H.S. 1, 2, 7, 13–15, 21, 23, 29, 49–51, 55, 58, 67, 71, 84, 92.

R. arvensis L.   (Map 11k)   *Corn Buttercup*   Ellis, 1750
Arable fields   Colonist
Considered by Coleman to be an abundant and troublesome weed on clay soils. It is still more common on the Boulder Clay than elsewhere but by no means abundant.

R. sardous Crantz   *Hairy Buttercup*   Coleman, 1841
In the mid-nineteenth century this was apparently a feature of muddy ground around the ponds of Hertford Heath. Since then it has been recorded only as a casual e.g. near St. Albans, 1909, *P. H. Cooke* and High Barnet, v.c. 20 [G.L.], 1919, *J. E. Cooper*; see *Kent and Lousley*, 5.

R. parviflorus L. *Small-flowered Buttercup* S. Woods, 1805

This was at one time a native of dry and exposed places such as Colney Heath where it was known to Salisbury. In recent years it has been found only as a garden weed at Chorley Wood, 1957 (09/H), det. Brit. Mus. (Nat. Hist.), *Mrs. K. M. Disney.*

R. auricomus L. (Map 11 l) *Goldilocks* Coleman, 1838
Woodland and hedgerows Native
Frequent throughout the county and, as elsewhere, very variable. H.S. 36, 63, 78.

R. lingua L. *Greater Spearwort* Coleman, 1844
Sides of ponds and marshy places ? Native
Coleman and his contemporaries considered this to be native in a pond at Thrift Wood, Stanstead, where it was eventually destroyed. It was apparently originally planted in all its present stations e.g. Totteridge Green (29/H), v.c. 20 [G.L.], where it has been known for over a hundred years, and the pond on Chorley Wood Common (09/I).

R. flammula L. (Map 11m) *Lesser Spearwort* Ellis, 1749
Marshy and muddy places Native
Common on the London Clay but only occasional elsewhere. H.S. 29, 87, 90, 91, 101, 108.

R. sceleratus L. (Map 11n) *Celery-leaved Crowfoot*
Coleman, 1838
Muddy shores of ponds and ditches Native
Frequent and well distributed. H.S. 20, 88.

R. ficaria L. (Map 11o) *Lesser Celandine* Franks, 1822
Ficaria verna Huds.
Meadows, roadside verges, wood borders, etc. Native
A common but variable species. Late-flowering plants with bulbils in the axils of the leaves and tending to grow in shade are frequent. H.S. 9, 12, 18, 19, 29, 35, 36, 39, 41, 44, 47, 60, 63, 65, 82, 95, 103.

The subgenus *Batrachium* (DC.) A. Gray (the Water Crowfoots) has presented many difficulties as the species limits of some of its members have not been clear. I wish to thank Dr. C. D. K. Cook for examining my herbarium material and assisting me in the treatment given here.

R. hederaceus L. *Ivy-leaved Water Crowfoot* Franks, 1820
Places which are perpetually wet and muddy Native
A species which has always been scarce in the county. Records were made during the period of the present survey at Hertford Heath (31/K), confirming an old record by Coleman; Golding's Wood, 1955 (31/Q), *Hb. H.M.*; meadow, Boxmoor, 1957 (00/N), *Hb. H.M.* Recorded also from Patmore Heath, *E. J. Douglas and J. L. Fielding.* It is apparently extinct in other places where it was known to earlier botanists e.g. Bricket Wood, Colney Heath, Burleigh Meadow and Totteridge Green.

R. peltatus Schrank Trimen and Dyer, 1869
Ponds, ditches, etc. Native
Frequent but with too few confirmed records to allow a satisfactory species map to be made.

R. penicillatus (Dumort.) Bab. Pryor, 1875
R. pseudofluitans (Syme) Newbould ex Baker & Foggitt
Rivers, gravel pits, etc. Native
A variable species including var. **calcareus** (Butcher) C. D. K. Cook which is apparently frequent in the chalk streams but lacks sufficient records to allow a distribution map to be presented, and var. **vertumnus** C. D. K. Cook (*R. sphaerospermus* auct. angl., non Boiss.). The latter is a feature of the river at Oughton Head (13/Q) where it was first collected by Pollard in 1886, *Hb. H.M.* and it is still

there, specimens having been gathered by G. L. Evans in 1951 and 1953, *Hb. H.M.* Collected also at Water End, 1966 (01/F), *Hb. H.M.*

R. aquatilis L. Pryor, 1875
R. heterophyllus Weber
Ponds, rivers, etc. Native
Owing to confusion with R. *peltatus* insufficient is known of the distribution and frequency of this species. Dr. Cook has referred only one gathering of mine to it: pond by Plashes Wood, 1958 (32/Q), *Hb. H.M.*

R. trichophyllus Chaix (Map 12a) Pryor, 1874
Ponds, ditches, etc. Native
An easily recognised species which is well distributed in the county.

R. circinatus Sibth. (Map 12b) Coleman, 1841
Deep stagnant water Native
A very distinct species which is a feature of the Tring Reservoirs and the canal system adjoining them and of the flooded gravel pits below Hoddesdon.

Adonis annua L., *Pheasant's Eye,* first recorded in *Pryor,* 3, has a number of subsequent records but very rarely have notes been given on its status. It appeared as a garden escape at Stocken's Green (21/P) in 1965, *Miss N. H. Johnson.*

Myosurus L.
M. minimus L. *Mousetail* J. Woods, 1805
Arable fields which become waterlogged in winter Native
Recorded a number of times from the river gravels but rarely established. During the period of the survey the following records were made: garden weed, Knebworth (22/L)!, *G. Bloom;* Rothamsted Experimental Farm (11/G)!, *K. Warington;* Redbournbury, 1959 (11/A)!, *Mrs. Charter;* abundant for one year only in field by Fanshaws Back Lane, 1958 (30/J), *H. B. Souster*!; field below Woodcroft Wood, 1956 (32/H), *Hb. H.M.*

Aquilegia L.
A. vulgaris L. *Columbine* Dickson, 1815
Recorded as a rare native species of 'woods and bushy places' by Coleman and it is possible that it may still appear as such in the south-west of the county. There are recent records from Whippendell Wood, 1958, *C. Leach,* and Chandler's Cross but they may well have been for garden escapes. It is now found occasionally as a naturalized species or on rubbish dumps.

Thalictrum L.
T. flavum L. (Map 12c) *Common Meadow Rue*
Blackstone, 1737
Water meadows and sides of rivers Native
Occasional in suitable places in meadows associated with the larger rivers. H.S. 75.

T. minus L. subsp. **minus** *Lesser Meadow Rue*
T. jacquinianum Koch H. Fordham, 1849
Limited to the eastern part of Therfield Heath (34/K, 33/J)!, *Hb. H.M.* where it is relatively abundant. It was considered scarce by nineteenth-century botanists as it was kept down by sheep and rarely flowered. H.S. 1.

The Ranunculaceae contain many attractive garden plants which may escape to adorn rubbish dumps or become naturalized elsewhere. *Winter Aconite* (**Eranthis hyemalis** (L.) Salisb.) first recorded by Webb and Coleman, 1843, has long been naturalized in a copse near Roxford Farm (31/A)! and has been recorded from Bengeo (31/G) – specimen collected by J. Pollard, 1875, *Hb. H.M.* – Tring,

Hertingfordbury, etc. *Love-in-a-Mist* (**Nigella damascena** L.) first recorded from Ware, 1917, by A. W. Graveson, *Hb. Gr.* occurs rarely on rubbish tips. *Monkshood* (**Aconitum napellus** L.) was recorded as a garden escape by Pryor and still occurs very rarely as such. *Larkspur* (**Consolida ambigua** (L.) P. W. Ball & Heywood (*Delphinium ajacis* auct., *D. consolida* auct.)) first recorded by J. Ansell, 1846, was apparently not unusual as a cornfield weed until about 1914 (specimen from Oughton Head Farm, 1875, *J. Pollard, Hb. H.M.*). It, or some closely allied species, is found occasionally on rubbish dumps.

BERBERIDACEAE
Berberis L.
B. vulgaris L.   *Barberry*   Steele MS., c. 1730
This was probably frequent in hedgerows in the eighteenth century but was destroyed by farmers as it caused wheat rust. It is now rare and some of the records given here may refer to planted shrubs. During the period of the survey it has been recorded from: copse, Mangrove Lane, Hertford, 1951, *Mrs. S. C. Mortis*; behind village hall, Tewin (21/S)!, *F. A. Robinson*; Brickendon Lane, Hertford, 1959, *H. Williams*; near Sawbridgeworth (41/S), *J. L. Fielding*; Hyde Farm, Bedmond (00/X), *H. B. Souster*!; roadside, Tyttenhanger, 1964 (10/X), *D. H. Kent*!.

Mahonia Nutt.
M. aquifolium (Pursh.) Nutt. (Map 12d) *Oregon Grape*
                                                      Little, 1922
Copses, plantations and woodland borders   Naturalized
Planted frequently and spreading to natural habitats.

NYMPHAEACEAE
Nuphar Sm.
N. lutea (L.) Sm.   (Map 12e)   *Yellow Water-lily,*
                          Brandy Bottle   Blackstone, 1737
Slow-flowing rivers   Native
Frequent in suitable places but not always flowering.

Nymphaea L.
N. alba L.   *White Water-lily*   Blackstone, 1746
                                        (Isaak Walton, 1653)
This was probably native at one time in the lower stretches of the Lea and Colne. It is now found only in ornamental ponds and lakes in private grounds having apparently been planted.

CERATOPHYLLACEAE
Ceratophyllum L.
C. demersum L.   (Map 12f) *Hornwort* Coleman, 1838
Canals, navigable rivers, lakes, etc.   Native
Frequent in the Grand Union Canal and the Lea Navigation. Probably introduced into ponds and lakes when being stocked with fish unless carried to them by waterfowl.

C. submersum L. was found by D. J. Hinson in 1956 in the Long Pond, Totteridge Lane. v.c. 20 [G.L.]!, *Hb. H.M.* It was apparently plentiful then but it cannot be refound now.

PAPAVERACEAE
Papaver L.
P. rhoeas L. (Map 12g) *Common Poppy* Blake, 1819
Cornfields, waste places, roadsides, etc.   Native
Abundant. It is a very variable species and previous botanists have recorded most of the named forms and varieties for the county.

P. dubium L.   (Map 12h) *Smooth long-headed Poppy*
P. lamottei Bor.   Coleman, 1838
Roadsides, waste places, etc.   Native
Occasional and well distributed in the county and less

common in arable fields than *P. rhoeas*. See also note on following species. H.S. 7.

P. lecoqii Lamotte   (Map 12i)   *Babington's Poppy*
                                              Pryor, 1874
Roadsides, arable fields, etc.   Colonist
Frequent on the Boulder Clay and Chalk but rare elsewhere. I have taken this to differ from *P. dubium* only in having dark-yellow sap. See my note on this species in *Flora of Bedfordshire*, 209.

P. hybridum L.   (Map 12j) *Prickly-headed Poppy*
                                              Coleman, 1840
Arable fields, etc.   Colonist
Frequent on the Chalk and to be found also but less frequently on the Boulder Clay.

P. argemone L. (Map 12k) *Rough long-headed Poppy*
                                              Blake, c. 1820
Sides of railway tracks, roadsides, etc.   Colonist
Well distributed being found most frequently on the railroads.

P. somniferum L. (Map 12 l), first recorded by Webb and Coleman, 1843, is found occasionally on rubbish dumps. In other places, e.g. fields near Benington Wood, where it has persisted for some years, it may be a relic of cultivation.

Chelidonium L.
C. majus L. (Map 12m) *Greater Celandine* Franks, 1823
Banks by roadsides   Colonist
Frequent but rarely found away from houses. Its yellow sap is still supposed by country folk to be a cure for warts.

Roemeria hybrida (L.) DC., **Glaucium corniculatum** (L.) Rudolph and **Eschscholzia californica** Cham. are garden plants which have been recorded rarely from rubbish tips.

FUMARIACEAE
Corydalis Vent.
C. lutea (L.) DC.   (Map 12n) *Yellow Fumitory*
                                              Blake, c. 1820
Old walls   Denizen
Occasional and always of garden origin.

C. bulbosa (L.) DC. has been recorded as a garden escape in shrubberies and apparently persisted for a number of years at Totteridge.
Fumaria L.
F. officinalis L.   (Map 12o)   *Common Fumitory*
                                              Franks, 1822
Arable fields, waste places, etc.   Colonist
Common except on the more acid soils. H.S. 83.

F. vaillantii Lois. (Map 13a) Webb and Coleman, 1843
Arable fields   Colonist
Rare and limited to the more calcareous soils.

F. densiflora DC.   (Map 13b)   Coleman, 1841
F. micrantha Lag.
Arable fields   Colonist
Not uncommon in fields on the Chalk.

F. parviflora Lam.   H. Fordham, 1842
Arable fields   Colonist
Very rare. Pollard recorded it from High Down, 1886, *Hb. H.M.* and Little knew it at Arbury Banks, Clothall and Great Wymondley. I have seen it only in the neighbourhood of Therfield and Royston (33/ILP) and near to Ardeley (32/H).

F. muralis Sond. ex Koch subsp. **boraei** (Jord.) Pugsl. occurs only as a casual and current records are: Hornbeam Lane, Essendon, 1963 (20/T), *J. C. Gardiner!*, *Hb. H.M.*; Perry Green, 1965 (11/P), *P. J. Ellison!*, *Hb. H.M.* **F. bastardii** Bor. was recorded from Benslow, Hitchin, by J. E. Little in *W.E.C. 1931–32 Rep.* 108, *Hb. Camb.*

CRUCIFERAE
Brassica L.
B. nigra (L.) Koch   (Map 13c)   *Black Mustard*
Sinapis nigra L.   Blake, c. 1820
Waste places, roadsides, etc.   Colonist
Occasional and usually an escape from cultivation.

B. rapa L. (Map 13d) *Bargeman's Cabbage* Coleman, 1838
B. campestris L.
Riversides   Colonist
Especially frequent on the Lea and Stort Navigation.

B. juncea (L.) Czern.   *Chinese Mustard*
                                          A. W. Graveson, 1911
A casual of waste places e.g. Blackbridge Dump, 1956 (11/X), *Hb. H.M.*, etc.

Other casuals include **B. tournefortii** Gouan, Hitchin U.D.C. refuse tip, 1965 (13/V), *Hb. H.M.* and various relics of cultivation such as cabbage, turnip, swede, rape, etc.

Sinapis L.
S. arvensis L.   (Map 13e)   *Charlock*   Ellis, 1744
Arable fields, waste places, etc.   Colonist.
Very common. H.S. 6, 53.

S. alba L.   (Map 13f)   *White Mustard*   Blake, c. 1820
Arable fields, waste places, etc.   Colonist
Abundant on the more calcareous soils

Diplotaxis DC.
D. muralis (L.) DC. (Map 13g) *Wall Rocket, Stinkweed*
                                          Pryor, 1874
Railway tracks, bare places on the Chalk, etc.   Colonist
Common in suitable habitats. H.S. 1.

D. tenuifolia (L.) DC.   (Map 13h) *Perennial Wall Rocket*
                                          Coles, 1657
Old walls, railway sidings, waste places, etc.   Colonist
This was at one time a feature of the walls of St. Albans Abbey. It now appears in bare and well drained sites where it becomes established.

D. erucoides (L.) DC. was recorded as a casual from Ware, 1916, by A. W. Graveson, *Hb. Gr.*

Raphanus L.
R. raphanistrum L. (Map 13i) *Wild Radish* Ellis, 1750
Raphanistrum innocuum Moench
Arable fields, waste places, roadsides, etc.   Colonist
Common. White-flowered forms are most frequent on arable land and yellow–flowered forms on newly-made roadside verges. H.S. 59.

R. sativus L., *Garden Radish*, occurs as an escape from cultivation.

Crambe maritima L., *Sea Kale*, was recorded from the face of a chalk pit at Hitchin, 1914. *J. E. Little.*

Rapistrum Crantz
R. rugosum (L.) All.   *Bastard Cabbage*   Pryor, 1874
R. orientale (L.) Crantz, *R. linneanum* auct., *R. tenuifolium* auct.
Recorded from time to time as a rare and very variable

casual on rubbish dumps, etc. It has increased in recent years as a bird-seed alien.

R. perenne (L.) All. was recorded from Ware, 1910, *G. C. Druce, Hb. Druce* and Cole Green, 1922, *A. W. Graveson, Hb. Gr.*

Conringia orientalis (L.) Dumort. (*Erysimum orientale* (L.) Crantz, non Mill.), *Hare's-ear*, was first recorded by Webb and Coleman (1843) and subsequently a few times as a casual in the neighbourhood of Ware. The only recent record is by Little from Great Wymondley in *B.E.C. 1929 Rep.* 103, *Hb. Camb.*

Lepidium L.
L. campestre (L.) R. Br.   (Map 13j)   *Pepperwort*
                                          Culpeper, 1652
Banks on field boundaries, railway banks, etc.   Colonist
Occasional but usually plentiful when it appears.

L. heterophyllum Benth., *Smith's Cress*, is a colonist of similar habitats to the above which had not been recorded before the present survey. Its known stations are: railway, Croxley Moor, 1957 (09/X), *F. M. Day!* (see *London Naturalist* 38 (1958), 74); railway, Bragbury End, 1961 (22/Q), *Lloyd-Evans!*, *Hb. H.M.*; abundant in gravel pit, Parkbury, 1966 (10/L, R).

L. ruderale L.   (Map 13k)   *Narrow-leaved Pepperwort*
                                          Blow, 1872
A frequent colonist of rubbish dumps and waste places especially on the London Clay and river gravels.

L. latifolium L. (Map 13 l) *Dittander* M. Brown, 1929
Riverbanks, roadsides, sides of disused pits, etc.   Colonist
A feature of the roadside near Baldock (23/M) where it was first recorded by Margaret Brown in *B.E.C. 1929 Rep.* 104. Locally abundant by the sides of the flooded pits south of Rickmansworth from where it was first recorded in *Proc. Herts. N.H.S.* 20 (1934), vii.

The following are recorded as casuals. **L. sativum** L., *Garden Cress*, frequent on rubbish dumps: **L. graminifolium** L., Pye Corner, 1962 (41/L), *L. Lloyd-Evans!*, *Hb. H.M.*: **L. densiflorum** Schrad., Royston, *H. Phillips, B.E.C. 1934 Rep.* 818, *Hb. Ph.*: **L. neglectum** Thell., Hitchin, *Little, B.E.C. 1923 Rep.* 375, *Hb. B.M.*: **L. virginicum** L., Ware, *A. W. Graveson, B.E.C. 1922 Rep.* 718, *Hb. Gr.*: **L. perfoliatum** L., *Hayllar, B.E.C. 1915 Rep.* 257; Ware, *A. W. Graveson, Hb. Gr.*

Coronopus Zinn
C. squamatus (Forsk.) Aschers. (Map 13m) *Swine's Cress*
C. procumbens Gilib.   Coleman, 1838
Farm tracks, well-manured ground, etc.   Colonist
A common species which has probably increased in recent years.

C. didymus (L.) Sm.   (Map 13n)   *Lesser Swine's Cress*
                                          J. Ransom, 1843
Waste ground   Colonist
Occasional on the more acid soils of the London Clay and river gravels. It has probably increased as it was considered to be rare a century ago.

Cardaria Desv.
C. draba (L.) Desv. (Map 13o) *Hoary Cress* Pollard, 1873
Lepidium draba L.
Roadsides, waste places, etc.   Colonist
A common and often pernicious weed on the Chalk which is also found occasionally on waste ground elsewhere. It

has much increased since its introduction less than a hundred years ago.

Iberis L.
I. amara L. *Candytuft* W. Christy
(New Botanist's Guide), 1835
A rare native of the edges of arable fields, rabbit warrens and similarly disturbed places on the Chalk. H.S. 52. R. B. Benson observes that it was common on the hills about Tring and Aldbury up to 1954 but seemed to become scarce afterwards owing to the absence of rabbit burrows. Other current records are fields near Therfield Heath where it was first recorded by Fordham, 1840 (33/J)!, *Hb. B.M.*; side of Prior's Wood from where it was first recorded by W. J. Blake (11/Y)!; to the south of Icknield Way, 1959 (12/J), *G. Bloom and B. Jennings*; chalkpit, Whiteway Bottom, 1960 (12/K).

Thlaspi L.
T. arvense L. (Map 14a) *Penny Cress* Blake, c. 1820
Arable fields Colonist
Considered by Coleman to be rare and limited to the southern half of the county. It is now frequent and widespread.

Teesdalia nudicaulis (L.) R. Br., *Shepherd's Cress*, a rare native of gravelly pastures was recorded from Colney Heath in 1859 by F. Walker (see *J. Bot. 1872*, 182). It was last seen there by Sir Edward Salisbury about 1940.

Capsella Medic.
C. bursa-pastoris (L.) Medic. (Map 14b) *Shepherd's Purse*
Ellis, 1750
Waste ground, arable fields, gardens, etc. Colonist
Ubiquitous H.S. 52, 53, 77.

Cochlearia danica L., *Danish Scurvy-grass*, was found sparingly in 1955 and 1956 on the railway track near to Berkhamsted (91/K, 90/Y, 00/D) *Hb. H.M.* I also found it about 1945 to be plentiful on the railway between Chiltern Green and Harpenden (11/HI). The occurrence of this species in the county is an interesting example of a plant of the coast spreading inland during the war years when labour was scarce on the railway.

Bunias L.
B. orientalis L. (Map 14c) *Warty Cabbage* Pryor, 1877
Old chalk pits, railway sidings, etc. Colonist
An introduced species which given favourable conditions becomes established for at least a limited period.

Alyssum alyssoides (L.) L. (*A. calycinum* L.), *Small Alison*, was introduced with crops, especially clover, in the mid-nineteenth century (see *Pryor*, 38). The most recent record was Little Offley, 1886, *J. Pollard, Hb. H.M.* **Lobularia maritima** (L.) Desv., *Sweet Alison*, is found frequently on rubbish dumps as a garden throw-out. **Berteroa incana** (L.) DC. was recorded earlier as a casual (see *Pryor*, 37) but the only recent record is from Letchworth, 1947, *A. Gavin Jones, Hb. B.M.*

Draba L.
D. muralis L. *Wall Whitlow Grass* Brown, 1925
Walls, gardens, etc. Colonist
Rare but often taking possession of a site for a number of years. It was first recorded from a wall at Berkhamsted, *Mrs.* (? Miss) *Brown, B.E.C. 1925 Rep.* 862. It is a feature of walls at Loudwater (09/M)! – see *Kent and Lousley*, 16. Other current records are: abundant in garden, Markyate Cell, 1962 (01/N); gravel pit, Nettleden, 1960 (01/A), v.c. 24 [Herts.].

Erophila DC.
E. verna (L.) Chevall. (Map 14d) *Whitlow Grass*
E. vulgaris DC. Kalm, 1748
Old walls, well drained sites, etc. Native
Occasional in the north of the county where it is found most frequently on gravel paths. H.S. 65.

E. spathulata Láng is known only from the embankment of Wilstone Reservoir, 1963 (91/B), *R. S. R. Fitter, Hb. H.M.* but may occur elsewhere. Wilstone Reservoir was a station given in *Pryor*, 38, for *E. praecox* (Stev.) DC. which in fact does not occur in Britain.

Armoracia Gilib.
A. rusticana Gaertn., Mey. & Scherb. (Map 14e)
Cochlearia armoracia L. *Horse Radish*
Webb and Coleman, 1843
Roadsides, waste ground, etc. Of garden origin
Common and well distributed.

Cardamine L.
C. pratensis L. (Map 14f) *Lady's Smock*
Coleman, 1838 (Isaak Walton, 1653)
Marshes, meadows, etc. Native
Frequent and well distributed. A variable species which merits closer study. H.S. 13, 18, 19, 27, 29, 74, 76, 78, 90, 91.

C. amara L., *Large Bittercress*, was recorded from the R. Colne close to the Middlesex boundary by Blackstone (1737) and subsequently by others. It was apparently last seen there by D. H. Kent in 1938 – see *Kent and Lousley*, 15. In 1966 C. W. Burton found it growing by the side of a pond at Pirton (13/L) where it had probably been introduced.

C. flexuosa With. (Map 14g) *Wavy Bittercress*
Webb and Coleman, 1843
Woods, riversides and shady places Native
Common on the London Clay but rare elsewhere H.S. 88, 103, 106.

C. hirsuta L. (Map 14h) *Hairy Bittercress* Coleman, 1838
Garden paths and plots, bare places, etc. Native
Occasional and well distributed.

C. bulbifera (L.) Crantz (Map 14i) *Coral-wort*
Dentaria bulbifera L. Webb and Coleman, 1843
Damp woods and shady places Native
Limited to a very small area in which it is locally abundant and from which it extends into Buckinghamshire and Greater London. It is restricted elsewhere in Britain to similar small areas and it must rank as one of the more interesting plants of the Hertfordshire flora.

Barbarea R. Br.
B. vulgaris R. Br. (Map 14j) *Wintercress* Franks, 1821
Sides of ditches and streams, roadsides, etc. Native
Frequent and well distributed. H.S. 41.

B. intermedia Bor. *Early Wintercress*
A. W. Graveson, 1919
A casual of roadsides and waste places. Colney Heath, 1919, *A. W. Graveson, Hb. Gr.*; near Whippendell Wood, 1957, *E. B. Bangerter, Hb. H.M.*; New Barnet, 1955 (29/T), v.c. 20 [G.L.], *Hb. H.M.*; canal bank, Berkhamsted, 1960 (90/Z), *Hb. H.M.*

B. verna (Mill.) Aschers. *Land Cress*
B. praecox (Sm.) R. Br. Webb and Coleman, 1849
A rare casual or escape from cultivation and recorded during the present survey from Oaklands, 1959 (10/Y), *Hb. H.M.*;

rubbish dump, Colney Street, 1963 (10/L), *Hb. H.M.*; Otterspool, 1966 (19/J).

Arabis L.

A. glabra (L.) Bernh.   *Tower Mustard*   Blake, 1820
A. perfoliata Lam., *Turritis glabra* L.
A native of disturbed gravelly soils which was a century ago frequent in the neighbourhood of Hertford and has been re-found twice in the same area during the present survey: gravel pit, Waterford, 1957 (31/C), *A. W. Graveson*!; roadside, east of Hatfield, 1961 (20/P).

A. caucasica Willd. (*A. albida* Stev.), *Garden Arabis*, has been recorded only as a garden escape.

Nasturtium R. Br.

N. officinale R.Br.   (Map 14k)   *Watercress*   Blake, 1819
Rorippa nasturtium-aquaticum (L.) Hayek
Streams and ditches   Native
Frequent and well distributed but becoming rare on the Boulder Clay. H.S. 9, 65, 66.

N. microphyllum (Boenn.) Reichb.   (Map 14 l)
Kent and Lousley, 1951
In similar situations to the previous species   Native
Frequent in streams on the Boulder Clay but absent from most of the larger rivers. H.S. 29, 74, 76.
N. microphyllum × officinale
This occurs frequently with the parents and is in addition very often the plant grown commercially in the watercress beds as at Whitwell and Boxmoor. From these it may escape and become established nearby.

Rorippa Scop.

R. sylvestris (L.). Bess. (Map 14m) *Creeping Yellow-cress*
Nasturtium sylvestre (L.) R. Br.   Webb and Coleman, 1843
Damp ground near streams, roadsides, gardens, etc. Native
This is considered rare by Coleman who knew it as a native plant in one station only. In the last twenty years it has increased to become an obnoxious weed in large gardens especially in the south of the county.

R. islandica (Oeder) Borbás   (Map 14n)   *Marsh*
Nasturtium palustre (L.) DC.,   *Yellow-cress*
N. terrestre R. Br., *N. anceps* auct.   Coleman, 1839
Muddy shores of ponds, waste places, etc.   Native
Occasional and most frequent on the London Clay and on ballast on railways. H.S. 20, 108.

R. amphibia (L.) Bess.   (Map 14o)   *Greater Yellow-cress*
Nasturtium amphibium (L.) R. Br.   Webb, 1840
Riversides, sides of canals, etc.   Native
Rare and limited to the larger rivers and Tring Reservoirs.

Hesperis matronalis L., *Dame's Violet*, is occasional as a garden escape and may have increased as Pryor considered it to be rare.

Erysimum L.

E. cheiranthoides L.   (Map 15a)   *Treacle Mustard*
Franks, 1820
Arable fields and waste places   Colonist
Occasional and well distributed.

E. repandum L. has been recorded as a rare casual e.g. Hertford, 1845, *J. Ansell, Hb. Druce*; Ware, 1914, *Mrs. Wedgwood, Hb. Druce*.

Cheiranthus cheiri L., *Wallflower*, was recorded by Coleman (1838) and most later botanists as a denizen on various old walls. It is still on Hertford Castle wall.

Alliaria Heist. ex Fabr.

A. petiolata (Bieb.) Cavara & Grande   (Map 15b)
A. officinalis Andrz. ex Bieb.,   *Garlic Mustard*   Ellis, 1750
Sisymbrium alliaria (L.) Scop.
Hedgerows, wood borders, etc.   Native
Abundant.

Sisymbrium L.

S. officinale (L.) Scop. (Map 15c) *Hedge Mustard*
Blake, c. 1820
Roadsides, waste places, etc.   Colonist
Abundant. A variable species and robust plants with glabrous seed pods, which are frequently found on the Hertfordshire rubbish dumps, appear to be distinct.

S. orientale L.   (Map 15d)   *Eastern Rocket*
A. W. Graveson, 1912
Waste places   Colonist
Frequent and much increased in recent years.

S. altissimum L.   (Map 15e)   *Tumbling Mustard*
A. W. Graveson, 1909
Waste places   Colonist
Frequent.

S. loeselii L., *False London Rocket*, first recorded by Little in *W.E.C. 1912–13 Rep.* 383, *Hb. B.M.* is frequent on rubbish dumps as at Blackbridge (11/X) and Park Street (10/L): **S. irio** L., *London Rocket*, first recorded by Webb and Coleman, 1849, has been found in recent years only by A. W. Graveson at Ware, 1917, *Hb. Gr.* and by Dymes at Letchworth, 1929. *Hb. Letch. Mus.*: **S. erysimoides** Desf. was found as a wool adventive at Wymondley, 1959 (22/D), *Hb. H.M.*

Arabidopsis (DC.) Heynh.

A. thaliana (L.) Heynh.   (Map 15f)   *Thale Cress*
Sisymbrium thalianum (L.) Gay   Coleman, 1838
Bare ground, railway tracks, old walls, etc.   Native
Frequent on gravelly soils but rare on the Chalk and Boulder Clay. H.S. 83, 96.

Camelina sativa (L.) Crantz, *Gold of Pleasure*, was recorded by Webb and Coleman, 1839, and later nineteenth-century botanists as a casual introduced with flax seed. It is now rare on rubbish dumps as a bird-seed alien. **C. alyssum** (Mill.) Thell. was recorded by Phillips from Welwyn in *B.E.C. 1931 Rep.* 552, *Hb. Druce* and **C. microcarpa** Andrz. (*C. sylvestris* Wallr.) from Ware, 1916, by A. W. Graveson, *Hb. Gr.* (see also *Pryor*, 39).

Descurainia Webb & Berth.

D. sophia (L.) Webb ex Prantl *Flixweed* Coleman, 1838
Sisymbrium sophia L.
Waste ground   Colonist
Recorded by earlier botanists mainly in the neighbourhood of Ware. It is now rare and occurs only as a casual as at Ashwell End, 1966 (24/K), *H. Bowry*; Royston, 1961 (34/K); Hitchin U.D.C. Dump, 1965 (13/V); Cole Green Dump, 1964 (21/Q); Blackbridge Dump (11/X); Tring U.D.C. Dump. (91/B).

D. brachycarpa (Richardson) O. E. Schulz (*Sisymbrium brachycarpon* Richardson) was recorded from Ware by A. W. Graveson in *B.E.C. 1924 Rep.* 556.

The following casuals in addition to those already accounted for are also recorded in the Cruciferae:

Carrichtera annua (L.) DC., Ware, *Hayllar in B.E.C. 1916 Rep.* 472: **Eruca vesicaria** (L.) Cav. subsp. **sativa** (Mill.) Thell., Hertford, 1873, *Blow, Hb. B.M.*; Ware,

1916, *A. W. Graveson, Hb. Gr.*: **Erucaria hispanica** (L.) Druce (*E. aleppica* Gaertn., *E. myagroides* auct.) has been recorded rarely and most recently from Hitchin (13/V) *H. Bowry, Hb. H.M.*: **Erucastrum gallicum** (Willd.) O. E. Schulz, Ware, 1920, *A. W. Graveson, Hb. Gr.*: **Hirschfeldia incana** (L.) Lagrèze-Fossat (*Erucastrum incanum* (L.) Koch), Ware, 1919, *A. W. Graveson, Hb. Gr.* – see also *Pryor*, 36: **Lunaria annua** L., *Honesty*, first recorded in *Pryor*, 37, occurs rarely as a garden relic: **Malcolmia africana** (L.) R. Br. (*Wilckia africana* (L.) F. Muell.), Ware, 1907, *G. C. Druce, Hb. B.M.*; Ware, 1916, *A. W. Graveson, Hb. Gr.*: **M. maritima** (L.) R. Br., *Virginian Stock*, Cole Green, 1922, *A. W. Graveson, Hb. Gr.*; Cock Lane, 1965 (30/U), *B. Wurzell, Hb. H.M.*: **M. ramosissima** (Desf.) Thell., rubbish dump, Pye Corner, 1964 (41/L), *Hb. H.M.*: **Moricandia arvensis** (L.) DC., Ware, *Hayllar, B.E.C. 1916 Rep.* 472: **Myagrum perfoliatum** L., Hertford, 1912, *A. W. Graveson, Hb. Gr.*: **Neslia paniculata** (L.) Desv., Hertford, 1875, *T. B. Blow, Hb. B.M.*; Hitchin, 1927, *J. E. Little*.

RESEDACEAE
Reseda L.
R. luteola L. (Map 15g) *Dyer's Rocket, Weld*
Blake, 1819
Waste ground on the Chalk and gravels   Native
Occasional and well distributed.

R. lutea L. (Map 15h) *Wild Mignonette* Blake, c. 1820
Waste and disturbed ground on chalky soils   Native
Common on the Chalk but only occasional elsewhere. H.S. 1, 7, 53.

R. alba L. was recorded as a casual from Letchworth by Phillips in *B.E.C. 1932 Rep.* 90, *Hb. Ph.* and **R. odorata** L., *Garden Mignonette*, was recorded in *Pryor*, 46.

VIOLACEAE
Viola L.
V. odorata L. (Map 15i) *Sweet Violet* Franks MS., 1822
Roadside banks, wood borders, etc.   Native
Apparently more frequent on the Chalk and Boulder Clay than elsewhere but it is difficult to distinguish introduced from genuinely wild plants. White-flowered forms are frequent but no adequate study has been made of the named varieties.

V. hirta L. subsp. **hirta** (Map 15j) *Hairy Violet*
J. Woods, 1805
Calcareous pastures   Native
Frequent on the chalk downs and chalk exposures elsewhere. H.S. 3, 11, 12, 14, 21, 41, 50–53, 56, 67, 100.
subsp. **calcarea** (Bab.) Warburg was recorded by Blow from Dawley Warren (see *Pryor*, 52) but it has not been found again in the county.
V. hirta × odorata (*V. × permixta* Jord.) was recorded by Blow (see *Pryor*, 51) and Little but I have not seen it in the county.

V. riviniana Reichb. (Map 15k) *Common Wood Violet*
Pryor, 1874
Woods, heathy places, etc.   Native
Frequent in woods on all soils throughout the county but found only occasionally on heaths and commons. H.S. 11, 16, 17, 41, 42, 45–47, 62, 77–80, 82, 87–89, 93–95, 104, 105, 107.

V. reichenbachiana Jord. ex Bor. (Map 15 l)
Pale Wood Violet Pryor, 1874
Woods   Native
Less common than *V. riviniana* and limited mainly to woods on calcareous soils. H.S. 17, 32, 36, 54, 60, 63.

V. canina L. subsp. **canina** (Map 15m) *Heath Violet*
Pryor, 1874
Heaths and heathy pastures   Native
Rare and readily hybridizing with *V. riviniana*. H.S. 70, 72

V. arvensis Murr. (Map 15n) *Heartsease, Field Pansy*
Coleman, 1838.
Arable fields, waste ground, etc.   Colonist
Common and well distributed. H.S. 52. The closely allied **V. tricolor** L., Wild Pansy, has been frequently recorded but often in error. I have seen it only once in the county: Bury Plantation, 1962 (23/S), *Hb. H.M.* These species are both variable and in addition probably hybridize. A number of names were applied to gatherings of pansies made by Little and his near contemporaries but no useful purpose would be gained by listing them here.

POLYGALACEAE
Polygala L.
P. vulgaris L. (Map 15o) *Common Milkwort* Franks, 1820
P. oxyptera Reichb.
Chalk downs and other calcareous pastures   Native
Occasional. H.S. 2, 3, 5, 14, 15, 49, 50, 55, 56, 100.

P. serpyllifolia Hose (Map 16a) *Heath Milkwort*
P. serpyllacea Weihe   Blow, 1872
Heaths and heathy pastures   Native
Rare. H.S. 57, 81.

GUTTIFERAE
Hypericum L.
H. androsaemum L. *Tutsan* Steele MS. c. 1730
Androsaemum officinale All.
Woods and copses   Native
Very rare. Coleman recorded this for a number of woods but it is probably extinct now. E. G. Kellett knew one plant in Sherrards Wood about twenty years ago which could have been indigenous but in places where I have seen it, e.g. Pond Bottom Wood (43/D), it had every appearance of having been originally planted.

H. perforatum L. (Map 16b) *Common St. John's Wort*
Franks, 1822
Hedgerows, wood borders, rough pastures, etc. Native
Common in most of the county but rare on the Boulder Clay. H.S. 4, 6, 21, 41, 45, 51, 58, 59, 62, 67, 69, 80, 83, 96.

H. maculatum Crantz (Map 16c) *Imperforate*
H. dubium Leers, *St. John's Wort* Sabine, 1805
H. quadrangulum auct.
Roadsides, wood borders, rough pastures, etc. Native
subsp. **maculatum** is very rare and has been found only in Hoo Wood, 1962 (01/G), *D. E. Allen!*, *Hb. H.M.*
subsp. **obtusiusculum** (Tourlet) Hayek is the usual form in the county and is rare except in the major square TL/20. where it is locally frequent.

H. tetrapterum Fr. (Map 16d) *Square-stemmed*
H. quadratum Stokes *St. John's Wort* Franks, 1820
Wet meadows, marshy places, etc.   Native
Occasional and well distributed H.S. 18, 19, 27, 33–35, 39, 44, 76, 77, 90, 100, 103.

H. humifusum L. (Map 16e) *Trailing St. John's Wort*
Blake, c. 1820
Heaths and heathy woodland rides   Native
Somewhat rare but generally to be found in suitable habitats.

H. pulchrum L.   (Map 16f)   *Slender St. John's Wort*
Woodward, 1787
Heathy woods   Native
More frequent and widely distributed than the preceding.
H.S. 64, 72, 77, 105.

H. hirsutum L.   (Map 16g)   *Hairy St. John's Wort*
Blake, c. 1820
Woods and hedgerows on calcareous soils   Native
Common in woods on the Chalk and Boulder Clay but
rare elsewhere. H.S. 11, 21, 32, 33, 35, 36, 41, 46, 54, 79, 80.

H. montanum L., *Pale St. John's Wort*, is a doubtful native
of Hertfordshire. Bentley reported one plant from Pirton
Cross in the *Phytologist* (*New Series*) 2 (1858), 493 and Sir
Edward Salisbury recorded it from near Hudnall, v.c. 24
[Herts.], in 1915, *Trans. Herts. N.H.S.* 16 (1917), 157 – there
is a photograph in *Hb. B.M.*
The following have been recorded as garden escapes:
H. calycinum L., *Rose of Sharon*, first recorded by Ed-
wards, 1857, and occasionally subsequently, has been re-
corded recently from Bayford, 1937, *P. H. Cooke in
Kent and Lousley*, 41; Watford, 1958, *C. Leach*: **H. inodor-
um** Mill. (*H. elatum* Ait. *H. grandifolium* Choisy), Hitchin,
Pryor, 82.

CISTACEAE
Helianthemum Mill.
H. nummularium (L.) Mill.   (Map 16h)   *Rockrose*
H. chamaecistus Mill.   Blackstone, 1746
Chalk hills, chalky exposures, etc.   Native
Frequent in suitable places. H.S. 1–3, 11, 14, 21, 22, 48, 50,
52, 67.

CARYOPHYLLACEAE
Silene L.
S. vulgaris (Moench) Garcke (Map 16i) *Bladder Campion*
S. cucubalus Wibel   Ellis, 1750
Roadsides, waste places, etc.   Native
Generally common but becoming scarce on the London
Clay. H.S. 4, 5, 11, 21, 22, 24, 50, 54, 80, 83.

S. noctiflora L.   (Map 16j)   *Night-flowering Catchfly*
Melandrium noctiflorum (L.) Fr.   Woods, 1805
Arable fields   Native
One of the weeds so much a feature of the Hertfordshire
Boulder Clay.

S. dioica (L.) Clairv.   (Map 16k)   *Red Campion* Blake,
Lychnis dioica L., *Melandrium rubrum* Garcke,   c. 1820
M. sylvestre (Hoppe) Roehl.
Hedges, copses, wood borders   Native
Locally common but with a peculiar distribution that I am
at a complete loss to explain. H.S. 43, 82.

S. alba (Mill.) E. H. L. Krause (Map 16 l) *White Campion*
Lychnis alba Mill.,   Coleman, 1838
Melandrium album (Mill.) Garcke,   *M. pratense* Roehl.
Roadsides, waste places, etc.   Native
Generally abundant but becoming scarce on the London
Clay. H.S. 22, 59, 83.
S. alba × dioica is found occasionally and Little claimed
to have found pink-flowered forms of *S. alba* (see *B.E.C.
1925 Rep.* 765).
The following are recorded as casuals. **S. armeria** L.,
Hatfield, 1850, *G. C. Churchill*, *Hb. B.M.* (see also *Pryor*, 62);
Welwyn, *Phillips*, *B.E.C. 1931 Rep.* 638: **S. conica** L.,
Pryor, 64, in error (see *B.E.C. 1929 Rep.* 107): **S.
conoidea** L., Ware, *Hayllar*, *B.E.C. 1915 Rep.* 258, *Hb.
Gr.*: **S. dichotoma** Ehrh., in quantity near Tring, 1914,

E. J. Salisbury, Trans. Herts. N.H.S. 16 (1916), 75; Ware,
Trower and Druce, B.E.C. 1925 Rep. 866 (see also *Pryor*,
63): **S. gallica** L. (*S. anglica* L., *S. quinquevulnera* L.),
Bishop's Stortford College grounds, 1941, *B. J. Adams,
Hb. J. L. Fielding*; for earlier records see *Pryor*, 63: **S. nutans**
L., *Nottingham Catchfly*, railway embankment, Harpenden,
Proc. Herts. N.H.S. 5 (1890), xxv, *Hb. Luton Mus.*: **S.
muscipula** L., Cole Green, 1924, *A. W. Graveson, Hb. Gr.*;
Welwyn, 1931, *H. Phillips, Hb. Ph.*: **S. cordifolia** All.,
Welwyn, *Phillips, B.E.C. 1931 Rep.* 564: **S. pendula**
L., Hertford, *A. W. Graveson, B.E.C. 1919 Rep.* 643,
Hb. Gr.: **S. rubella** L. Ware, *Druce, B.E.C. 1919 Rep.* 643

Lychnis L.
L. flos-cuculi L. (Map 16m) *Ragged Robin* Franks, 1822
Marshes and wet meadows   Native
Occasional and well distributed. H.S. 9, 19, 29, 30, 35,
38, 39, 66, 73, 76–8, 80, 90, 91, 99, 100.

L. viscaria L. (*Viscaria vulgaris* Bernh.), field near Radlett,
Ada Selby, Trans. Herts. N.H.S. 6 (1890), 74 – see also
Pryor, 59: **L. chalcedonica** L., Welwyn, *H. Phillips*, 1933,
Hb. Ph.

Agrostemma L.
A. githago L.   *Corn Cockle*   Ellis, 1750
Lychnis githago (L.) Scop., *Githago segetum* Link
At one time a frequent cornfield weed but it began to
decrease about fifty years ago. It was, I think, last seen in
the county in 1950.

Dianthus L.
D. armeria L. *Deptford Pink* Newton MS. (see *Pryor*, 499),
c. 1683
Recorded by Coleman and subsequent workers as a very
rare native species of dry gravelly banks. Salisbury knew
it about 1935 on a bank near Radlett and the Gravesons
from a site near Water End, Wheathampstead (11/X),
Hb. Gr. where it can no longer be found. I have seen it only
in rough pasture near Thickney Wood, 1960 (21/J),
Lloyd-Evans!, *Hb. H.M.*

D. deltoides L., *Maiden Pink*, was first recorded by Coleman (1846) and known to him only at Easneye and Amwell
Marsh in which places it has long been extinct. Like *D.
armeria* it is a native of dry gravelly banks. The only recent
records are Bishop's Stortford golf course, 1942 (52/A),
H. J. Holland, Hb. Fielding and it may still survive here;
Wilbury Hill, 1948, *W. H. Fordham*.

D. barbatus L., *Sweet William*, garden escape, Mardock,
J. W. Higgens, B.E.C. 1917 Rep. 99: **D. carthusianorum**
L., St. Albans, 'Dickenson', *B.E.C. 1914 Rep.* 475.

Vaccaria pyramidata Medic. (*Saponaria vaccaria* L.),
a casual first recorded by Webb and Coleman (1843), still
occurs occasionally e.g. Cock Lane Dump, 1965 (30/U),
B. Wurzell; Park Street Dump, 1965 (10/L), *Hb. H.M.*

Saponaria L.
S. officinalis L.   (Map 16n)   *Soapwort*
Webb and Coleman, 1843
Roadsides and waste places   Colonist
Rare, as it has always been. Double-flowered forms are as
frequent as single-flowered ones.

S. ocymoides L. was recorded by Little as a garden escape
at Knebworth in *B.E.C. 1914 Rep.* 9 and **S. calabrica** Guss.
by Phillips from Welwyn in *B.E.C. 1923 Rep.* 468, *Hb. Ph.*

Cerastium L.

C. arvense L. (Map 16o) *Field Mouse-ear Chickweed*
Coleman, 1839
On chalky soils that are more or less disturbed   Native
Rare but by no means limited to the chalk escarpment.
H.S. 69, 83.

C. tomentosum L., (Map 17a) *Snow-in-Summer*, first
recorded by J. E. Dandy from Tring in 1946, *Hb. B.M.*
is found rarely but usually well established as a garden
escape.

C. fontanum Baumg. subsp. **triviale** (Murb.) Jalas
C. holosteoides Fr.,   (Map 17b)   *Mouse-ear Chickweed*
C. vulgatum auct.   Kalm, 1748
Pastures, waste ground, etc.   Native
Very common H.S. 4, 8, 9, 11, 18, 19, 21–23, 27–29, 33, 34,
39, 42, 44, 50, 52, 55–57, 60, 65, 66, 69, 71–80, 90, 91, 100,
105.

C. glomeratum Thuill.   (Map 17c)   *Sticky*
C. viscosum auct.   *Mouse-ear Chickweed* Franks, 1821
Rough pastures, sides of trackways, etc.   Native
Frequent especially on gravelly soils. H.S. 34, 41, 60, 69, 77,
80, 88, 96, 99, 105.

C. diffusum Pers. (Map 17d) *Dark-green Mouse-ear Chick-*
C. atrovirens Bab., *C. tetrandrum* Curt.   *weed* Dony, 1953
A plant of the sea coast which has spread inland along the
railway. It is still frequent on the permanent way of the
railroads but less so than it was twenty years ago when
labour was scarce and the tracks were not regularly cleaned.

C. pumilum Curt.   *Curtis's Mouse-ear Chickweed*
Dony, 1953
Limited to the now disused line from Hitchin to Bedford
for a distance of about two miles from the outskirts of
Hitchin to the county boundary.

C. semidecandrum L. (Map 17e) *Little Mouse-ear*
Chickweed Coleman, 1838
Well drained gravelly banks   Native
Rare but easily overlooked. It is now to be found most
frequently on railway banks.

Myosoton Moench

M. aquaticum (L.) Moench (Map 17f) *Water Chickweed*
Stellaria aquatica (L.) Scop.,   Blake, 1819
Malachia aquatica (L.) Fr.
Riversides, wet ditches and marshy places.   Native
Occasional but absent from considerable areas through a
lack of suitable habitats. H.S. 20, 74.

Stellaria L.

S. media (L.) Vill.   (Map 17g)   *Chickweed*   Ellis, 1733
Arable land, waste places, etc.   Native
Ubiquitous. H.S. 9, 26, 45, 46, 52, 60, 61, 80.

S. neglecta Weihe (*S. umbrosa* Opiz) is recorded from near
Park Wood, Bramfield, by Little in *W.E.C. 1915–16 Rep.*
530 and from Hertford, 1919, *A. W. Graveson, Hb. Gr.*
Otherwise it may have been mistaken for robust forms of
S. media.

S. holostea L.   (Map 17h)   *Greater Stitchwort*
Blake, c. 1820
Hedgerows   Native
Frequent in most of the county but avoiding the Chalk.
H.S. 28, 47, 58, 59, 78, 80.

S. graminea L. (Map 17i) *Lesser Stitchwort* Franks, 1822
Pastures, heaths, etc.   Native
Frequent except on the Chalk and Boulder Clay. H.S. 26,
28, 42, 55, 68, 72, 77, 78, 90, 96.

S. palustris Retz.   *Marsh Stitchwort* Coleman, 1839
This grew previously in the marshes by the river between
Hoddesdon and Broxbourne and also at Amwell. It is now
without doubt extinct having last been seen by Hayllar in
1914.

S. alsine Grimm (Map 17j) *Bog Stitchwort* Franks, 1820
S. uliginosa Murr.
Marshy places on the more acid soils.   Native
Occasional on the London Clay and river gravels. H.S. 65,
66, 76, 77, 91.

Moenchia Ehrh.

M. erecta (L.) Gaertn., Mey. & Scherb.   *Upright Chick-*
M. quaternella Ehrh.   *weed.* Coleman, 1838
Exposed heathy and gravelly places.   Native
Very rare. Coleman knew this in about fifteen places all on
gravelly soils and the Gravesons and Little knew six stations
including Hertford Heath, Colney Heath, Codicote High
Heath, Broxbourne Common and Broxbourne Woods.
I have seen it once only – Gustardwood Common, 1957
(11/S), *Hb. H.M.*

Sagina L.

S. apetala Ard. (Map 17k) *Common Pearlwort* Coleman, 1838
S. ciliata Fr., *S. filicaulis* Jord., *S. reuteri* auct.
Bare soil, paths, old walls, etc.   Native
Occasional. British botanists have previously considered this
to comprise at least two species the limits of which have
been difficult to determine. The *Flora Europaea* treats it as
one variable species and that treatment is followed here.

S. procumbens L.   (Map 17 l)   *Procumbent Pearlwort*
Blake, 1820
Bare soil, wet pastures, garden paths, lawns, old walls, etc.
Native
Common and well distributed. H.S. 29, 42, 44, 62, 77, 78,
80, 91, 105.

S. nodosa (L.) Fenzl *Knotted Pearlwort* Blackstone, 1746
Wet sandy and gravelly places   Native
Very rare and recorded for few stations by Coleman. At
Oughton Head Common, the one remaining locality
known to Pryor, it was last seen by Pollard in 1868,
Hb. H.M.. I have seen it only once – Green End, Sandon,
1957, *Hb. H.M.*, a welcome discovery of a plant believed
to be extinct in the county.

Minuartia L.

M. hybrida (Vill.) Schischk.   *Fine-leaved Sandwort*
Arenaria tenuifolia L.,   H. Fordham, 1840
Alsine tenuifolia (L.) Crantz
Well drained habitats, old walls, etc.   Native
Very rare and known to Coleman and other early workers
from few stations outside the neighbourhood of Hitchin.
Little recorded it from a number of places near Hitchin and
distinguished two varieties. I have seen it only on the En-
gineer's Sidings, Hitchin, 1957 (12/Z, 22/E).

Moehringia L.

M. trinervia (L.) Clairv.   (Map 17m)   *Three-nerved*
Sandwort Plukenet, 1690
Woods and copses   Native
Common except on the Chalk. H.S. 26, 41, 43, 45, 60, 77,
80, 82, 95, 107.

Arenaria L.

A. serpyllifolia L.   (Map 17n)   *Thyme-leaved Sandwort*
                                                                   Blake, 1820
Arable land, old walls, etc.   Native
Frequent. H.S. 7, 14, 21, 22, 77.

A. leptoclados (Reichb.) Guss.   (Map 17o)   Pryor, 1874
In similar situations to *A. serpyllifolia* from which it is
scarcely distinguishable.
Occasional. H.S. 83.

Spergula L.

S. arvensis L.   (Map 18a)   *Corn Spurrey*   Blake, c. 1820
S. vulgaris Boenn., *S. sativa* Boenn.
Arable fields   Colonist
Frequent on the river gravels but rare elsewhere.

Spergularia (Pers.) J. & C. Presl

S. rubra (L.) J. & C. Presl   (Map 18b)   *Sand Spurrey*
Lepigonum rubrum (L.) Wahlb.   Coleman, 1839
Bare sandy and gravelly places.   Native
Occasional on the Lea and Colne Gravels.

S. marina (L.) Griseb. (*Lepigonum neglectum* Kindb.), a
plant of salt marshes, was recorded in *Pryor*, 76, from Ware
Park brickfield. It persisted here until at least 1924, *Hb. Gr.*

Polycarpon tetraphyllum (L.) L. was recorded as a
casual from Hitchin by Little in *B.E.C. 1927 Rep.* 391 and
Gypsophila elegans Bieb. from Welwyn by Phillips
in *B.E.C. 1931 Rep.* 638.

ILLECEBRACEAE
Scleranthus L.

S. annuus L.   (Map 18c)   *Knawel*   Blake, c. 1820
Arable fields   Colonist
Frequent on the gravelly soils, rare on the clays and absent
on the Chalk.

Corrigiola littoralis L., *Strapwort*, abundant on Oakleigh
Park railway sidings, 1958 (29/S), *B. Clay*!, still there, 1966.
Herniaria glabra L., *Rupture-wort*, behind Ware Park
Mill, 1904–9, *A. W. Graveson*.

PORTULACACEAE
Montia L.

M. fontana L.   *Blinks*   Coleman, 1838
Moist pastures, wet rides, lawns, etc.   Native
Rare, as it has always been. Most of our plants are subsp.
chondrosperma (Fenzl) Walters, e.g. Ayot Green, 1956
(21/H)!, *Mrs. J. Foster, Hb. H.M.*; Hertford Heath, confirming old records, 1956 (31/K)!, *Lloyd-Evans, Hb. H.M.*;
ride, Plashes Wood, 1966 (32/V), *Lloyd-Evans*!; lawn,
Briggens, 1966 (41/A): subsp. **amporitana** Sennen (*M. intermedia* Beeby) occurs on a lawn at Wrotham Park, 1965
(29/P), v.c. 21 [Herts.], *Hb. H.M.* Dr. Walters has confirmed
as intermediate between the two subspecies above specimens
from lawn, Ashridge House, 1966 (91/W), v.c. 24 [Herts.],
Hb. H.M.

M. perfoliata (Willd.) Howell   (Map 18d)   *Spring Beauty*
              Hibbert-Ware (Proc. Herts. N.H.S. 12: xvi), 1902
Claytonia perfoliata Donn ex Willd.
Gardens, waste sandy ground, etc.   Colonist
Rare until about 1920 after which it was recorded frequently
for about ten years mainly from the south of the county.
It is now rare again.

One plant of **M. sibirica** (L.) Howell (*Claytonia sibirica* L.)
was found by R. Morse on Norton Common in 1931.

AMARANTHACEAE
Amaranthus L.

I wish to thank Mr. J. P. M. Brenan for his assistance in
naming my material.
A. retroflexus L.   *Pigweed*   Ansell, 1846
A casual of waste places recorded occasionally by earlier
workers. Recent records are from Blackbridge Dump
(11/X); Cock Lane Dump, 1956 (30/U), *Hb. H.M.*;
Sawbridgeworth, 1964 (41/X), *J. L. Fielding*.
The following species have also been recorded:
A. albus L., Blackbridge Dump, 1959 (11/X), *Hb. H.M.*:
A. blitoides S. Wats., Park Street Dump, 1964 (10/L),
Hb. H.M.; Cock Lane Dump, 1958 (30/U), *Hb. H.M.*;
Cole Green Dump, 1956 (21/Q), *Hb. H.M.*: **A. caudatus**
L., *Love Lies Bleeding*, Blackbridge Dump (11/X): **A.
hybridus** (*A. chlorostachys* Willd.), Cole Green Dump,
1956 (21/Q), *Hb. H.M.*; wool adventive, Wymondley,
1959 (22/D), *Hb. H.M.*: **A. lividus** L., Hitchin U.D.C.
Dump, 1959 (13/V), *Hb. H.M.* – it is possible that records
of *A. blitum* made by Phillips and Graveson should be
referred to this: **A. quitensis** Kunth, Cock Lane Dump,
1958 (30/U), *Hb. H.M.*: **A. thunbergii** Moq., Hitchin
U.D.C. Dump, 1959 (13/V): **A. viridis** L., Bulls Mill
Dump, 1959 (31/C), *Hb. H.M.* A record of *A. angustifolius*
Lam. from Welwyn by Phillips in *B.E.C. 1932 Rep.* 108
lacks a specimen to allow for a closer determination.

CHENOPODIACEAE
Chenopodium L.

I wish to thank Mr J. P. M. Brenan for his assistance in
naming my material of the more difficult members of this
genus.
C. bonus-henricus L.   (Map 18e)   *Good King Henry*
                                                                   Blake, 1819
Waste ground usually near to houses   Denizen
Occasional and well distributed in the county.

C. polyspermum L.   (Map 18f)   *Many-seeded Goosefoot*
                                               Webb and Coleman, 1843
Cultivated ground, recently cleared woodland, etc.
                                                                    Colonist
Frequent on the London Clay and rare elsewhere.

C. vulvaria L.   *Stinking Goosefoot*   Webb and Coleman,
                                                                       1843
A casual in waste places and rare as it has always been. I
have seen it only on Blackbridge Dump, 1959 (11/X),
Hb. H.M. and Park Street Dump, 1966 (10/L). *Hb. H.M.*

C. album L.   (Map 18g)   *Fat Hen.*   *White Goosefoot*
                                                                  Franks, 1822
Arable fields, gardens, waste places, etc.   Colonist
Abundant.

C. ficifolium Sm.   (Map 18h)   *Fig-leaved Goosefoot*
                                                              G. S. Gibson, 1851
Arable fields, dung heaps, etc.   Colonist
Occasional and well distributed.

C. rubrum L.   (Map 18i)   *Red Goosefoot*   Coleman, 1840
Waste places, dung heaps, dried mud by ponds, etc.
                                                                    Colonist
Occasional and a feature of most rubbish dumps.

C. hircinum Schrad., a casual, was recorded by A. W.
Graveson from Hertford, *Hb. Gr.* and J. E. Little from
Hitchin. I have found it only on Park Street Dump, 1964
(10/L), *Hb. H.M.*

C. murale L.   *Nettle-leaved Goosefoot*   Coleman, 1841
A rare casual which has been found during the present
survey at Bishop's Stortford U.D.C. Dump, 1962 (42/V),
J. L. Fielding, Hb. H.M.; Bull's Mill Dump, 1958 (31/C),
Hb. H.M.; Cock Lane Dump, 1958 (30/U), *Hb. H.M.*

C. hybridum L.   *Sowbane*   Franks, 1822
A rare casual of waste ground. Hertford, 1957 (31/G),
confirming an old record, *A. W. Graveson!*; allotment
garden, Hertford, 1966 (31/B); gravel pit, Rye Meads,
1966 (31/V); Bishop's Stortford U.D.C. Dump, 1964
(42/V); garden, Cheshunt, 1966 (30/L).

C. glaucum L.   *Glaucous Goosefoot*   J. Woods, 1830
A rare casual which has appeared regularly at intervals in
the county. It was recorded from 'near Rye House' (31/V)
in *B.E.C. 1910 Rep.* 583 and subsequently, and I refound
it there on new gravel workings in 1965 in company with
J. Lovell, *Hb. H.M.* It was also found on a rubbish dump
near Aldenham, 1955 (19/I)!, *R. A. Graham, Hb. H.M.*

C. opulifolium Schrad. was recorded by Little from a
waste heap near Welwyn, 1912, *Herb. Camb.* and from
various places near Hitchin e.g. lane to Oughton Head,
1925, *Herb. Camb.* (see also *B.E.C. 1929 Rep.* 922). It
appeared also on Cock Lane Dump, 1965 (30/U), *Hb. H.M.*

C. pratericola Rydb. var. **thellungianum** Aellen (*C.
leptophyllum* auct.) was recorded from Welwyn, 1912,
Little, Hb. Camb.; Ware, *Druce, B.E.C. 1915 Rep.* 278;
Hertford, *A. W. Graveson, Hb. Gr.*

C. capitatum (L.) Aschers. was recorded as a casual from
Rabley Heath, 1956, *T. D. V. Swinscow, Hb. H.M.* and
still persists in this neighbourhood. **C. berlandieri** Moq.
was recorded from Ware by Druce in *B.E.C. 1923 Rep.* 209.
C. probstii Aellen appears as a wool adventive: e.g.
Wymondley, 1957 (22/DJ).

C. urbicum L. was recorded by Webb and Coleman (1843)
as a rare casual but there were no subsequent records.

Atriplex L.
A. patula L. (Map 18j) *Common Orache* Coleman, 1838
A. erecta Huds., *A. angustifolia* Sm.
Arable fields, waste places, etc.   Colonist
Common and well distributed but most abundant in the
southern half of the county. H.S. 35.

A. hastata L. (Map 18k) *Hastate-leaved Orache*
Coleman, 1838
Cultivated ground, manure heaps, etc.   Colonist
Abundant on the London Clay and occasional elsewhere.
H.S. 94.

A. hortensis L., a rare casual of garden origin and first
recorded by Pryor has been seen during the period of the
present survey on refuse tips at Aldenham, 1955 (19/I),
Welwyn, 1959 (21/T) and Luffenhall (22/Z). **A. tatarica**
L. was recorded from Ware by Druce in *B.E.C. 1915 Rep.*
279, *Hb. Gr.* and **A. spongiosa** F. Muell. from Ware
by A. W. Graveson, 1921, *Hb. Gr., Hb. B.M.*

Kochia sieversiana (Pall.) C. A. Meyer (*K. scoparia* var.
densiflora Moq.), a casual, was frequent on Cock Lane
Dump, 1964, *Hb. H.M.*

Salsola kali L. subsp. **ruthenica** (Iljin) Soó (*S. kali* subsp.
tragus auct., *S. pestifera* A. Nels.), Ware, 1875, *T. B. Blow,
Hb. B.M.*; Hertford, 1913, 1921, *A. W. Graveson, Hb. Gr.*;

Park Street Dump, 1966 (10/L), *Hb. H.M.*: **Axyris amar-
anthoides** L., Hitchin, *J. E. Little, B.E.C. 1927 Rep.* 415;
Ware, 1926, *A. W. Graveson, Hb. Gr.*

Phytolacca americana L. (PHYTOLACCACEAE),
Pokeweed, is sometimes found on sites of old gardens.

TILIACEAE
Tilia × vulgaris Hayne (*T. europaea* auct.) *Common Lime*,
occurs as a planted tree throughout the county and according to Ellis was planted at Ashridge in 1660. **T. cordata**
Mill., *Small-leaved Lime*, is planted less frequently and usually in towns. **T. platyphyllos** Scop., *Large-leaved Lime*,
was recorded by A. W. Graveson from Wormley Wood,
1919, *Hb. Gr.* also as a planted tree.

MALVACEAE
Malva L.
M. moschata L. (Map 18 l) *Musk Mallow* Gerard, 1597
Roadsides and wood borders   Native
Frequent on the river gravels and Clay-with-Flints, rare on
the Boulder Clay and absent on the Chalk. H.S. 59.

M. sylvestris L. (Map 18m) *Common Mallow*
Coleman, 1838
Roadsides, waste places, etc.   Native
Common and well distributed.

M. neglecta Wallr. (Map 18n) *Dwarf Mallow*
M. rotundifolia auct.   Blake, c. 1820
Waste ground usually near houses   Colonist
Occasional but well distributed.

M. parviflora L.   *Small-flowered Mallow*   Blow, 1878
A casual found during the period of the present survey at
Park Street Dump, 1965 (10/L)!, *B. Goater, Hb. H.M.*;
Blackbridge Dump, 1962 (11/X), *Hb. H.M.*; Cock Lane
Dump (30/V), *Hb. H.M.*; Cole Green Dump, 1964 (21/Q).

M. pusilla Sm. (*M. borealis* Wallm.) was recorded from
Hitchin by Little in *B.E.C. 1925 Rep.* 868 and from Welwyn
by Phillips, *Hb. Ph.* – see also *Pryor*, 80.

Abutilon theophrasti (L.) Medic., *Chinese Jute*, a
casual, is recorded from near Ware, 1949, *D. C. Lucas,
Hb. B.M.*; refuse tip, Hadham Towers, 1964 (41/I), *Hb.
H.M.*; refuse tip, Rickmansworth, 1958 (09/G).

Hibiscus trionum L., *Flower-of-the-Day*, has been recorded
from Hitchin, 1920 by Little and from Stevenage, 1951,
G. L. Evans, Hb. H.M.

Lavatera cretica L. was recorded from Ware as *L. sylvestris* Brot. by J. W. Higgens in *B.E.C. 1916 Rep.* 477.
Althaea hirsuta L. was found at Stanstead Abbots (1871)
by Emily Buxton (see *Pryor*, 78). D. McClintock has sent
me an extract from a letter saying that the naming of the
specimen was confirmed by Sir Joseph Hooker. The
Gravesons later found the same species at Ware and Hertford. **Anoda cristata** (L.) Schlecht., was recorded from
Bushey U.D.C. refuse tip, 1958 (19/I), *R. A. Graham,
R. M. Harley and D. H. Lewis, Hb. Kew.*

LINACEAE
Linum L.
L. catharticum L. (Map 18o) *Purging Flax, Fairy Flax*
Kalm, 1748
Well drained pastures   Native
Abundant on the Chalk, occasional elsewhere. H.S. 1–6,
14, 15, 48–53, 56, 67, 69, 71, 73, 84, 100.

L. usitatissimum L. (Map 19a) *Flax* Coleman, 1839
Waste places Casual
Frequent as a bird-seed alien and in recent years white-flowered forms have become more frequent than the blue Coleman accounted for its earlier frequency from having probably 'been dropped by bird catchers'.

Radiola linoides Roth, *All-seed*, was recorded by Coleman from Colney Heath and from near Northaw but it was not known to any later botanists.

GERANIACEAE
Geranium L.
G. pratense L. (Map 19b) *Meadow Cranesbill* Blake, 1820
Meadows, roadsides, etc. ? Native
This is occasional on the Chalk where it may in some places be native e.g. Rushy Meadow (91/B). In its roadside stations, whether on the Chalk or not, it is no doubt naturalized but at times makes a spectacular stand as at Little Gaddesden (91/W.)

G. pyrenaicum Burm. f. (Map 19c) *Mountain Cranesbill* Blake, c. 1820
Roadsides, railway banks, etc. Colonist
Occasional and appearing to be more frequent on the river gravels and in the neighbourhood of houses.

G. columbinum L. (Map 19d) *Long-stalked Cranesbill* L. Manser, 1838
Disturbed ground, newly cut scrub, etc. Native
Rare and limited to the more calcareous soils. It is a species which has no doubt decreased.

G. dissectum L. (Map 19e) *Cut-leaved Cranesbill* Blake, 1820
Edges of arable fields, roadsides, waste places, etc. Native
Common. H.S. 11, 20, 24, 50, 96, 100.

G. molle L. (Map 19f) *Dove's-foot Cranesbill* Blake, c. 1820
Rough pastures, waste ground, roadsides, etc. Native
Frequent and well distributed. H.S. 22, 65, 100.

G. pusillum L. (Map 19g) *Small-flowered Cranesbill* Coleman, 1839
Pastures, waste ground, etc. Native
Occasional and most frequent on the gravelly soils but by no means limited to them.

G. rotundifolium L. *Round-leaved Cranesbill* Pryor, 1874
Railway banks Colonist
Known to Pryor from one station only, Sopwell Lane, St. Albans, the habitat of which he did not specify. It is now limited to railway banks where it is rare but usually well established. Current records are: railway between Hitchin and Ickleford, 1964 (13/V), *H. Bowry*; railway, south-east of Berkhamsted, 1960 (90/Z, 00/D); railway, south of Harpenden Central Station, 1960 (11/G); railway near Watford Junction Station, 1961 (19/D), *Hb. H.M.*

G. lucidum L. (Map 19h) *Shining Cranesbill* Webb and Coleman, 1843
Old walls, banks, etc. Denizen or colonist
Rare and appearing occasionally as a garden weed when it is not established as it is in its other habitats.

G. phaeum L. *Dusky Cranesbill* I. Brown, 1840
Hedge banks, rough pastures, etc. Denizen
Rare and of garden origin but persisting for a long time as at Clothall (23/R) where it has been known since 1915

and Bower Heath, 1962 (11/N), *Hb. H.M.* It is also recorded by Mrs. Foster from St. Albans, 1958 (10/M), *Hb. H.M.* and Priory Dell, Bedwell, 1964 (22/M), *M. Mullin.*

G. endressii Gay occurs as a garden escape at Gilston Park (41/L), *J. L. Fielding*!; Pirton Cross, 1965 (12/V) and near Bramfield, 1965 (21/X). **G. versicolor** L. (*G. striatum* L.), another garden escape, was recorded from near Elstree by D. H. Kent in *London Naturalist* 26 (1946), 59. See also *Pryor*, 85. **G. endressii × versicolor** was recorded from roadside near Waterford, 1956 (31/C)!, *Lloyd-Evans.*

G. nodosum L. *English Botany* tab. 1091, November, 1802, was drawn from a specimen collected by Charles Abbot between Hatfield and Welwyn. It was probably a garden escape.

G. robertianum L. (Map 19i) *Herb Robert* Blake, c. 1820
Shady places, banks by roadsides, old walls, etc. Native
Very common. H.S. 16, 32, 35, 36, 47, 54, 61, 77, 78, 80, 93, 95, 106, 107.

Erodium L' Hérit.
E. cicutarium (L.) L'Hérit. (Map 19j) *Common Storksbill* Blake, c. 1820
Disturbed ground, edges of gravel pits, etc. Native
Occasional on both river and glacial gravels but it has also occurred as a wool adventive in the neighbourhood of Wymondley and Hitchin. Pryor and Little considered the species to be critical but the forms recognised by them are now thought to be of little significance.

E. moschatum (L.) L'Hérit., *Musky Storksbill*, first recorded as a rare casual by Webb and Coleman, 1843, now occurs as a wool adventive. It was also found near to Welwyn Garden City, 1963 (21/L). **E. crinitum** Carolin (*E. cygnorum* sensu Little), **E. botrys** (Cav.) Bertol. and **E. obtusiplicatum** (Maire, Weiller & Wilczek) J. T. Howell have all occurred regularly as wool adventives.

OXALIDACEAE
Oxalis L.
O. acetosella L. (Map 19k) *Wood Sorrel* Blake, c. 1820
Damp woods Native
Frequent in woods on the Clay-with-Flints, Colne Gravels and London Clay, occasional elsewhere except on the Chalk where it is absent. H.S. 16, 45, 60, 61, 95, 103, 106. Some species of *Oxalis* occur as garden weeds and throwouts on rubbish dumps but they have not been completely accounted for in the county. Dr. D. P. Young has named gatherings of mine as **O. europaea** Jord., Cock Lane Dump, 1964 (30/U), *Hb. H.M.*; Berkhamsted U.D.C. tip, 1959 (90/D) *Hb. H.M.*: **O. corniculata** L. var. **repens** (Thunb.) Zucc., garden weed, Wrotham Park, 1965 (29/P) v.c. 21 [Herts.], *Hb. H.M.*

BALSAMINACEAE
Impatiens, L.
I. capensis Meerb. (Map 19 l) *Orange Balsam*
I. fulva Nutt. J. E. Littleboy, 1875
This spread rapidly along the Grand Junction Canal after its introduction and now appears in Hertfordshire to be limited to that water system except for one outlying occurrence at Water End (01/F).

I. parviflora DC. (Map 19m) *Small Balsam* Blow, 1874
Waste places, copses, etc. Naturalized
This occurs chiefly in three areas near to towns. One of its favoured habitats is timber yards and it is possible that it is introduced with imported timber.

I. glandulifera Royle (Map 19n) *Policeman's Helmet*
Crutwell (B.E.C. 1932 Rep.), 1932
A recent introduction which appears to be spreading rapidly by waterways in the Hertford area. Otherwise it is found occasionally in waste places. It is to be hoped that it will increase no further.

ACERACEAE
Acer L.
A. pseudoplatanus L. (Map 19o) *Sycamore* Ellis, 1733
Hedgerows, woods, etc.   Introduced
Apparently more common than it was a century ago as Pryor listed stations for it. In some of our woods, especially on the Chalk, sycamore is gaining a hold and ousting a native flora. H.S. 3, 11, 12, 16, 17, 48, 54, 70, 79, 80, 94, 95, 106.

A. campestre L.   (Map 20a)   *Maple*   Ellis, 1742
Hedgerows, wood borders, etc.   Native
Generally common but absent from a small area on the Chalk where there is insufficient body in the soil to support it. H.S. 11, 17, 21, 24, 32, 36, 39–41, 46, 47, 50–52, 54, 61, 63, 67, 84.

A. platanoides L., *Norway Maple*, occurs occasionally as a planted tree.

Aesculus hippocastanum L. (HIPPOCASTANACEAE), *Horse Chestnut*, was noted as an unusual tree 'planted about a mile away from me twenty years ago' by Ellis (1733). It is now frequently planted and may sometimes be self-sown. It has little effect on the native flora. H.S. 14, 17.

AQUIFOLIACEAE
Ilex L.
I. aquifolium L.   (Map 20b)   *Holly*   Ellis, 1742
Hedges, woods, etc.   Native
Holly has a peculiar but interesting distribution in the county. Its absence from the Chalk in the north of the county is not surprising considering that it is recorded only with doubt as a native in Cambridgeshire and Huntingdonshire. It is, however, present on the Chalk in the western part of the county but is absent from the Gault. It would appear that both climatic and soil factors play a part in determining its distribution. In the greater part of the county it is without doubt native although it is also frequently planted. H.S. 16, 84, 104, 106.

CELASTRACEAE
Euonymus L.
E. europaeus L.   (Map 20c)   *Spindle*   Turner, 1548
Hedgerows, wood borders, etc.   Native
Occasional on calcareous soils and more frequent on the Boulder Clay than elsewhere. H.S. 11, 21, 47.

Buxus sempervirens L. (BUXACEAE), *Box*, was probably at one time native on the chalk downs as box is an element in a number of place names e.g. Boxmoor (*Place Names of Hertfordshire*, 41). William Ellis observed in 1742 that box 'will grow on a chalky gravelly soil as may be seen in the Box-warren about two miles off Gaddesden . . . at first planted here for the refreshment, shelter and security of rabbits and where, if not cut too much, it will remain for ever'. Pehr Kalm in 1748 noted that the Duke of Bridgewater planted box on the hills near to Tring and that the wood was used by London block-makers. It is possible that the box so planted replenished an older native stock but it is strange that the tree cannot now be seen on the hills at Tring or on those around Dunstable where Woodward

in 1787 recorded it as being in plenty. Coleman, Pryor and Little did not consider box to be a Hertfordshire tree but must have known it in old parkland where it still occurs. There are a few box trees on the hill slopes at Boxmoor but nothing is known of their origin.

RHAMNACEAE
Rhamnus L.
R. catharticus L. (Map 20d) *Buckthorn* Morell, c. 1835
Hedges, wood borders, etc.   Native
Frequent on the Chalk, occasional on the Boulder Clay, rare elsewhere. H.S. 21, 53, 54.

Frangula Mill.
F. alnus Mill.   *Alder Buckthorn*   Coleman, 1839
Rhamnus frangula L.
Wet woods   Native
Very rare as it always has been. It is locally plentiful on Bricket Wood Common (10/F) where it has been known for many years. Other recent records include: Oxhey Woods, *D. H. Kent, Kent and Lousley*, 53; Bull's Green, 1911, *Little, Hb. Camb.*; near Bulls Mill (31/C), *Lloyd-Evans*.

Vitis vinifera L. (VITACEAE), *Vine*, occurs rarely on refuse tips e.g. Hitchin U.D.C. Dump, 1964 (13/V).

LEGUMINOSAE
Laburnum anagyroides Medic. was planted some time ago in great quantity on the Hexton Estate and self-sown trees may be found occasionally in that neighbourhood. Otherwise it occurs rarely on refuse tips.

Genista L.
G. tinctoria L. (Map 20e) *Dyer's Greenweed* Coleman, 1838
Rough pastures on clay soils   Native
Rare and found mainly on the London Clay and Boulder Clay. H.S. 71, 72, 92.

G. anglica L. (Map 20f) *Petty Whin* J. A. Hankey (Herb. Druce), 1834
Heathy places   Native
Rare and revealing no distribution pattern. Its survival in so many places in Hertfordshire is of special interest as it is extinct in Bedfordshire and Cambridgeshire. H.S. 72, 85, 92, 97, 98, 101.

Ulex L.
U. europaeus L.   (Map 20g)   *Furze, Gorse*   Ellis, 1742
Heathy and gravelly pastures
Frequent in open habitats on the Colne Gravels and Clay-with-Flints and Ellis observed that it is 'the most common and cheapest fuel our Hertfordshire commons afford'. It is no doubt planted in most of its scattered stations on the Chalk and Boulder Clay. H.S. 57, 64, 84–86, 98, 101.

U. minor Roth   *Dwarf Furze*   Blake, 1830
U. nanus T. F. Forst.
Sandy heaths   Native
Rare as it has always been but persisting in most of the stations in which it was known to Coleman, such as Nomansland (11/R) where it is still abundant and the Furze Field at Colney Heath (20/C). It occurs also at Arkley Manorial Lands (29/C). It is not recorded for Bedfordshire or Cambridgeshire. H.S. 85, 101.

Records of *U. gallii* Planch., e.g. by Crespigny, are in error except no doubt that in *Pryor*, 97, which was for an introduced plant.

Sarothamnus Wimm.

S. scoparius (L.) Wimm. ex Koch (Map 20h) *Broom*
Coleman, 1838
Heathy and gravelly pastures Native
Frequent on the river gravels, rare elsewhere. H.S. 70, 79, 92.

Ononis L.

O. repens L. (Map 20i) *Rest-harrow* Woodward (see
O. arvensis auct. Withering, Third Edition, 1796), 1779
Pastures, roadsides, etc. Native
Frequent, being most common on the calcareous soils. H.S. 3, 5, 7, 11, 22.

O. spinosa L. (Map 20j) *Spiny Rest-harrow*
O. campestris L. Webb and Coleman, 1843
A native of marshy places on the Chalk Marl where it is occasional. It is rare elsewhere.

O. salzmanniana Boiss. & Reut. is recorded as a bird-seed alien from R. I. Sworder's garden, Little Dudswell, 1965 (90/U), *Hb. H.M.*

Medicago L.

M. falcata L. *Sickle Medick* Doody, 1706
This was not known to either Coleman or Pryor but since 1910 it has been recorded from time to time as a casual or colonist. Current records are Cock Lane Dump, 1965 (30/U), *B. Wurzell*; railway, Garston, 1956 (10/F); clearing, Upwick Wood, 1959 (42 M), *Hb. H.M.*; railway sidings, Hitchin, 1963 (12/Z), *Hb. H.M.* **M. falcata × sativa** (*M. × varia* Martyn), railway sidings, Hitchin, with both parents, 1959 (12/Z), *Hb. H.M.*

M. sativa L. (Map 20k) *Lucerne, Alfalfa* Blake, c. 1820
Roadsides, field borders, etc. A relic of cultivation
More frequent on the Chalk than elsewhere. H.S. 50.

M. lupulina L. (Map 20 l) *Black Medick* Ellis, 1736
Pastures, roadside verges, arable land, etc. Native
A native of well established pasture but frequent elsewhere as a colonist. H.S. 3–8, 11, 15, 20–22, 24, 48–53, 56, 66, 67, 84, 96, 100.

M. arabica (L.) Huds. (Map 20m) *Spotted Medick*
Andrews, 1861
Pastures, waste places, etc. Colonist
Recorded a few times before 1920 after which time it apparently increased on gravelly soils around Hitchin and in the east of the county. It is a common wool adventive and may have been introduced by this means.

M. polymorpha L. (Map 20n) *Toothed Medick*
M. denticulata Willd. Andrews, 1861
Waste places, arable fields, etc. Casual
Occasional as a wool adventive but rare otherwise.

M. minima (L.) Bartal., **M. laciniata** (L.) Mill. and **M. proecox** DC., all first recorded by Little, still appear as wool adventives in the neighbourhood of Wymondley.

Melilotus Mill.

M. altissima Thuill. (Map 20o) *Tall Melilot*
Franks, 1822
Pastures, roadsides, etc. Native
Frequent on the Boulder Clay but rare elsewhere H.S. 6.

M. officinalis (L.) Pall. (Map 21a) *Common Melilot*
Webb and Coleman, 1851
Roadsides, waste places, etc. Colonist
Frequent and more widely distributed than the preceding.

M. alba Medic. (Map 21b) *White Melilot* Coleman, 1839
Roadsides, waste places, etc. Colonist
Considered rare by Pryor it is now occasional but widely distributed.

M. indica (L.) All. (Map 21c) *Small-flowered Melilot*
Pryor, 1887
Waste places Casual
Recorded for only one station by Pryor.

M. sulcata Desf. has been found only on Cole Green Dump, 1955 (21/Q), *Hb. H.M.*

Trifolium L.

T. pratense L. (Map 21d) *Red Clover* Kalm, 1748
Pastures, roadsides, etc. Native
Abundant but it is very difficult to distinguish genuine native material from relics of cultivation. H.S. 5, 6, 8, 9, 11, 13, 15, 18, 19, 23, 24, 26–29, 48–51, 55, 56, 65–67, 69–71, 73, 74, 84, 90–92, 96, 100, 105.

T. ochroleucon Huds. (Map 21e) *Sulphur Clover*
Woodward, 1787
Pastures, roadsides, etc. Native
Occasional on the Boulder Clay. It has a similar distribution in Bedfordshire and has the western limit of its distribution in Britain in the two counties. H.S. 24.

T. medium L. (Map 21f) *Zigzag Clover* Coleman, 1838
Pastures mainly on clay soils. Native
Scattered over the county but avoiding the Chalk. It is particularly frequent on railway banks where it forms, as elsewhere, large patches produced by vegetative reproduction as it sets little seed. H.S. 55, 100.

T. arvense L. (Map 21g) *Hare's-foot Clover* Blake, c. 1820
Bare or disturbed ground on gravelly soils Native
Mainly on the river gravels where it is occasional but does not appear continuously in any given site.

T. striatum L. (Map 21h) *Knotted Clover* Coleman, 1838
Pastures with short grass on gravelly soils Native
Occasional and well established on the Lea gravels.

T. subterraneum L. *Subterranean Clover*
H. D. Henslow, 1834
This was recorded by earlier botanists as a rare native of gravelly heaths such as Colney Heath and Nomansland and was last observed as such by Little in 1913, *Hb. B.M.* It occurs now only as a wool adventive.

T. hybridum L. (Map 21i) *Alsike Clover* Pryor, 1887
T. elegans Savi
Roadsides, waste places, etc. Relic of cultivation
Apparently a recent introduction in Pryor's time. It is now common and well distributed.

T. repens L. (Map 21j) *White or Dutch Clover*
Kalm, 1748
Pastures, lawns, etc. Native
Abundant. H.S. 8, 13, 18–22, 24, 27–29, 49, 50, 56, 65, 66, 69–71, 73–75, 77, 78, 84, 88, 90–92, 105.

T. fragiferum L. (Map 21k) *Strawberry Clover*
Coleman, 1838
Pastures on calcareous soils Native
Occasional on the Boulder Clay and in water meadows near Hertford but rare elsewhere. H.S. 29.

T. campestre Schreb.   (Map 21 l)   *Hop Trefoil*
T. procumbens auct.   Blake, c. 1820
Bare ground, waste places, etc.   Native
Frequent and well distributed. H.S. 20, 52.

T. dubium Sibth.   (Map 21m)   *Common Yellow Trefoil*
                                                        Franks, 1823
Grassy places, waste ground, etc.   Native
Very common. H.S. 22, 26, 58, 62, 65, 69, 70, 73, 78, 92, 96, 100, 105.

T. micranthum Viv.   (Map 21n)   *Slender Trefoil*
T. filiforme L., nom. ambig.   Blake, c. 1820
Pastures with short grass, lawns, etc.   Native
Occasional except on the Chalk and Boulder Clay. H.S. 69.

T. ornithopodioides L. (*Trigonella purpurascens* Lam.)
Birdsfoot Fenugreek, was recorded by Coleman as a rare native of gravelly pastures near to Northaw but there have been no subsequent records.

The following casuals are recorded: **T. angustifolium** L., a wool adventive, Wymondley, 1959: **T. aureum** Poll. (*T. agrarium* auct.), Welwyn, 1931, *H. Phillips, Hb. Ph.*: **T. echinatum** M. Bieb., Ware, 1912, *A. W. Graveson, Hb. Gr.*: **T. glomeratum** L., Easneye, Buxton (see Pryor, 111): **T. incarnatum** L., *Crimson Clover*, Cock Lane Dump, 1965 (30/U), *Hb. H.M.*, once occasional as a relic of cultivation: **T. lappaceum** L., Royston, 1926, *A. W. Graveson, Hb. Gr.*; Elstree, 1961 (19/T), *Hb. H.M.*: **T. michelianum** Savi, Welwyn, 1875, *T. B. Blow, Hb. B.M.*: **T. resupinatum** L., *Reversed Clover*, recorded a few times e.g. Hertford, 1924, *A. W. Graveson, Hb. Gr.*: **T. tomentosum** L., probably a wool adventive, Wymondley, *H. Phillips, B.E.C. 1928 Rep. 733, Hb. Ph.*

Trigonella L.
The following species have been recorded. **T. corniculata** (L.) L., Hertford, 1876, *R. T. Andrews, Hb. B.M.*: **T. foenum-graecum** L., Hertford, *A. W. Graveson, B.E.C. 1919 Rep. 647, Hb. Gr.*: **T. procumbens** (Bess.) Reichb., Ware, *Druce, B.E.C. 1928 Rep. 731*: **T. hamosa** L., Lea Navigation near Ware, 1932, *A. H. Carter, Hb. B.M.* In addition A. W. Graveson's herbarium contains specimens named **T. caerulea** (L.) Ser., Ware, 1912, Hertford, 1920, and **T. polyceratia** L., Ware, 1916.

Anthyllis L.
A. vulneraria L. (Map 21o) *Kidney Vetch, Ladies' Fingers*
                                                        Kalm, 1748
Chalk hills   Native
Occasional on the Chalk and chalk exposures with a preference for places where the soil has been disturbed. H.S. 6.

Lotus L.
L. corniculatus L. (Map 22a) *Birdsfoot Trefoil* Ellis, 1750
Pastures, roadside verges, etc.   Native
Abundant. H.S. 1–3, 5, 7, 8, 13, 15, 22, 23, 25, 26, 28, 29, 48–51, 55, 56, 58, 59, 65, 67, 69, 70, 71, 73, 84, 92, 96, 100.

L. tenuis Waldst. & Kit. ex Willd.   *Slender Birdsfoot*
                                          Trefoil Ansell, 1845
Found by earlier workers as a rare native of pastures and field borders on calcareous soils but it is now found more often on rough ground and often by railway tracks. During the present survey it has been found at Scrubs Wood, Sarratt, *L. J. Stearn*; Bulls Mill, c. 1961 (31/C), *H. B. Souster*; railway siding, Stapleford, 1957 (31/D), *Hb. H.M.*; railway siding, Mardock, 1964 (31/X).

L. uliginosus Schkuhr (Map 22b) *Large Birdsfoot Trefoil*
L. pilosus Beeke, non Medic.   Kalm, 1748
Marshy places and wet woods   Native
Common on the London Clay and occasional elsewhere. H.S. 9, 18, 27–29, 33, 34, 38, 39, 42, 62, 72, 76, 78, 87, 89–91, 99, 100, 104.

Galega L.
G. officinalis L.   (Map 22c)   *Goat's Rue, French Lilac*
                                          Trower and Druce, 1915
A naturalized plant of waste places and much increased since its introduction.

Colutea L.
C. arborescens L. (Map 22d) *Bladder Senna* Little, 1913
An introduced plant which is often a feature of railway banks but may occur less frequently on refuse tips.

Astragalus L.
A. danicus Retz.   *Purple Milk-vetch*   Ray, 1690
Chalk hills   Native
A rare and attractive species which can now be found abundantly on Therfield Heath (34/K, 33/JP), H.S. 2, from where it was originally recorded by Ray. It occurs also on Icknield Way, Lilley Hoo (12/E), where it was first recorded by Maria Ransom, 1838–40, *Hb. H.M.* and Arbury Banks (23/P), *H. and D. Meyer.*

A. glycyphyllos L. (Map 22e) *Milk-vetch, Wild Licorice*
                                                        Dawson, 1840
Scrub, wood borders, etc.   Native
A rare species of calcareous soils.

Ornithopus L.
O. perpusillus L. (Map 22f) *Birdsfoot* Coleman, 1838
Heaths   Native
Rare and limited to the more acid soils. H.S. 26

Coronilla L .
C. varia L.   *Crown Vetch*   Trower and Druce, 1916
A plant of garden origin but well established on the railway at Hitchin sidings (12/Z); Letchworth (23/B) and near Hunton Bridge (00/V), *Hb. H.M.*

C. scorpioides (L.) Koch (*Ornithopus scorpioides* L.) was recorded from Ware by Trower and Druce in *B.E.C. 1915 Rep.* 262 and from Hertford, 1920, by A. W. Graveson, *Hb. Gr.* Recent records are: bird-seed alien, Dudswell, 1965 (90/U), *R. I. Sworder, Hb. H.M.*; Park Street Dump, 1966 (10/L), *Lady Anne Brewis and Miss A. M. Hugh-Smith, Hb. H.M.*

Hippocrepis L.
H. comosa L. (Map 22g) *Horseshoe Vetch* L. Manser, 1838
Chalk pastures   Native
Frequent on the chalk downs in the north of the county but rare on chalk exposures elsewhere. H.S. 1, 2, 7.

Onobrychis Mill.
O. viciifolia Scop. (Map 22h) *Sainfoin* Blake, c 1820
Chalky banks and roadside verges   Relic of cultivation
Occasional on the Chalk and chalky exposures but I have not seen it as a convincingly native species as it appears to be in neighbouring parts of Bedfordshire (see *Flora of Bedfordshire*, 255).

Vicia L.
V. hirsuta (L.) Gray (Map 22i) *Hairy Tare* Ellis, 1750
Ervum hirsutum L.
Pastures, railway banks, roadside verges, etc.   Native
Frequent and well distributed. H.S. 4, 38, 59, 83, 96.

V. tetrasperma (L.) Schreb.   (Map 22j)   *Smooth Tare*
Ervum tetraspermum L.   Coleman, 1838
In similar situations to *V. hirsuta*   Native
Occasional and well distributed. H.S. 38, 39, 79, 100.

V. tenuissima (Bieb.) Schinz & Thell. (*Ervum gracile* DC.), a colonist, was first recorded by Coleman from Hertford, 1843, *Hb. H.M.* It was found by others there and by Pollard at High Down. Its last record was from Norton Common, 1916, by H. C. Littlebury, *Hb. Letch. Mus.* In 1955 I found it a few yards over the county boundary at Little Chishill and it may well be found in neighbouring parts of Hertfordshire.

V. cracca L.   (Map 22k)   *Tufted Vetch*   Kalm, 1748
Hedges, wood borders, sides of marshes, etc.   Native
Frequent but with a peculiar distribution as it is absent from some considerable areas. H.S. 5, 9, 10, 18, 19, 27, 28, 30, 75, 76, 99.

V. sylvatica L., *Wood Vetch*, a native species, was first recorded by Maria Ransom c. 1839, an earlier record by Dickson (1815) from Tring having referred to Bucks. It was known from Hitch and Wain Woods and there remains one plant in Wain Wood (12/X)!, *Hb. H.M.*

V. sepium L.   (Map 22 l)   *Bush Vetch*   Coleman, 1838
Hedgerows, wood borders, etc.   Native
Common except on the Chalk. H.S. 5, 24, 34, 36, 39, 41, 46, 61, 63, 82.

V. sativa L.   (Maps 22m, n)   *Common Vetch*   Ellis, 1750
Pastures, waste places, roadsides, etc.   Native
Common and well distributed but very variable: subsp. **sativa** is robust and a relic of cultivation but subsp. **angustifolia** (L.) Gaud., first recorded by Coleman (1838), is slender and procumbent forms of this are no doubt native H.S. 4, 7, 24, 50, 59, 69, 78, 79, 83, 84, 96, 100, 105.

V. dasycarpa Ten., a casual was first recorded by A. W. Graveson from Ware, 1916, *Hb. Gr.* Its recent records are: Baldock, 1965 (23/L), *H. Bowry, Hb. H.M.*; railway sidings, Bishop's Stortford, *J. L. Fielding, Hb. H.M.*

The following casuals are also recorded. **V. benghalensis** L. (*V. atropurpurea* Desf.) Stansteadbury, *Trower, B.E.C. 1925 Rep. 871*; Ware, *A. W. Graveson, Hb. Gr.*: **V. bithynica** (L.) L., Ware, *G. C. Druce, B.E.C. 1914 Rep. 65*: **V. cretica** Boiss. & Heldr. (*V. spruneri* Boiss.), Hoddesdon, 1915, *J. E. Little, Hb. Camb.*: **V. hybrida** L., between Hertford and Ware, *A. W. Graveson, Hb. Gr.*: **V. lutea** L., railway bank, Berkhamsted, *Griffiths, Trans. Herts. N.H.S. 4* (1887), 118; Ware, *G. C. Druce, B.E.C. 1915 Rep. 262, Hb. Gr.*; Hitchin, 1914, *J. E. Little, Hb. Camb.*: **V. melanops** Sm. Ware, *G. C. Druce, B.E.C. 1928 Rep. 734*; between Hertford and Ware, 1920, *A. W. Graveson, Hb. Gr.*: **V. monantha** Retz. (*V. calcarata* Desf.), Ware, *Trower and Druce, B.E.C. 1919 Rep. 649*: **V. narbonensis** L., Ware, *Druce, B.E.C. 1928 Rep. 734*; Hertford, 1920, *A. W. Graveson, Hb. Gr.*; near Wymondley Springs, 1927, *J. E. Little, Hb. Camb.*: **V. peregrina** L., Ware, *Trower and Druce, B.E.C. 1919 Rep. 650*: **V. varia** Host, *G. C. Druce, B.E.C. 1919 Rep. 649*: **V. villosa** Roth, waste ground, Hitchin, 1907, *E. F. Linton, Hb. B.M.*; Ware, 1922, *A. W. Graveson, Hb. Gr.*; Welwyn, *H. Phillips, B.E.C. 1932 Rep. 93, Hb. Ph.*: **V. tenuifolia** Roth, Wheathampstead, *D. M. Higgins, W. E. C. 1901–2 Rep. 10*: **V.elegans** Guss., bed of Startops End Reservoir, 1945, *J. E. Dandy, Hb. B.M.*

Lathyrus L.

L. aphaca L.   *Yellow Vetchling*   H. Fordham, 1841
Arable fields, gardens, etc.   Colonist
Rare and seldom established. It has been recorded more or less at regular intervals but during the period of the present survey it has been reported only from a few places in the Welwyn area.

L. nissolia L.   (Map 22o)   *Grass Pea*
                    Miss Hume (Herb. J. E. Smith), 1801
Rough grassland, recently cleared woodland, etc.   Native
Occasional and having no distribution pattern. H.S. 96.

L. hirsutus L.   *Hairy Vetchling*
                    W. H. Hutchings (Herb. Brit. Mus.), 1894
A casual which has been recorded from time to time. The only records made during the period of the present survey are Danesbury, 1956 (21/I), *L. Crewdson, Hb. H.M.*; railway siding. Wheathampstead, 1960 (11/S).

L. pratensis L.   (Map 23a)   *Meadow Vetchling*   Kalm, 1748
Pastures, roadside verges, etc.   Native
Abundant. H.S. 4, 8–10, 18, 19, 24, 25, 27, 28, 30, 32, 33, 35, 38, 59, 69, 71, 73, 75, 76, 83, 90, 96, 99, 100.

L. tuberosus L., *Tuberous or Fyfield Pea*, a colonist, has recently been found in a hedgerow between Kensworth village and church, 1961 (01/J), v.c. 20 [Beds.], by G. Elwell. This is a welcome addition to the flora.

L. sylvestris L.   *Narrow–leaved Everlasting Pea*
                                      J. Woods, 1805
Wood borders, hedgerows, etc.   ? Native
Very rare and known to Little only from Titmore Green, near Wymondley. Hunsdon Mill, 1943, *D. McClintock*; Briggens Park, 1959 (41/A), *P. C. and J. Hall.*

L. latifolius L.   (Map 23b)   *Everlasting Pea*   Pryor, 1874
A naturalized plant of hedgerows, old gardens and waste places which has apparently much increased in recent years.

L. montanus Bernh.   (Map 23c)   *Bitter Vetch*
Orobus tuberosus L.   Coleman, 1838
Heathy woods   Native
Rare and limited mainly to the London Clay. H.S. 103.

The following have been recorded as casuals: **L. annuus** L., Hayllar in *B.E.C. 1915 Rep. 262*: **L. cicera** L., Ware, *Trower and Druce, B.E.C. 1915 Rep. 262*: **L. hierosolymitanus** Boiss., Ware, *Trower and Druce, B.E.C. 1914 Rep. 194*: **L. inconspicuus** L., Hertford, *A. W. Graveson, B.E.C. 1921 Rep. 380, Hb. Gr.*: **L. ochrus** (L.) DC., Ware, *Trower and Druce, B.E.C. 1915 Rep. 262*: **L. odoratus** L., *Sweet Pea*, Webb (see *Pryor*, 117): **L. sphaericus** Retz., Cole Green, *Pryor, J. Bot. 1874*, 205; Ware, 1920, *A. W. Graveson, Hb. Gr.*

The Leguminosae contain a number of plants of commerce that given suitable conditions may become casuals and account for many of the introduced species listed below: **Arachis hypogaea** L., *Ground Nut*, Hitchin U.D.C. Dump 1959 (13/V), *Hb. H.M.*: **Cicer arietinum** L., for which there are also earlier records, Cock Lane Dump, 1959 (30/V), *Hb. H.M.*: **Lens culinaris** L., *Lentil*, Knowling, *B.E.C. 1916 Rep.* 481: **Psoralea americana** L., Dump at Pye Corner, 1959 (41/L), *P. C. and J. Hall, Hb. H.M.*; Hitchin U.D.C. Dump, 1964 (13/V): **Scorpiurus subvillosus** L., Cole Green Dump (21/Q), *Hb. H.M.*: **S. sulcatus** L., lawn at St. Albans, 1922, *H. B. M. Miller, Hb. B.M.* Species of Pea (*Pisum*) and Bean (*Phaseolus*) are found as relics of cultivation and appear also on rubbish dumps.

ROSACEAE
Filipendula Mill.

F. vulgaris Moench   (Map 23d)   *Dropwort*   Kalm, 1748
Spiraea filipendula L.
Chalk downs and chalk exposures   Native
Rare but locally frequent where it occurs. H.S. 1–3, 14.

F. ulmaria (L.) Maxim. (Map 23e) *Meadow Sweet*
Spiraea ulmaria L. Ellis, 1750
Marshes, wet places, etc.
Frequent when conditions are suitable for it. H.S. 9, 13, 18, 19, 20, 28, 30–32, 34–36, 38, 39, 46, 73, 75, 76, 90, 99, 100.

Spiraea salicifolia L. occurs rarely on the sites of old gardens – see also *Pryor*, 501.

Rubus L.
R. idaeus L. (Map 23f) *Raspberry* Woodward, 1787
Woods, heaths, etc. Native
Frequent except on the Chalk and Boulder Clay. It has, however, often been introduced. H.S. 45, 68, 79.

R. caesius L. (Map 23g) *Dewberry* Ellis, 1750
Hedges, wood borders, etc. Native
Frequent on the Chalk and Boulder Clay but rare elsewhere. H.S. 11, 21, 33, 37, 41, 42, 46, 107.

R. fruticosus L. (Map 23h) *Bramble, Blackberry*
Kalm, 1748
Hedges, wood borders, heaths, commons, etc. Native
The brambles of Hertfordshire have attracted the attention of botanists for many years and a number of names have been applied to material collected in the county. Nothing would be gained by listing these names here as they could not be related to any accepted treatment of the genus. W. C. R. Watson, the most recent authority on the subject, made a number of visits to restricted areas and over such a long period of time that the earliest names he used bear little relationship to those he was using during his later visits. The county, especially on the Clay-with-Flints and river gravels, must be as rich as any in its bramble flora and this needs to be studied. Among the segregates **R. ulmifolius** Schott, a sexual diploid, is distinct and it hybridizes with dewberry and other brambles. It is very common and I very much regret now that I have not accounted for its distribution in the county. Some garden species *e.g.* **R. procerus** P. J. Muell. and **R. laciniatus** Willd. have escaped and become naturalized. The aggregate species is recorded for all tetrads. H.S. 4, 6, 7, 10, 11, 16, 17, 21, 22, 24, 26, 30–39, 41–47, 52, 53, 55–57, 59–62, 64, 67–70, 77–82, 84, 86, 88, 89, 93–96, 98–101, 103–107.

Potentilla L.
P. palustris (L.) Scop. *Marsh Cinquefoil* Webb, 1840,
Comarum palustre L. Coleman, 1840
Marshy places Native
Extinct. This was previously known only from Rickmansworth Common and a few places in the Wormley Wood area. It was last seen about 1919.

P. sterilis (L.) Garcke (Map 23i) *Barren Strawberry*
P. fragariastrum Pers. Blake, 1820
Woods, roadside banks, etc. Native
Frequent and well distributed but absent from the Chalk. H.S. 11, 32, 36, 39, 41, 42, 44–47, 54, 56, 60, 62, 69, 77, 78, 80, 82, 84, 88, 93, 94, 103, 105.

P. anserina L. (Map 23j) *Silver Weed* Blake, c. 1820
Wet pastures, roadsides, etc. Native
Common and well distributed. J. E. Little separated varieties based mainly on the hairiness of the leaves. H.S. 8–11, 18, 20, 21, 33, 34, 62, 88, 90.

P. argentea L. (Map 23k) *Hoary Cinquefoil*
D. Leach (Herb. Brit. Mus.), 1817
Old gravel pits, gravelly pastures, etc. Native
Rare and limited mainly to the river gravels. H.S. 22.

P. erecta (L.) Räusch. (Map 23 l) *Tormentil* Franks, 1822
P. tormentilla Stokes
Heathy pastures Native
Occasional and more frequent on the London Clay than elsewhere. H.S. 9, 10, 26, 55, 57, 58, 68, 70, 72, 78, 81, 86, 87, 89–91, 97–105.
P. erecta × **reptans** (*P.* × *italica* Lehm.) is found frequently with both parents and is much confused with *P. anglica.*

P. anglica Laichard. *Creeping Tormentil* Woodward, 1787
P. procumbens Sibth., *Tormentilla reptans* L.
A very rare native of heathy places which Coleman doubted was a Hertfordshire species. Pryor listed three stations and Little only one (Burleigh Meadow, 1924 det. H. W. Pugsley). Apparently good material was collected by Miss Elwell at Beechwood, 1964 (01/M), det. P. Benoit.
P. × *mixta* (*P. anglica* × *reptans*) was recorded by Pryor and Little but it is difficult to know what was intended.

P. reptans L. (Map 23m) *Creeping Cinquefoil* Blake, 1819
Meadows, roadsides, etc. Native
Abundant. H.S. 4, 5, 10, 11, 20–22, 24, 28, 33–35, 37, 38, 44, 46, 47, 50, 53, 62, 67, 69, 71, 77–80, 82, 83, 88, 94, 96, 98, 99, 104, 107.

P. hirta L. was recorded from 'near Herts'. [? Hertford] by Hayllar in *B.E.C. 1915 Rep.* 264: **P. inclinata** Vill., Bayfordbury, 1922, *H. Clinton Baker, Hb. B.M.*: **P. intermedia** L., Ware, *Druce and Hayllar, B.E.C. 1915 Rep.* 264: **P. norvegica** L., first recorded by Saunders, 1881 (see *Pryor*, 501), has been recorded occasionally. The only current record is from railway sidings, Oakleigh Park, v.c. 20 [G.L.], 1964 (29/S), *Hb. H.M.*: **P. recta** L., first recorded from the Anchusa Pit, Hertford, 1910, *A. W. Graveson, Hb. Gr.*, has been found during the period of the present survey at Stevenage, 1964 (22/L)!, *M. Mullin, Hb. H.M.*; Knebworth, 1960 (22/K), *B. Jennings*; Danesbury, 1956 (22/I); Furneux Pelham, 1965 (42/I), *Hb. H.M.*

Fragaria L.
F. vesca L. (Map 23n) *Wild Strawberry* Kalm, 1748
Woods, woodland clearings, exposed banks, etc. Native
Frequent and well distributed. H.S. 11, 14, 16, 17, 21, 33, 36, 37, 39, 42, 50–54, 60, 62, 77–80, 88, 93, 94, 100, 104, 105, 107.

F. ananassa Duchesne (Map 23o) is frequent on railway banks. It was first recorded by Little in 1924 but there was for some time confusion with **F. moschata** Duchesne (*F. elatior* Ehrh.) which was recorded by Dickson (1815) in its own right. Both are of garden origin.

Geum L.
G. urbanum L. (Map 24a) *Herb Bennet, Wood Avens*
Coleman, 1838
Roadsides, wood borders, etc. Native
Abundant. H.S. 11, 17, 22, 32–37, 39, 41, 43–47, 61–63, 77–79, 82, 88, 93–95, 103, 107.

G. rivale L. *Water Avens* Webb and Coleman, 1849
A very rare native species of marshes and wet woods which was known to earlier botanists from four isolated stations. It was found once during the present survey; Sarratt Bottom, 1963 (09/J).
G. rivale × **urbanum** (*G.* × *intermedium* Ehrh.) was recorded in *Pryor*, 141, from Flaunden Bottom and by Eyles (*Trans. Herts. N.H.S.* 16 (1917), 159) from Bricket Wood, a station from which *G. rivale* has not been recorded.

Agrimonia L.

A. eupatoria L. (Map 24b) *Common Agrimony*
Blake, 1819
Roadsides, wood borders, pastures, etc. Native
Common. H.S. 3–5, 11, 14, 21–25, 28, 33, 42, 51–53, 56, 62, 65, 67, 71, 79, 82, 84, 94.

A. odorata Mill., *Fragrant Agrimony*, was recorded from Broxbourne Wood, near the brook, 1909, *A. W. Graveson, Hb. Gr.*; Cuffley, *L. B. Hall* in *Kent and Lousley*, 104; Highfield Wood, 1953 (30/P), *R. M. Payne* in *Kent and Lousley*, 347. I have found no satisfactory material in the county.

Alchemilla L.

A. vestita (Buser) Raunk. (Map 24c) *Lady's Mantle*
A. vulgaris auct. Gerard, 1597 but more certainly Blake, c. 1820
Pastures, grassy rides in woods, etc. Native
Occasional but well distributed.

A. xanthochlora Rothm. was first recorded from near to Tring as *A. pratensis* by Druce in *B.E.C. 1915 Rep.* 265. I have found it in and near Grove Wood, 1956 (90/EJ) and R. F. Turney has shown it to me on the county boundary by Phillips Hill Wood (09/C).

Aphanes L.

A. arvensis L. (Map 24d) *Parsley Piert* Franks MS., 1820
Alchemilla arvensis (L.) Scop.
Arable fields, disturbed places in short grass, etc. Native
Frequent and widely distributed on a variety of soils. H.S. 22, 77.

A. microcarpa (Boiss. & Reut.) Rothm. (Map 24e) has only recently been recognised as a distinct species. It grows mainly in sandy and gravelly fields and is found occasionally in the south of the county. H.S. 60, 69.

Sanguisorba L.

S. officinalis L. *Great Burnet* Morice, 1840
A very rare plant of damp pastures which until recently had been recorded only from Ashwell by Mrs. Morice. It was reported by D. J. Hinson from Totteridge Green, 1956 (29/S), v.c. 20 [G.L.] and by Lloyd-Evans from Standon Lordshp, 1956 (32/V)! I saw one plant in 1956 at the south end of Aldenham Reservoir (19/S).

S. minor Scop. subsp. **minor** (Map 24f) *Salad Burnet*
Poterium sanguisorba L. Blake, c. 1820
Pastures, railway banks, etc. Native
Common on the Chalk and chalky outcrops. H.S. 1–5, 11, 14, 15, 21, 22, 48–50, 52, 53, 67, 84.
subsp. **muricata** Aschers. & Graebn. *Fodder Burnet*
Poterium muricatum Spach Pryor, 1875
This was at one time grown frequently as a crop and became naturalized especially on railway banks. I found it near Royston in 1955 and at Preston in 1956 but I have not seen it since.

Rosa L.

I wish to thank Dr. R. Melville for his assistance in naming my rose specimens and also for his very helpful suggestions regarding the limits of the species to be included here.
R. arvensis Huds. (Map 24g) *Field Rose* Blake, c. 1820
Hedges, wood borders, etc. Native
Frequent and well distributed. H.S. 17, 32, 36, 38, 39, 41, 46, 47, 61, 78, 79, 88, 93, 94, 99, 103, 106, 107.

R. stylosa Desv. (Map 24h) Monro (see Pryor, 142), c. 1820
A rare native rose of hedgerows mainly on clay soil. Distribution imperfectly known.

R. canina L. (including *R. dumetorum* Thuill., *R. dumalis* Bechst. *R. obtusifolia* Desv.) (Map 24i) *Dog Rose*
Kalm, 1748
Hedgerows, scrub, etc. Native
Abundant. H.S. 3–5, 11, 16, 21, 22, 24, 26, 32, 33, 35, 37, 38, 45, 48, 50–52, 61, 62, 67, 69, 71, 73, 79, 84, 95, 96, 106, 107.

R. tomentosa Sm. (Map 24j) *Downy Rose* Sabine, 1815
A rare native mainly of hedgerows and scrub on the Chalk and Boulder Clay. H.S. 46.

R. rubiginosa L. *Sweet Briar* Steele MS., c. 1730
Chalk downs and chalky exposures Native
Rare but its distribution is not fully known. Dawley Warren, 1961 (21/M)!, *J. C. Gardiner*; Therfield Heath (33/J)!, *Little*; Oxshott Hill, 1964 (22/W)!, *M. Mullin*; slope below Benington High Wood, H.S. 41, 1962 (22/X); Sheethanger Common, 1963 (00/M).

R. micrantha Borrer ex Sm. Sabine, 1815
Hedgerows, field borders, etc. Native
Probably more widespread than *R. rubiginosa* but distribution imperfectly known. Wormley Wood (30/I)!, *R. A. Boniface*; below Aldbury Nowers, 1964 (91/L); above Aldbury, 1965 (91/Q); Northchurch Common, 1965 (91/V); Hudnall Common, 1963 (01/C).

Prunus L.

P. spinosa L. (Map 24k) *Sloe, Blackthorn* Kalm, 1748
Hedgerows, etc. Native
Abundant. H.S. 5, 7, 21, 24, 25, 33, 36, 39, 46, 49, 53, 58, 61, 67, 84, 106, 107.

P. domestica L. *Wild Plum, Bullace* Coleman, 1838
P. insititia L.
A garden escape or planted tree of hedgerows which is found occasionally but rarely far from houses. Earlier workers, including Little, recognised two species and it is indeed possible that the true Bullace (*P. insititia*) was grown more frequently than it is now and consequently found more often growing wild.

P. cerasifera Ehrh. (Map 24 l) *Cherry Plum* Little, 1912
A comparatively recent introduction and a still uncommon tree which is sometimes deliberately planted in hedgerows. Unlike *P. domestica* it may occasionally be found remote from houses when it is probably bird-sown.

P. avium (L.) L. (Map 24m) *Gean, Wild Cherry*
Steele MS., c. 1730
Woods Native
One of our most attractive native trees. It is frequent especially on the Clay-with-Flints. H.S. 17, 55, 61, 84, 93.

P. cerasus L. *Sour Cherry* Webb and Coleman, 1843
A small introduced tree of hedgerows which is very rare. I have seen it only by the side of West Wood, 1957 (12/S), *Hb. H.M.*, where it was also found by Little, and at Scratch Wood, 1963 (01/R), *Hb. H.M.*

P. padus L., *Bird Cherry*, has been recorded only as a planted shrub.

Crataegus L.

C. monogyna Jacq. (Map 24n) *Hawthorn* Ellis, 1742
Hedgerows, scrub, etc. Native
This is our common hawthorn. H.S. 2–6, 11, 12, 14–17, 21–24, 26, 28, 31–33, 35–42, 45–56, 59–64, 67, 69–71, 75, 78–80, 82, 84, 88, 89, 92, 95, 96, 98, 100, 101, 103–107.
Coleman recognised only one hawthorn – *C. oxyacantha* L.

– and Pryor, retaining this as the common species, added *C. monogyna* which he considered to be rare. Little was the first worker to separate the Hertfordshire species in the way that we now know them. Ellis in 1742 noted that hawthorn was plentiful in the Chiltern country but scarce in the vale open-field lands. It was apparently becoming much in demand for hedgerows as a result of the increasing enclosure of open fields and commons.

C. laevigata (Poir.) DC. (Map 24o) *Midland Hawthorn*
C. oxyacanthoides Thuill. Pryor, 1874
Woods, hedgerows, etc. Native
Frequent on the London Clay especially in the Barnet area and scattered over the rest of the county where it is more frequent within woods than in hedgerows. It hybridizes freely with *C. monogyna* and plants of hybrid origin are common. H.S. 36.

Sorbus L.
S. aucuparia L. (Map 25a) *Rowan, Mountain Ash*
Coles, 1657
Woods, scrub, etc. Native
Occasional on the river gravels, London Clay and Clay-with-Flints and either absent or rare, except as a planted tree, on the Chalk and Boulder Clay. Coleman considered it to be rare and no doubt a great deal of our material has been introduced. H.S. 82, 106.

S. intermedia (Ehrh.) Pers. has been found as an introduced tree by the roadside east of Barkway, 1961 (33/H), *Hb. H.M.* and at Westbrook Hay, 1955 (00/H).

S. aria (L.) Crantz (Map 25b) *White Beam* Ellis, 1742
Woods Native
Frequent in woods on the Chalk in the west of the county but elsewhere rare and possibly planted. It is a most attractive tree which can be recognised on the slopes of the hills from a considerable distance. H.S. 17, 51.

S. torminalis (L.) Crantz (Map 25c) *Wild Service Tree*
Sabine, 1815
Woods on clay soils Native
Mainly in woods on the London Clay where it is very rare.

Pyrus communis L., *Wild Pear*, occurs rarely in hedgerows and woods having been planted or escaped from cultivation. It was first recorded by Coleman, 1839. **Cotoneaster horizontalis** Decne. is well naturalized on Boxmoor golf course, 1963 (00/H). **Mespilus germanica** L., *Medlar*, was recorded in *Pryor*, 154, but only as a planted tree.

Malus Mill.
M. sylvestris Mill. sensu lato (Map 25d) *Crab Apple*
Pyrus malus L. Coleman, 1838
Hedgerows, wood borders, etc. Native
The native species **M. sylvestris** Mill. sensu stricto is less frequent than **M. domestica** Borkh. (*M. sylvestris* subsp. *mitis* (Wallr.) Mansf.) which is of garden origin. The detailed distribution of the two species in the county remains to be studied. H.S. 84.

CRASSULACEAE
Sedum L.
S. telephium L. (Map 25e) *Orpine, Livelong*
S. vulgare (Haw.) Link., *S. fabaria* Koch Steele MS., c. 1730
Woodland rides, field borders, railway banks, etc. Native
Considered to be frequent by earlier workers and Pryor gave a number of stations including a few on railway banks which is now one of its main habitats. Both Coleman and Pryor considered it to be variable but no recent study has been made in the county of its named forms.

S. acre L. (Map 25f) *Wall-pepper* Blake, 1824
Bare waste ground, railway banks, old walls, etc. Denizen
This was recorded by earlier workers as being frequent on walls and roofs but it is now found more often on bare ground not yet colonized by other plants.

S. album L. (*S. micranthum* Bast. ex DC.), *White Stonecrop*, first recorded by Webb, 1840, was a rare wall denizen but its only recent record is from a roadside bank at Amwell cross-roads (31/Q) by various workers, e.g. *S. C. Mortis*, 1950, see *Kent and Lousley*, 118. **S. reflexum** L. was similarly recorded and during the period of the survey has been recorded from South Mimms, 1957, *E. Warmington*; roadside, Oxhey Wood, 1956 (19/B).

S. dasyphyllum L. was recorded from Markyate by T. Knowlton (1724) and was found there a century later by Dr. Wollaston who 'according to Blake, gave his specimens to Miss Sebright' (see *Pryor*, 171). Otherwise it was recorded by early nineteenth-century botanists as a rare denizen of old walls and roofs but there are no recent records.

Sempervivum tectorum L., *Houseleek*, first recorded by Coleman, 1838, is often seen on roofs of old houses but it has apparently always been originally planted.

SAXIFRAGACEAE
Saxifraga L.
S. tridactylites L. *Rue-leaved Saxifrage* Webb, 1838
Old walls, bare ground, etc. Native
Apparently frequent in the nineteenth century but it is rare now. Recorded during the present survey from the banks of Wilstone Reservoir, 1964 (91/B), *R. S. R. Fitter*; on walls at Hitchin, 1965 (12/Z), *H. B. Souster*; Ware, 1963 (31/M)!, *Lloyd-Evans*; Hadham Hall (41/L)!, *E. J. Douglas*; old wall, Stapleford, 1966 (31/D); wall, Cheshunt, 1966 (30/L).

S. granulata L. (Map 25g) *Meadow Saxifrage*
Blackstone, 1737
Pastures Native
Occasional in well-established turf in meadows on base-rich soils in various parts of the county. H.S. 13, 22.

S. cymbalaria L., has been recorded as a garden escape from Chorley Wood, 1962, by R. F. Turney.

Chrysosplenium L.
C. oppositifolium L. (Map 25h) *Golden Saxifrage*
Coleman, 1838
On perpetually wet ground in woods and shady places
Native
Occasional in a very limited area on the Lea Gravels and London Clay. H.S. 43.

PARNASSIACEAE
Parnassia L.
P. palustris L. *Grass of Parnassus* Blackstone, 1737
Boggy pastures Native
Recorded in the nineteenth century from various places in the county and said to be especially frequent in the riverside meadows between Harpenden and Hertford. J. E. Little found that it was last seen at Oughton Head in 1901 and Dr. Brenchley told Sir Edward Salisbury that she saw it in the meadows below Harpenden until 1907 or 1908. The Gravesons knew it at Wilstone Reservoir as late as 1922.

GROSSULARIACEAE
Ribes L.

R. rubrum L. (Map 25i) *Red Currant* Coleman, 1838
R. sylvestre (Lam.) Mert. & Koch
Woods, open spaces, etc. Colonist
Occasional and apparently increasing. It is no doubt bird
sown. H.S. 63.

R. nigrum L. (Map 25j) *Black Currant* Coleman, 1838
Woods, wet places, river banks, etc. Native
More scarce than the preceding and probably native in some
of the wetter situations in which it grows. Otherwise it is
bird sown or accidentally introduced.

R. uva-crispa L. (Map 25k) *Gooseberry* Coleman, 1838
Woods, hedgerows, scrub, etc. Colonist
Occasional but never appearing with the look of a native
species.

R. sanguineum Pursh, *Flowering Currant*, is found only
on the sites of old gardens.

DROSERACEAE
Drosera L.

D. rotundifolia L. *Sundew* Webb, 1838
This grew a century ago as a native in a few bogs between
Bell Bar and Little Berkhampstead. It was last seen in
1914 by Hayllar in a bog near Barber's Lodge Farm.

LYTHRACEAE
Lythrum L.

L. salicaria L. (Map 25 l) *Purple Loosestrife* Blake, 1819
Riversides, marshy places, etc. Native
Occasional and mainly in the neighbourhood of the larger
rivers. H.S. 30, 76.

L. hyssopifolia L., *Grass Poly*, a native of bare wet places,
was recorded by Webb in 1848 from Colney Heath but
was apparently extinct there when Crespigny visited it
c. 1877. Saunders recorded it as a casual at Putteridge in
Trans. Herts. N.H.S. 4 (1887), 118.

L. junceum Banks & Solander (*L. meonanthum* Link ex
Steud.), a casual, was recorded from Hertford, 1914,
A. W. Graveson, *Hb. Gr.* Current records are: refuse
tip, Rickmansworth, 1958, *Hb. H.M.*; Park Street Dump,
1965 (10/L), *Hb. H.M.*

Peplis L.

P. portula L. (Map 25m) *Water Purslane* Coleman, 1838
Sides of ponds, muddy trackways in woods, etc. Native
Occasional on the London Clay, rare elsewhere.

THYMELAEACEAE
Daphne L.

D. laureola L. (Map 25n) *Spurge Laurel*
Steele MS., c. 1730
Woods, mainly on the Chalk. Native
Occasional. H.S. 17, 54.

D. mezereum L., *Mezereon*, was recorded on slender
evidence by Webb and Coleman, and by Pryor. If it were
wild it must have been only a garden escape.

ONAGRACEAE
Epilobium L.

My early gatherings were examined by the late G. M. Ash
whose intimate knowledge of the genus allowed him to
recognise hybrids which would otherwise have passed
undetected.

E. hirsutum L. (Map 25o) *Great Hairy Willow-herb,
Codlins and Cream* Blake, 1818
In varied habitats but having a preference for river sides.
Native
Common. H.S. 19, 20, 31, 32, 35, 37–39, 65, 74, 99, 105,
107. White-flowered forms have been observed.

E. parviflorum Schreb. (Map 26a) *Hoary Willow-herb*
Blake, c. 1820
Marshy places Native
Occasional but well distributed. H.S. 8, 9, 18–20, 27, 29, 30,
39, 45, 66, 74, 76, 90.

E. montanum L. (Map 26b) *Broad-leaved Willow-herb*
Franks, 1820
Woods, waste places and occasionally a garden weed
Native
Frequent and well distributed. H.S. 16, 17, 25, 32, 33, 35,
37, 39, 41, 45–47, 54, 77, 78, 80, 88, 93, 95, 103–107.

E. lanceolatum Seb. & Mauri, *Spear-leaved Willow-herb*,
had not been recorded before the present survey. It has been
found on railway embankments south of Elstree (19/XY),
1960, *Hb. H.M.* and at Bragbury End (22/Q).

E. roseum Schreb. (Map 26c) *Pale Willow-herb*
E. Forster (see Pryor, 158), 1800
Damp places and rarely as a garden weed Native
Generally rare. H.S. 34, 44, 88.

E. adenocaulon Hausskn. (Map 26d) *American Willow-
herb* Brenan, 1937
Woods, waste places, etc. Colonist
Probably introduced about 1925 it has now spread all over
the county and could no doubt with close enough search
be found in every tetrad. H.S. 33, 34, 39, 41, 42, 44, 45,
77, 80, 88.

E. tetragonum L. subsp. **tetragonum** (Map 26e)
Square-stalked Willow-herb Franks, 1822
Wet places, stream sides, railway sidings, etc. Native
Occasional but well distributed.
subsp. **lamyi** (F. W. Schultz) Nyman
G. M. Ash referred no fewer than five of my specimens to
'E. lamyi' but in the field I have preferred to consider this
to be an extreme form of *E. tetragonum*.

E. obscurum Schreb. (Map 26f) *Short-fruited Willow-
herb* Pryor, 1874
Woods, damp places, etc. Native
Occasional but not easily distinguished from the more
common *E. adenocaulon*. G. M. Ash named as *E. obscurum*
seven of my specimens collected in 1955 and 1956. H.S.
37, 107.

E. palustre L. *Marsh Willow-herb* Coleman, 1839
On boggy ground Native
The least common of our willow-herbs which during the
period of the survey has been recorded from Hertford
Heath, *S. C. Mortis*; Kimpton Mill (11/Z), *Hb. H.M.*;
Patmore Heath (42/M); Sawbridgeworth Marsh (41/X),
H.S. 76.

E. angustifolium L. (Map 26g) *Rosebay Willow-herb,
Fireweed* Woodward, 1787
Chamaenerion angustifolium (L.) Scop.
Cleared woodland, waste places, etc. Native
Common. H.S. 4, 16, 17, 35–37, 39, 41, 42, 45, 46, 56, 62,
64, 77, 79–81, 89, 93, 98, 100, 101, 104–7. This is one of the
most interesting plants entering into the flora, as it was,
as elsewhere in Britain, rare until comparatively recently.

Coleman thought it to be a feature of woods on moist soils and osier beds. Salisbury noted that it was becoming more frequent in 1924 and it was observed to be increasing in the Broxbourne Woods in 1929, 1930 and 1931 by Hayllar. It was at about this time that I observed its increase in Bedfordshire but I failed to put it on record.

E. neterioides Cunn. was found on Potters Bar golf course, v.c. 21 [Herts.] by R. P. Libbey, c. 1945, *Hb. Lousley, Kent and Lousley*, 348.

The following hybrids have been recorded: **E. adenocaulon × montanum** *Hb. H.M.*, **E. adenocaulon × obscurum** *Hb. H.M.*, **E. adenocaulon × parviflorum** *Hb. H.M.*, **E. hirsutum × parviflorum**, **E. montanum × parviflorum**, **E. palustre × parviflorum**.

Oenothera L.
O. erythrosepala Borbás, *Evening Primrose*, first recorded by Webb and Coleman (1843), is frequent in waste places as is a smaller-flowered species which may be *O. biennis* L. They are, however, only garden escapes the nomenclature of which is much confused. **O. laciniata** Hill (*O. sinuata* auct.) was recorded from between Ware and St. Margarets, 1926, *A. W. Graveson, Hb. Gr.*

Circaea L.
C. lutetiana L. (Map 26h) *Enchanter's Nightshade*
Rudge, c. 1810
Woods, shady places and also rarely a garden weed Native
Frequent. H.S. 16, 17, 32, 34–37, 39–41, 43–47, 60, 63, 77, 80, 82, 88, 93–95, 103, 106, 107.

HALORAGACEAE
Myriophyllum L.
M. spicatum L. (Map 26i) *Spiked Water-milfoil*
Rudge, c. 1810
Lakes, flooded pits, slow-flowing rivers, canals, etc. Native
Occasional but rarely flowering.

M. verticillatum L. (Map 26j) *Whorled Water-milfoil*
Webb and Coleman, 1843
Flooded pits, slow-flowing rivers, etc. Native
Not infrequent in the Stort and Lea Navigations and probably carried to flooded pits by birds.

M. alterniflorum DC. *Alternate Water-milfoil*
Webb and Coleman, 1843
This was recorded by nineteenth-century botanists as a rare native of ponds in the more heathy areas of the county. It was found to be still at Aldenham Reservoir in 1916 by Sir Edward Salisbury and at Colney Heath in 1916 by Mrs. A. White. I know of no more recent records for the county.

HIPPURIDACEAE
Hippuris L.
H. vulgaris L. (Map 26k) *Mare's-tail* Blackstone, 1737
Slow-flowing rivers, lakes, flooded pits, etc. Native
Occasional in its genuinely native stations but probably originally introduced and surviving in artificial lakes in parks.

CALLITRICHACEAE
Callitriche L.
The comparative completeness of the records for this genus is due almost entirely to the work of P. M. Benoit on a number of visits to the county.

C. stagnalis Scop. (Map 26 l) *Water Starwort*
Franks MS., 1823
Ditches, streams and wet ruts in woodland rides. Native
Our most common Water Starwort and to be found scattered throughout the county. H.S. 60, 77, 78, 88, 89.

C. platycarpa Kütz. (Map 26m) Coleman, 1846
C. verna auct.
Clear running streams and rivers Native
Rare to occasional but only because the habitat is.

C. obtusangula Le Gall (May 26n) Pryor, 1876
In similar situations and of like rarity to *C. platycarpa* with which it is often found growing.

C. intermedia Hoffm. (Map 26o) Coleman, 1846
C. pedunculata DC., *C. hamulata* Kütz. ex Koch
Flooded pits, reservoirs, etc. Native
Occasional and the species usually found in deep stagnant water.

LORANTHACEAE
Viscum L.
V. album L. (Map 27a) *Mistletoe* Knowlton, c. 1750
Parasite on various trees Native
The status and frequency of this appears to have been unchanged in the past hundred years but it may at all times have been under-recorded. It is still found growing on a variety of trees including lime (principally), poplar, apple and hawthorn.

SANTALACEAE
Thesium L.
T. humifusum DC. *Bastard Toadflax* H. Fordham, 1840
A native species of close turf on chalk downland which is still locally plentiful on Therfield Heath (33/J, 34/K), H.S. 2. From here it extends eastwards into Cambridgeshire but it is absent on the chalk westwards in Bedfordshire and Buckinghamshire.

CORNACEAE
Swida Opiz
S. sanguinea (L.) Opiz (Map 27b) *Dogwood* Blake, 1818
Cornus sanguinea L., *Thelycrania sanguinea* (L.) Fourr.
Hedgerows, wood borders, chalk scrub, etc. Native
Very common. H.S. 4, 11, 16, 17, 21, 24, 32, 33, 39, 45, 46, 48, 49, 51, 52, 54, 56, 78–80, 84, 94, 107.

ARALIACEAE
Hedera L.
H. helix L. (Map 27c) *Ivy* Ellis, 1742
Woods, hedges, sides of old buildings, etc. Native
Very common. H.S. 17, 35, 41, 45–47, 52, 54, 61, 63, 78–80, 84, 95.

UMBELLIFERAE
Hydrocotyle L.
H. vulgaris L. (Map 27d) *Marsh Pennywort*
Coleman, 1838
Boggy places Native
Rare, but apparently no more so than it was a hundred years ago. H.S. 10, 31.

Sanicula L.
S. europaea L. (Map 27e) *Wood Sanicle*
Steele MS., c. 1730
Woods Native
Frequent in woods on chalky soils but rare elsewhere. H.S. 11, 12, 17, 46, 50, 52, 54, 61, 63, 77, 80, 84, 93, 95.

Chaerophyllum L.

C. temulentum L.   (Map 27f)   *Rough Chervil*
Coleman, 1838
Hedgerows   Native
Generally common but becoming less so on the river gravels and London Clay.

Anthriscus Pers.

A. sylvestris (L.) Hoffm.   (Map 27g)   *Cow Parsley*
Ellis, 1750
Hedgerows, shady places and occasionally in woods   Native
Abundant. H.S. 17, 24, 25, 47, 59, 61, 63, 83, 100.

A. caucalis Bieb. (Map 27h) *Bur Chervil* Coleman, 1838
A. vulgaris Pers., non Bernh.
Gravel pits and waste gravelly places where it is a rare colonist.

A. cerefolium (L.) Hoffm. has been recorded, e.g. *Pryor*, 183, only as an escape from cultivation.

Scandix L.

S. pecten-veneris L.   (Map 27i)   *Shepherd's Needle*
Ellis, 1733
Arable fields   Colonist
Occasional and with a slight preference for calcareous soils.

Myrrhis odorata (L.) Scop., *Sweet Cicely*, has been recorded only as a naturalized plant e.g. on Norton Common (23/B), *Hb. H.M.* or as a garden escape.

Torilis Adans.

T. japonica (Houtt.) DC.   (Map 27j)   *Hedge-parsley*
T. anthriscus (L.) C. C. Gmel., non Gaertn.,   Franks, 1822
Caucalis anthriscus (L.) Huds.
Roadsides, wood borders, etc.   Native
Common and well distributed. H.S. 4, 5, 25, 47, 84, 100.

T. arvensis (Huds.) Link   (Map 27k)   *Spreading Hedge-*
T. helvetica (Jacq.) C. C. Gmel.,   *parsley*   Franks, 1821
Caucalis arvensis Huds.
Arable fields   Colonist
This was considered by Coleman to be an obnoxious weed but it has much decreased and is apparently still diminishing. H.S. 52.

T. nodosa (L.) Gaertn.   (Map 27 l)   *Knotted Hedge-parsley*
Coleman, 1839
Dry bare pastures   Native
Coleman considered this to be especially common on chalky soil. It is still more frequent on the Chalk than elsewhere but it is definitely rare.

Caucalis platycarpos L. (*C. daucoides* L.), a rare colonist of arable fields, was first recorded by Blake, 1821. It was reported from time to time and its last certain record was from Potters Bar, v.c. 21 [Herts.], 1914, *J. E. Cooper, Hb. B.M.*

Turgenia latifolia (L.) Hoffm. (*Caucalis latifolia* L.) was recorded as a rare casual by Webb and Coleman and its last record was from Ware by Hayllar in *B.E.C. 1915 Rep.* 286.

Coriandrum sativum L., *Coriander*, first recorded by T. Walker, 1873, *Hb. B.M.* is now occasional on refuse tips probably as a bird-seed alien e.g. Cole Green, 1957 (21/Q); Cock Lane, 1958 (30/U); Bulls Mill, 1958 (31/C) etc.

Smyrnium L.

S. olusatrum L.   *Alexanders*   Blake, 1824
Roadside verges, field borders, etc.   Naturalized
Very rare as it has always been. It is now known only from Holy Cross, near Ware, an old station, 1955 (31/R)!, *Lloyd-Evans*; edge of Welwyn Garden City Golf Course, 1952, *E. G. Kellett.*

Conium L.

C. maculatum L.   (Map 27m)   *Hemlock*   Blake, 1820
Sides of rivers, waste ground, etc.   Native
Occasional but well distributed by riversides; it also appears regularly on the Hertfordshire rubbish dumps.

Bupleurum L.

B. rotundifolium L.,   *Thorow-wax*   Steele MS., c. 1730
This was at one time a common weed of cornfields on calcareous soils but it is now probably extinct. The last certain record was no doubt made by H. W. Pugsley from Allens Green, 1941, *Hb. B.M.*

B. lancifolium Hornem. (*B. protractum* Hoffmanns. & Link) first recorded in *Pryor*, 193, has increased as a bird-seed alien and is often reported in error as *B. rotundifolium*. Recent records include South Road, Bishop's Stortford, 1941, *B. J. Adams, Hb. J. L. Fielding*; waste ground, Hitchin; garden weed, Wigginton; garden, St. Albans. **B. petraeum** L. was recorded from waste heap, Welwyn, *H. Phillips, B.E.C. 1934 Rep.* 827.

Apium L.

A. nodiflorum (L.) Lag.   (Map 27n)   *Fool's Watercress*
Helosciadium nodiflorum (L.) Koch   Blake, 1819
Streams, ditches, etc.   Native
Occasional but widely distributed. H.S. 29, 65, 66.

A. inundatum (L.) Reichb. f.   (Map 27o)   *Least Marshwort*
Helosciadium inundatum (L.) Koch   Coleman, 1838
Ponds on heathy ground   Native
Rare and occurring mainly on the London Clay. Its present records are Hertford Heath, 1956 (31/K), *Hb. H.M.* and Aldenham Reservoir, 1956 (19/S), *Hb. H.M.* both confirming old records; Potten End, 1956 (00/E); near Bricket Wood, 1957 (10/F); Goose Green, 1956 (30/P), *Hb. H.M.*; Hadley Green, 1957 (29/N), v.c. 21 [Herts. 1904-65, G.L.]

A. graveolens L., *Wild Celery*, was recorded by Webb and Coleman and by Pryor but apparently Garden Celery was intended. **A. dulce** Mill., *Garden Celery*, occurs occasionally in waste places as a garden throw-out.

Petroselinum Hill

P. segetum (L.) Koch   *Corn Caraway*   I. Brown, 1841
This native of bare banks on calcareous soils which may become also a colonist in arable fields was considered rare by Coleman most of whose stations were in the Hitchin area. Little found it 'quite common near Hitchin' but I have only seen it twice in the county: rubbish dump, Rickmansworth, 1958, *Hb. H.M.*; arable field between Sandridge and Smallford, 1960 (10/U), *Hb. H.M.*

P. crispum (Mill.) Airy Shaw (*P. sativum* Hoffm.), *Parsley*, has been recorded as a garden escape.

Sison L.

S. amomum L.   (Map 28a)   *Stone Parsley*   Franks, 1822
Roadside verges, field borders, etc.   Native
Occasional and more plentiful on the London Clay than elsewhere.

Cicuta L.

C. virosa L. *Cowbane* J. Goodyer, 1625
A rare native recorded by Goodyer from Moor Park and by Crespigny from Applebury (i.e. Appleby Street), two miles west of Cheshunt, *Hb. B.M.* It was known to Coleman and later nineteenth-century botanists from a few ponds in the Wormley Wood area. It was last seen there by A. W. Graveson in 1929 but may have survived a little longer.

Ammi majus L. was recorded from Ware Park Mill as a casual in *Pryor*, 186. There are a few subsequent similar records but it has in the period of the survey been recorded only as a wool adventive.

Falcaria Fabr.

F. vulgaris Bernh. *Longleaf* Andrews (Hb. Brit. Mus.), 1899
Rough grassland Colonist
Recorded from time to time but not always established. Current records are: White Hall, Aston, 1957 (22/V), *A. W. Graveson*!, it has been known to the Gravesons here for forty years, *Hb. Gr.*; roadside, Lilley Bottom, 1961 (12/I), *Hb. H.M.*; sides of fields below Arbury Banks (23/U) where it was plentiful in 1964 and an apparent newcomer. It was recorded from Pirton as 'getting to be a pest' by Van de Weyer in *B.E.C. 1923 Rep.* 186. I have no other record of it here.

Carum carvi L., *Caraway*, was recorded by previous workers (e.g. *Pryor*, 190) from railway banks. I have found it only as a casual on Cole Green Dump, 1955 (21/Q), *Hb. H.M.*

Bunium L.

B. bulbocastanum L. (Map 28b) *Great Earthnut*
Bulbocastanum linnaei Schur Coleman, 1840
Arable fields and rough pastures on the Chalk Native
Coleman was the first botanist to recognise this as a British species. He found it first at Cherry Hinton in Cambridgeshire in 1835 and later in a number of places in Hertfordshire and Bedfordshire. Its unusual distribution is exactly the same now as it was then.

Conopodium Koch

C. majus (Gouan) Loret (Map 28c) *Earthnut, Pig Nut*
C. denudatum Koch Blake, 1820
Woods, heathy pastures, etc. Native
Common except on the Chalk and Boulder Clay. H.S. 41, 55, 57, 58, 60, 65, 70, 72, 103.

Pimpinella L.

P. saxifraga L. (Map 28d) *Burnet Saxifrage* Blake, 1819
Pastures with a short turf, roadsides, railway banks, etc.
 Native
Very common on the Chalk and frequent on all other soils except the river gravels. H.S. 2, 4, 14, 15, 23, 26, 48, 49.

P. major (L.) Huds. (Map 28e) *Greater Burnet Saxifrage*
 Alchorne, 1748
Sides of woods, roadsides, etc. Native
Common in the northern part of the Boulder Clay but with a disjunct distribution elsewhere which is not related to any geological formation. H.S. 28. Forms with cut leaves have been found near St. Albans.

Aegopodium L.

A. podagraria L. (Map 28f) *Goutweed, Ground Elder*
 Blake, c. 1820
Gardens, roadsides, waste ground, etc. Colonist
Abundant having probably increased in the past century.

Sium latifolium L., *Greater Water-parsnip*, has been recorded in error (see *Pryor*, 186). It occurs now by a pond at Rydal Mount, Potters Bar, 1965 (20/K), v.c. 21 [Herts.], *D. H. Kent*!, *Hb. H.M.* It was probably originally planted here.

Berula Koch

B. erecta (Huds.) Coville (Map 28g) *Lesser Water-*
Sium erectum Huds. *parsnip* Blake, 1822
Rivers, streams, etc. Native
Occasional in the upper courses of rivers but rare in the navigable and fouled waterways. H.S. 76.

Seseli L.

S. libanotis (L.) Koch (*Libanotis montana* Crantz), *Moon Carrot*, a rare native, is known only from Arbury Banks (23/U)!, *Hb. H.M.* where it was recorded by Coleman in 1841. There is doubt regarding the location of 'inter St. Albans et Stoney Stratford' which is the basis of the record in Hudson's *Flora Anglica* (1762).

Oenanthe L.

O. fistulosa L. (Map 28h) *Tubular Water Dropwort*
 Blackstone, 1737
A rare native of ponds and ditches which has probably diminished in recent years with the filling in of ponds.

O. pimpinelloides L., a very rare native of ditches, was found in 1962 by A. R. Paterson at Bulls Mill (31/C), *Hb. H.M.* Close search has failed to reveal another plant.

O. lachenalii C. C. Gmel., a very rare native of marshes on the Chalk Marl, was first recorded by Isaac Brown in 1841. It has been found by previous workers at Ashwell Common; Oughton Head Common, *Hb. B.M.* and Norton Common (23/B)! *Hb. B.M.*, *Hb. Letch. Mus.* It still survives on Norton Common, H.S. 10.

O. crocata L., *Hemlock Water Dropwort*, a native of wet places, was first recorded with certainty by D. H. Kent from Watford and Rickmansworth, 1952, in *Kent and Lousley*, 132. Its only other record is from Dobbs Weir, 1960 (30/Z) by Lloyd-Evans.

O. aquatica (L.) Poir. *Fine-leaved Water Dropwort*
O. phellandrium Lam. Blake, 1824
Ponds mainly on clay soils Native
Rare: records made during the present survey are: pond, Watery Grove (22/G); pond, Combs Wood (32/A); pond between Collier's End and Plashes Wood (32/Q); pond, Latchford (32/V); Gobion's Pond (20/L), *Hb. H.M.*; ditches near to Cole Green Dump (21/Q). In none of these stations was it known to Pryor.

O. fluviatilis (Bab.) Colem. (Map 28i) *River Water Drop-*
 wort Webb and Coleman, 1843
O. phellandrium Lam. var. *fluviatilis* Bab.
Running water Native
Occasional in the lower stretches of the Lea and its main tributaries and in the Colne. It should be of special interest to Hertfordshire botanists as it was Coleman who first realised that *O. fluviatilis* was deserving of specific rank.

Aethusa L.

A. cynapium L. (Map 28j) *Fool's Parsley* Blake, 1819
Gardens, arable fields, waste places, etc. Colonist
Very common. H.S. 52.

Foeniculum Mill.

F. vulgare Mill. (Map 28k) *Fennel* Webb and Coleman,
F. officinale All. 1849
Railway banks, waste ground, etc. Colonist
Rare but more frequent on railways and in the south of the county than elsewhere.

Silaum Mill.
S. silaus (L.) Schinz & Thell. (Map 28 l) *Pepper Saxifrage*
Silaus pratensis Bess.   Blake, c. 1820
Well established pastures   Native
Occasional on the Boulder Clay and London Clay but
rare elsewhere. H.S. 28, 72, 73.

Angelica L.
A. sylvestris L.   (Map 28m)   *Wild Angelica*
                                                    Blackstone, 1737
Marshes, wet woods, etc.   Native
Common on the London Clay and frequent in woods on
the Boulder Clay but absent from considerable areas of
the county. H.S. 19, 28, 30–33, 35, 37–39, 75–78, 99, 100,
103.

Pastinaca L.
P. sativa L.   (Map 28n)   *Wild Parsnip*   Franks, 1820
Rough pastures   Native
Common on the Chalk and occasional on chalk outcrops
and other calcareous soils elsewhere. H.S. 3, 5, 6, 10, 21,
51–53.

Heracleum L.
H. sphondylium L. (Map 28o) *Hogweed* Doody, 1696
Roadsides, rough pastures, etc.   Native
Very common. It is variable in the width of its leaf segments
but I have not seen any extremely narrow-leaved forms.
H.S. 3, 5, 10, 24, 28, 39, 46, 47, 52, 54, 59, 73, 79, 80, 82, 84,
95, 96, 103.

H. mantegazzianum Somm. & Levier, *Giant Hogweed*,
occurs only as a garden escape or relic of old gardens but it
is most spectacular when it does so.

Daucus L.
D. carota L.   (Map 29a)   *Wild Carrot*   Blake, c. 1820
Rough pastures, waste places, etc.   Native
Frequent on the Chalk and Colne Gravels and often a
feature of railway banks on any soils. H.S. 1, 4, 6, 50–52,
83, 84, 96.

Anethum graveolens L. (*Peucedanum graveolens* (L.).
Hiern., non S. Wats.), *Dill*, first recorded by A. W.
Graveson, 1920, *Hb. Gr.* is found occasionally on rubbish
dumps e.g. Abbots Langley, 1961 (00/V), *Hb. H.M.*;
Cock Lane, 1964 (30/U), *Hb. H.M.*; Hitchin (13/V);
Pye Corner (41/L); Park Street 10/L).

The following casuals are also recorded: **Trachyspermum
ammi** (L.) Sprague, Hitchin U.D.C. Dump, 1965 (13/V),
Hb. H.M.: **Ridolfia segetum** (L.) Moris, Hitchin, 1926,
Little, Hb. Camb.

CUCURBITACEAE
Bryonia L.
B. dioica Jacq. (Map 29b) *White Bryony* Blake, c. 1820
Hedgerows, wood borders, etc.   Native
Common and becoming rare only on the London Clay.
H.S. 22, 25, 53.

The Cucurbitaceae contains many plants of economic
importance and this accounts for a number which appear on
rubbish dumps such as cucumber and vegetable marrow.
Also recorded are **Citrullus lanatus** (Thunb.) Mansf.
(*C. vulgaris* Schrad.), Welwyn, *Phillips, Hb. Ph.*; Blackbridge
Dump (11/X), *Hb. H.M.*: **Cucumis melo** L., *Melon*, Hit-
chin U.D.C. Dump (31/V); Blackbridge Dump (11/X):
Cucurbita pepo L., *Pumpkin*, Bushey U.D.C. Dump
(19/I), *Hb. H.M.*: **Ecballium elaterium** (L). A. Rich.,
Squirting Cucumber, Hitchin, *A. W. Graveson, B.E.C. 1922
Rep.* 728, *Hb. Gr., Hb. Ph.*

Asarum europaeum L., *Asarabacca*, and **Aristolochia
clematitis** L., *Birthwort*, both members of the ARIS-
TOLOCHIACEAE were recorded in the old floras as
garden relics. There have been no subsequent records.

EUPHORBIACEAE
Mercurialis L.
M. perennis L. (Map 29c) *Dog's Mercury* Ellis, 1750
Woods and shady places   Native
Common. H.S. 11, 12, 16, 17, 24, 32, 36, 40, 41, 43, 44,
46, 47, 53, 56, 61–63, 80, 82, 94, 95.

M. annua L.   (Map 29d)   *Annual Mercury*
                    R. T. Andrews (Herb. Brit. Mus.), 1873
Waste places, gardens, etc.   Colonist
This has much increased as a garden weed and rubbish
dump casual.

Euphorbia L.
E. lathyris L. *Caper Spurge* Blake (see Pryor, 368), 1827
Copses, waste places, etc.   ? Native
This was a feature of a copse near to Goldings (*Hb. Gr.* no
date) where it may well have been native. It now appears
mainly on rubbish dumps as a garden throw-out.

E. platyphyllos L.   (Map 29e)   *Warty Spurge*
                                                     Doody, c. 1700
Arable fields especially those under root crops   Colonist
One of the more interesting weeds of the Boulder Clay
where it is locally frequent.

E. helioscopia L. (Map 29f) *Sun Spurge* Blake, 1820
Cultivated ground, waste ground, etc.   Colonist
Frequent and well distributed. It is especially common
on allotments and vegetable plots.

E. peplus L.   (Map 29g)   *Petty Spurge*   Blake, 1820
Cultivated ground, waste places, etc.   Colonist
The most common of our spurges and no doubt to be
found in every garden. Recorded for all tetrads except 33/R
where there is no house with a garden.

E. exigua L. (Map 29h) *Dwarf Spurge* Blake, c. 1820
Arable fields, waste places, etc.   Colonist
Common on the more calcareous soils and found frequently
in cornfields which is rarely the case with *E. helioscopia*
and *E. peplus*. H.S. 39, 52, 53.

E. uralensis Fisch. ex Link (Map 29i) *Leafy Spurge*
E. virgata Waldst. & Kit., non Desf.,   Rudge, c. 1810
E. esula sensu Pryor
Roadsides, rough grassland, etc.   Colonist
Rare but usually well established.

E. cyparissias L.   *Cypress Spurge*   Morse, 1918
Rare but well established as a garden escape on roadsides,
waste land, etc. Welwyn, near Little Viaduct, *R. Morse,
W.E.C. 1918–9 Rep.* 114; Hertford, *A. W. Graveson,
B.E.C. 1919 Rep.* 678; Roughdown Common, 1945,
R. B. Benson, Hb. B.M. I have seen it in the following
tetrads: 33/P, 41/S, 30/EQ, 09/M, 19/CE.

E. amygdaloides L.   (Map 29j)   *Wood Spurge*
                                                    Coleman, 1838
Woods   Native
Common in the west of the county and to a less extent on
the London Clay. H.S. 80, 104.

POLYGONACEAE
Polygonum L.

P. aviculare L. *sensu stricto* (Map 29k) *Knotgrass*
Coleman, 1838
Arable fields, waste ground, etc. Native
Very common. H.S. 7, 20, 35, 38, 39, 53, 59, 66, 77, 80, 82, 105.

P. aequale Lindm. (Map 29 l) Pryor, c. 1880
P. arenastrum Bor.
Trackways, sides of fields, etc. Native
Occasional but well distributed. In addition to this Pryor recorded *P. humifusum* Jord. ex. Bor., *P. rurivagum* Jord. ex. Bor. and *P. microspermum* Jord. ex Bor. as microspecies of the aggregate for *P. aviculare*.

P. bistorta L. (Map 29m) *Bistort, Snake-root* Coles, 1657
Wet meadows Native
Rare and showing no distribution pattern. It has probably decreased in frequency as Coleman considered it to be not uncommon.

P. amphibium L. (Map 29n) *Amphibious Bistort*
Ellis, 1750
Lakes, ponds, slow-flowing rivers, etc. Native
Frequent in suitable habitats. Terrestrial forms are met with occasionally on river banks etc. but they rarely flower. H.S. 20, 73, 74, 76, 108.

P. persicaria L. (Map 29o) *Red Shank, Persicaria*
Blake, 1819
Wet places, cultivated land, etc. Native
Frequent but diminishing slightly in quantity on the Boulder Clay. H.S. 66, 91.

P. lapathifolium L. (Map 30a) *Pale Persicaria* Blake, 1819
P. nodosum Pers., *P. maculatum* (Gray) Dyer ex Bab.
Cultivated ground, rubbish heaps, etc. Colonist
A species of man-made habitats. It has a similar distribution to *P. persicaria* but is less common.

P. hydropiper L. (Map 30b) *Water-pepper* Blake, c. 1820
Wet places, woodland rides, etc. Native
Common on the London Clay and occasional on the river gravels but becoming rare on the Boulder Clay and Chalk. H.S. 88, 94, 106.

P. mite Schrank was recorded from Broxbourne Wood by J. W. Higgens in *B.E.C. 1916 Rep.* 501. I have found no specimen to support this record which should be doubted especially as *P. minus* was known from stations nearby.

P. minus Huds. *Least Water-pepper* Coleman (Herb.
Bolton Mus.), 1842
Marshy places which are kept perpetually wet Native
Known to the nineteenth-century botanists from Hertford Heath, Goose Green and Hoddesdon Marsh and from the Colney Heath and London Colney area. It has not been reported for many years from any of the places in which they found it. I have found it only in a meadow at Boxmoor, 1964 (00/N), *Hb. H.M.*

P. convolvulus L. (Map 30c) *Black Bindweed*
Franks, 1822
Arable fields, cleared woodland, etc. Native
Abundant. H.S. 1, 35, 39, 52, 53.

P. dumetorum L., *Copse Bindweed*, a rare native of hedgerows, was first recorded by Coleman in 1838 and was found mainly on the Lea Gravels. Its last certain record was from Tewin by H. Groves in 1875, *Hb. B.M.*

P. cuspidatum Sieb. & Zucc. (Map 30d) *Japanese
Knotweed* Little, 1912
Waste places, derelict gardens, etc. Colonist
Common.

P. baldschuanicum Regel, *Russian Vine*, is found scrambling over hedges and walls but never looks genuinely wild. **P. polystachyum** Wall. ex Meisn., a colonist of waste places, Mardley Heath (21/P)!, *H. Phillips and Miss Cable, B.E.C. 1927 Rep.* 416; gravel pits, Hoddesdon (30/T): **P. sachalinense** F. Schmidt, canal bank, Berkhamsted, 1960 (90/Z), *Hb. H.M.*; gravel pits, Hoddesdon (30/T); near Otterspool (19/Z). Also recorded are **P. arenarium** Waldst. & Kit., Ware, *Druce, B.E.C. 1915 Rep.* 208: **P. patulum** Bieb., Ware, *Higgens, B.E.C. 1918 Rep.* 397.

Fagopyrum esculentum Moench, *Buckwheat*, occurs as a relic of cultivation and is found also on rubbish dumps but it is not common. **F. tataricum** (L.) Gaertn. was found by A. W. Graveson at Cole Green, 1924, *Hb. Gr.*

Rumex L.

R. acetosella L. (Map 30e) *Sheep's Sorrel* Blake, c. 1820
Dry heathy and gravelly pastures Native
Common on all soils except the Chalk and Boulder Clay. H.S. 22, 26, 57, 58, 62, 69, 70, 72, 81, 85, 86, 92, 98, 101, 102.

R. acetosa L. (Map 30f) *Common Sorrel* Kalm, 1748
Meadows, roadsides, etc. Native
Common except on the most calcareous soils. H.S. 1, 7–9, 13, 18, 22, 23, 25, 26, 28, 29, 55, 58, 59, 65, 66, 68–73, 75, 76, 79, 83, 90, 91, 96, 98, 100, 101, 105, 109.

R. hydrolapathum Huds. (Map 30g) *Great Water Dock*
Coleman, 1838
Riversides Native
Limited to the large rivers and the canals. H.S. 65.

R. crispus L. (Map 30h) *Curled Dock* H. D. Henslow
(Herb. Druce), 1833
Roadsides, waste and cultivated ground Native
Abundant. H.S. 9, 20, 21, 25, 33, 35, 38, 39, 41, 46, 66, 74, 80, 83, 96, 108.
R. crispus × **obtusifolius** (R. × *acutus* L.) has been recorded frequently and there is good material in *Hb. Gr.* and *Hb. H.M.* The records of 'R. pratensis' in Webb and Coleman's Flora should no doubt be referred to this.

R. obtusifolius L. subsp. **obtusifolius** (Map 30i)
Broad Dock Coleman, 1838
Roadsides, waste ground, etc. Native
Abundant. H.S. 18, 33, 36, 44, 66, 77, 90, 93, 100, 106.
subsp. **sylvestris** (Wallr.) Reching. (R. *sylvestris* Wallr.) A casual recorded in Pryor, 355. More recent records are Wormley, *C. E. Britton, B.E.C. 1929 Rep.,* 239, *Hb. Druce* and Stanstead St. Margarets, *J. E. Lousley, B.E.C. 1938 Rep.* 127, *Hb. Lousley*.
R. obtusifolius × **pulcher** was recorded by Little from Hitchin in *B.E.C. 1924 Rep.* 595 and was found at Sarratt Bottom (09/J) in 1964, *Hb. H.M.*
R. obtusifolius × **sanguineus** was found at Hoo Wood, 1966 (01/G), *P. M. Benoit!, Hb. H.M.*

R. pulcher L. (Map 30j) *Fiddle Dock*
Webb and Coleman, 1843
Pastures Native
Rare and following no distribution pattern. Coleman and Little thought that it was particularly frequent in churchyards but this has not been my experience. H.S. 22.

R. sanguineus L. (Map 30k) *Wood Dock* Coleman, 1839
Wood borders, roadside verges, etc.   Native
Generally common. H.S. 16, 21, 32–39, 41, 43–47, 60, 62,
77–80, 82, 88, 93, 95, 100, 103, 105–107.

R. conglomeratus Murr.   (Map 30 l)   *Clustered Dock*
R. acutus sensu Webb & Coleman   Coleman, 1838
Wet places, ditches, etc.   Native
Frequent and well distributed. H.S. 9, 19, 27, 29, 45, 65,
66, 74, 76, 88, 90, 91.

R. palustris Sm.   *Marsh Dock*   Coleman, 1840
R. limosus auct.
Wet places   Native
Frequent in the gravel pits to the south of Hoddesdon but
rare elsewhere; the Node, Codicote, 1955 (21/E), *Hb. H.M.*;
Cock Lane Dump, 1963 (30/V), *Hb. H.M.*; gravel pit,
Broxbourne, 1965 (30/T), *Hb. H.M.*; gravel pit, Hoddesdon,
1966 (30/U); gravel pit near Dobbs Weir, 1966 (30/Z),
gravel pit, near Rye House, 1966 (31/V).

R. maritimus L. *Golden Dock* D. Martha Higgins, 1899
Frequent in the upper stretches of the Lea into which it was
probably introduced from Luton Hoo having been pre-
viously recorded there in 1885 (see *Flora of Bedfordshire*,
306). Its Hertfordshire records are: Coldharbour (11/I)!,
D. M. Higgins, W.E.C. 1899–1900 Rep. 19, *Hb. H.M.*;
Stanborough, 1959 (21/G), *P. C. and J. Hall*!, *Hb. H.M.*;
Batford, 1964 (11/H), *Hb. H.M.*; below Blackbridge, 1965
(11/X), *Hb. H.M.*; Cheshunt Marsh, 1964 (30/R), *Hb. H.M*.
It has also been recorded from Totteridge, 1912, *C. S.
Nicholson*, and St. Margarets, 1933, *A. W. Graveson*, both
in *Kent and Lousley*, 245.

The following have been recorded as casuals. **R. bucepha-
lophorus** L. from Ware by *Druce* in *B.E.C. 1917 Rep.*
126: **R. dentatus** L., Ware, *Druce, B.E.C. 1922 Rep.*
745, *Hb. Druce*; Bulls Mill, 1958 (31/C), *Hb. H.M.*: **R.
obovatus** Danser, Ware, *Druce, B.E.C. 1922 Rep.* 621;
Hitchin, 1932, Little, *Hb. B.M.*: **R. patientia** L. (*R.
consersus* auct.), Hitchin, Little, *B.E.C. 1920 Rep.* 145,
B.E.C. 1922 Rep. 745; Hertford (det. J. E. Lousley), *A. W.
Graveson, Hb. Gr.*: **R. scutatus** L., Hitchin, Bentley,
Phytologist (New Series), 2 (1858), 497: **R. triangulivalvis**
(Danser) Reching. f. (*R. salicifolius* auct.), Hertford,
A. W. Graveson, B.E.C. 1920 Rep. 146, *Hb. Gr.*; Ware,
Druce, B.E.C. 1928 Rep. 757, *Hb. Druce.*

URTICACEAE
Urtica L.
U. dioica L. (Map 30m) *Stinging Nettle* Kalm, 1748
Waste ground, wood borders, old gardens, etc. Native
Very common and often an indication of high nitrogen
content in the soil. H.S. 5, 11, 12, 20, 22, 25, 34–37, 40–45,
56, 60, 63, 65, 74, 80, 82, 105–107.

U. urens L. (Map 30n) *Small Stinging Nettle* Blake, 1820
Arable land, gardens, etc.   Colonist
Frequent in well manured plots but absent or rare in
considerable areas.

Parietaria L.
P. diffusa Mert. & Koch (Map 30o) *Pellitory-of-the-Wall*
                                                Blake, 1820
Old walls and ground at the base of walls   Native
Occasional but well distributed and found most often on
church walls.

Soleirolia soleirolii (Req.) Dandy, *Mind-your-own-
business*, is found rarely in gardens and usually near to
the greenhouses from which it has escaped.

CANNABACEAE
Humulus L.
H. lupulus L.   (Map 31a)   *Hop*   Ellis, 1750
Hedges   Naturalized
Scattered over the county but usually found near to houses
as it was at one time generally cultivated.

Cannabis sativa L., *Hemp*, was recorded by Pryor as a
rare casual. It occurs now as a bird-seed alien on rubbish
dumps and is probably more frequent than at any earlier
period.

ULMACEAE
Ulmus L.
The Hertfordshire elms have caused botanists much
trouble. Webb and Coleman recognised four species but
confessed to 'have paid no great attention to this obscure
genus'. Pryor upheld these species but the editor of his
Flora reduced them to two. Little gave the genus more
attention and allowed for four species and some hybrids.
     Later on the elms were studied more thoroughly by Dr.
R. Melville, some of whose early work on the genus was
done in Hertfordshire. Melville used a biometric method
to distinguish the four species already recognised by earlier
workers: **U. glabra** Huds., **U. procera** Salisb., **U. carpinifolia** Gled. and **U. plotii** Druce (another species, the Cornish
Elm, *U. angustifolia* (Weston) Weston, did not enter
Hertfordshire as a native tree). He described a new species,
U. coritana Melville, the Midland Elm, which was present
in north Hertfordshire. He found that there was also an
'East Anglian Small-leaved Elm' which was undescribed
and entered into the east of the county. Melville allowed for
hybridization between his species and described one new
hybrid, **U. × diversifolia,** the type of which was a tree
on the roadside between Hatfield and Hertford. This has
since been destroyed in converting the road into a dual
carriageway. Dr. Melville gave me great assistance with the
genus in the early years of my work on the flora but I
found it impossible to study the distribution of the various
species on a tetrad basis.
     Still more recently R. H. Richens embarked upon an
independent biometric survey of the elms of Eastern
England. He considers that there are a few species which
are very variable but which can be divided into 'biometri-
cally defined groups'. He thinks that hybrids in elms are
rare. Richens collected a large number of Hertfordshire
elms in the field and in 'Studies on *Ulmus*. III. The Village
Elms of Hertfordshire' *Forestry*, 32, No. 2, 1959, he described seven groups in *U. carpinifolia* and two groups in
U. procera. He considered *U. glabra* also to be present and
that there was one putative hybrid of *U. glabra* and *U.
carpinifolia*.
     Elms are found generally throughout the county and
are more frequent in the east on the Boulder Clay than
elsewhere. *U. procera* is the most common species except
near the Essex border where it is replaced by *U. carpinifolia*.
I regret that I did not make sufficient field records to be
able to present satisfactory distribution maps of any species.

Ficus carica L. (MORACEAE), *Fig*, was recorded by L. J.
Tremayne from Watford Churchyard, growing out of a
tomb, 1924, *Kent and Lousley*, 252. Seen also on tunnel
top, Oakleigh Park, 1966 (29/S), v.c. 20 [G.L.], *Hb. H.M.*

Juglans regia L. (JUGLANDACEAE), *Walnut*, occurs
in fields near farmhouses where it has no doubt been planted. J. E. Little recorded seedlings, presumably bird sown,
in *B.E.C. 1920 Rep.* 147.

BETULACEAE
Betula L.
B. pendula Roth (Map 31b) *Silver Birch* Moses Cook, 1676 (Webb and Coleman, 1851, for the restricted species) *B. verrucosa* Ehrh.
Woods, heaths, etc. Native (but often planted)
Occasional except on the Chalk and Boulder Clay. H.S. 32, 45, 48, 62, 64, 67, 70, 78, 79, 87, 89, 97, 98, 101, 104, 105.

B. pubescens Ehrh. (Map 31c) *Birch*
Webb and Coleman, 1851
Wet heaths, damp parts of woodland, etc. Native
Occasional and generally more tolerant of wettish conditions than *B. pendula*. H.S. 64, 67, 77, 81, 89, 101, 105.

Alnus Mill.
A. glutinosa (L.) Gaertn. (Map 31d) *Alder* Ellis, 1733
Banks of rivers, marshy places near rivers, etc. Native
Frequent in suitable places. There are specimens in *Hb. B.M.* named var. *laciniata* Willd. from Cassiobury Park, 1911, *A. B. Jackson* and from Colney Street, 1921, *H. S. Redgrove*. Similar trees have been seen by me at Oughton Head (13/Q) and at Poplar's Green (21/R). Mr. B. F. C. Sennitt has also reported it from Old Parkbury (10/R).

A. incana (L.) Moench was recorded as an introduced tree at the Folly, Hitchin by Little in *J. Bot. 1923*, 146, *Hb. B.M.*, *Hb. Ph.*

CORYLACEAE
Carpinus L.
C. betulus L. (Map 31e) *Hornbeam, Haybeech* Ellis, 1733
Woods, hedges, etc. Native
Abundant in the southern half of the county where it is native but it is also planted throughout the county. It is rare except as a planted tree in Bedfordshire and Cambridgeshire, and in Hertfordshire it probably reaches the northern limits of its distribution as a native tree in southeastern England. In the area of its greatest abundance it was coppiced frequently and pollarded trees were general but in more recent years with a change in woodland management a greater number of trees are being allowed to grow to their full stature. H.S. 21, 33, 36, 41, 43–45, 47, 48, 52, 53, 60, 64, 67, 77, 78, 80, 81, 93, 94, 99, 103, 105, 106.
Corylus L.
C. avellana L. (Map 31f) *Hazel* Ellis, 1733
Hedgerows, woods, etc. Native
Very common. H.S. 11, 17, 21, 32–34, 36, 37, 39, 45, 46, 51, 52, 61–64, 67, 80, 82, 87, 88, 93, 95, 103, 104, 107.

FAGACEAE
Fagus L.
F. sylvatica L. (Map 31g) *Beech* Ray, 1690
Woods, hedgerows, etc. Native
Common on the Chalk and no doubt native at least in the western part of the county. On the Chalk eastwards from Hexton it has been extensively planted and is less likely to be native. It is scattered over the rest of the county as a planted tree. H.S. 16, 17, 51, 52, 54, 61, 62, 80, 95, 106.

Castanea sativa Mill., *Sweet Chestnut*, occurs only as a planted tree. Ellis in 1742 noted that some large trees had been felled at Ashridge 'some fourteen years since'.

Quercus L.
Q. robur L. (Map 31h) *Common Oak* Ellis, 1733
Q. pedunculata Ehrh. ex Hoffm.
Woods, hedgerows, etc. Native
Common and becoming scarce only on the bare chalk. H.S. 3, 14, 16, 21, 25, 26, 28, 32–37, 39, 44, 47, 48, 50–52, 54–62, 64, 67, 68, 70, 77–79, 86–89, 93, 94, 97–101, 103–105, 107.

Q. petraea (Mattuschka) Liebl. (Map 31i) *Durmast Oak*
Q. sessiliflora Salisb. Webb and Coleman, 1843
This occurs in woods on the more heathy soils but it is doubtful if it exists in the county in a pure state and no doubt most of our trees are hybrids with *Q. robur*. Salisbury recorded the hybrid from Symondshyde Great Wood in *Trans. Herts. N.H.S.* 14 (1912), 301 and considered it to be the dominant tree there and to occur also at Bricket Wood and Hertford Heath. H.S. 57, 64, 103.

Q. cerris L., *Turkey Oak*, occurs scattered over the county as a planted tree and in some remote areas it may have been accidentally introduced. H.S. 11, 64, 69. **Q. ilex** L., *Holm Oak*, occurs only as a planted tree.

SALICACEAE
Populus L.
J. E. Little wrote a very valuable paper on the 'Hertfordshire Poplars' in the *Journal of Botany 1916*, 233–6, and there is not much to add to his conclusions.

P. alba L. (Map 31j) *White Poplar* Ellis, 1750
Hedges, wet meadows, etc. Planted
Rare: Little observed only female trees.

P. canescens (Ait.) Sm. (Map 31k) *Grey Poplar*
Webb and Coleman, 1849
Hedges, damp woods, etc. Planted
More frequent than *P. alba* but still rare. Little, who observed both male and female trees, said that he had seen no evidence that would lead one to think that it is indigenous.

P. canescens × tremula (*P. × hybrida* Bieb.) was recorded by Little from Grove Mill, Hitchin, det. C. E. Moss, in *B.E.C. 1912 Rep.* 286.

P. tremula L. (Map 31 l) *Aspen* Ellis, 1750
Damp woods, heaths, etc. Native
Occasional but well distributed. Little observed trees of both sexes and two varieties. H.S. 39, 42, 61, 78, 87, 89, 97, 104, 105.

P. nigra L., *Black Poplar*, a tree of wet places, was considered by Little to be probably native in the Lower Lea Valley confirming the earlier view of Moses Cook (1676), 'I suppose this (i.e. Water Poplar) is the same which some people call Black Poplar: it growes in several places about Ware by the Ditch sides'. Little gave a few stations for what he considered to be var. **betulifolia** (Pursh) Torr., the native tree.

P. × canadensis Moench (Map 31m) *Black Italian Poplar*
P. serotina Hartig, *P. deltoides × nigra* Little, 1916
Planted throughout the county. Little made notes on trees which he considered to be hybrids of this and various varieties of *P. nigra*.

The following have been recorded as planted trees: **P. italica** Moench, *Lombardy Poplar*; **P. gileadensis** Rouleau (*P. tacamahacca* auct.); **P. × marilandica** Bosc.

Salix L.
I have had much assistance from Mr. R. D. Meikle in dealing with the problems of this difficult genus. Willows are often planted and the trees chosen for planting are usually either selected strains or hybrids and to complicate matters triple hybrids may be encountered. J. E. Little was

as much interested in willows as poplars and his notes have been most useful. In the field my fellow workers and I have recorded the species in their broadest concept and specimens have been taken only when the trees appeared to be widely divergent from this.

S. alba L. (Map 31n) *White Willow* Coleman, 1838
Sides of rivers and ditches Native
Occasional but well distributed. Little recorded var. **vitellina** (L.) Stokes frequently and Meikle has referred a number of my specimens to this.
S. alba × fragilis (*S. × rubens* Schrank *S. alba* var. *caerulea* Sm.), *Cricket-bat Willow*, was recorded by Little and is occasionally planted. Current records include: side of Cheshunt Marsh, 1956 (30/Q) *Hb. H.M.*; gravel pits, Smallford, 1956 (10/Y) *Hb. H.M.*

S. pentandra L., *Bay Willow*, first recorded by Webb and Coleman (1843) occurs only as a planted tree. Recent records are West Mill (i.e. leading to Oughton Head Common), 1920 (13/Q)!, *J. E. Little, B.E.C. 1923 Rep.* 404, *Hb. B.M.*; Tedmanbury Lock, 1961 (41/Y), *J. L. Fielding*; Kimpton Mill, 1956 (11/Z), *Lloyd-Evans! Hb. H.M.*; streamside, Luffenhall, 1955 (22/Z).

S. fragilis L. (Map 31o) *Crack Willow* Coleman, 1838
S. russelliana Sm.
Banks of rivers, sides of ponds, etc. Native
Frequent in those parts of the county where there are rivers. H.S. 108.

S. triandra L. (Map 32a) *Almond Willow* Coleman, 1838
Riversides, ditches, etc. Native
Rare but well distributed. It is easily recognised in flower but may have been overlooked in leaf.

S. purpurea L. (Map 32b) *Purple Willow* Coleman, 1839
River banks and low-lying land by rivers. Native
Occasional but absent from the lower courses of the Lea and Colne. Little recorded *S. purpurea × viminalis* from Purwell in *B.E.C. 1924 Rep.* 738.

S. viminalis L. (Map 32c) *Common Osier* Coleman, 1838
Riversides, disused gravel pits, etc. Mainly planted
Occasional and well distributed. Although this has been extensively planted it may occur also as a self-set tree.

S. caprea L. (Map 32d) *Great Sallow* Ellis, 1750
Hedges, wood borders, etc. Native
Common and widely distributed. H.S. 6, 26, 32, 34, 37–39, 42, 45, 62, 75, 77, 84, 88, 104–106. Meikle has determined as **S. caprea × viminalis** specimens which were collected at Bulls Mill, 1956 (31/C), *Hb. H.M.* and Rowley Green, 1957 (29/D).

S. cinerea L. (Map 32e) *Common Sallow*
Webb and Coleman, 1843
Pondsides, ditches, hedges, etc. Native
A frequent but very variable species. H.S. 26, 31, 33, 35 87, 89, 90, 97, 99, 101, 105, 108; subsp. **cinerea** is to be found in marshy places only e.g. wet depression, Westbury Wood, 1956 (12/M), det. R. D. Meikle, *Hb. H.M.*, but its distribution in the county remains to be studied; subsp. **oleifolia** Macreight (*S. atrocinerea* Brot.) is common in the county and grows in a wide variety of habitats such as streamsides, wood borders, hedgerows, etc. usually, but not invariably, in marshy areas.
S. cinerea × viminalis (*S. × smithiana* Willd.) was recorded by both Coleman and Pryor and by Little from Hitchin in *B.E.C. 1927 Rep.* 589.
S. cinerea × purpurea × viminalis (*S. × forbyana* Sm.) was found at Kimpton Mill, 1956 (11/Z), *Hb. H.M.*

S. aurita L. (Map 32f) *Eared Willow* Coleman, 1839
Wet heathy places Native
Limited to a few stations in which it may be locally frequent. H.S. 89.
S. aurita × caprea (*S. × capreola* J. Kerner ex Anderss.) was recorded from Hitchin by Little in *B.E.C. 1924 Rep.* 739 and from near Dyes Farm, Langley, 1927, *Hb. Ph.*
S. aurita × cinerea (*S. × multinervis* Doell) was recorded by Little from Oughton Head in *B.E.C. 1924 Rep.* 740 and during the present survey recorded from Bricket Wood, 1956 (10/F), *Hb. H.M.* and Aldenham Reservoir, 1956 (19/S) *Hb. H.M.*

S. repens L. subsp. **repens** *Creeping Willow*
Coleman, 1838
Wet heathy places Native
Rare and known to nineteenth-century botanists from only a few stations. Current records are Bricket Wood, 1955 (10/F); Hertford Heath, 1955 (31/K).

S. calodendron Wimm. (*S. acuminata* auct.) a planted tree, Ickleford, *J. E. Little, B.E.C. 1920 Rep.* 397; Brook End, St. Ippolyts, *J. E. Little, B.E.C. 1923 Rep.* 405.

ERICACEAE
Calluna Salisb.
C. vulgaris (L.) Hull (Map 32g) *Heather, Ling*
C. erica DC. Blake, 1819
Heathy ground Native
Occasional in the south of the county. H.S. 57, 58, 64, 68, 70, 81, 85, 86, 97, 98.

Erica L.
E. tetralix L. *Cross-leaved Heath*
Webb and Coleman, 1843
In the nineteenth century this was a very rare native plant of heathy ground mainly in the west of the county. Salisbury found one plant at the Furze Field, Colney Heath, in 1913 and it survived here until about 1927. It was also found by Salisbury at Bricket Wood in 1939, *Trans. Herts. N.H.S.* 21 (1940), 159. Neither Coleman nor Pryor knew it at either Colney Heath or Bricket Wood. A plant found by Mr. F. C. Studley growing on the edge of Moor Park golf course, 1966 (09/W)!, had been apparently planted there.

E. cinerea L. *Bell Heather* Coleman, 1840
This was known to Coleman from Pré Wood and Wigginton Common and may be presumed to have been extinct in both by 1880 as it was not known at all to Pryor. It was found at Bricket Wood in 1939 by R. B. Benson, *Trans. Herts. N.H.S.* 21 (1940), 175.

Vaccinium myrtillus L., *Bilberry*, was first recorded in 1861 by Pidcock from Oxhey Wood and known from here and the adjoining Eastbury Wood by Pryor. Its only recent record is from a patch of rough woodland at the side of Chipperfield Common (00/K)!, *R. B. Benson, Proc. Herts. N.H.S.* 20 (1935), x. I see no reason to suppose that it is not native here as it must also have been at Oxhey Wood.

PYROLACEAE
Pyrola L.
P. minor L. *Wintergreen* Woodward, 1787
Heathy woods Native
Plentiful in Grove Wood and Stubbings Wood (91/A, 90/E), *Hb. H.M.* where it was first recorded by T. Woodward, *Hb. B.M.* There are early records from the Ashridge and Beechwood areas but no recent ones. E. G. Kellett found it in Sherrards Wood (21/G) in 1952. It is still there and possibly native as A. W. Graveson knew it for a number of years at Ayot which is nearby.

P. media Sw. was recorded almost certainly in error from 'beech woods about Tring' on the authority of Pamplin in the *New Botanist's Guide* (1835). P. rotundifolia L. recorded in *Pryor*, 269, on the authority of Pidcock from woods at Redheath (i.e. south of Chandler's Cross (09/T)) needs more certain evidence before it can be claimed as a Hertfordshire species.

MONOTROPACEAE
Monotropa L.
M. hypopitys L.   (Map 32h)   *Yellow Bird's-nest*
Doody, 1696
Parasite on the roots of beech trees and conifers   Native
Very rare and possibly diminishing. **M. hypopitys** sensu stricto appears in the wood at Aldbury Nowers (91/L), *Hb. H.M.* and **M. hypophegea** Wallr. in Grove and Stubbings Woods (91/A, 90/E), *Hb. H.M.* and by the side of Tingley Wood (13/F). Recent records for the aggregate are from Solomon's Wood (09/H) and Bottom Wood (09/G), *R. F. Turney*; wood, south of Baldock (23/L); woods near Church Hill, Therfield Heath (33/J); Offley Holes (12/T).

PRIMULACEAE
Primula L.
P. veris L.   (Map 32i)   *Cowslip*   Isaak Walton, 1653
P. officinalis (L.) Hill
Pastures   Native
Common on the Chalk and diminishing in frequency to become scarce on the least calcareous soils. Near to the London area it appears mainly on railway banks. H.S. 1–3, 5, 13, 18, 24, 25, 28, 67, 73.
P. veris × vulgaris is rare and occurs mainly in woods on the Boulder Clay.

P. elatior (L.) Hill, *Oxlip*, occurs only at Great Hormead Park Wood (42/E), H.S. 36 where it is limited to one part and appears with hybrids with *P. vulgaris*: see Dony, J.G. (1961).

P. vulgaris Huds.   (Map 32j)   *Primrose*   Kalm, 1748
Woods   Native
Frequent in woods on the Boulder Clay and becoming rare elsewhere. H.S. 11, 21, 32, 35, 39, 41, 43–47.

Hottonia L.
H. palustris L.   *Water Violet*   Coleman, 1838
Ponds and ditches   Native
Rare and sometimes originally planted. Recorded during the period of the survey from: pond near Shephall, 1961 (22/L), *A. Carlton Smith*; Hertford Heath (one of Coleman's stations), 1955 (31/K); Watery Grove, 1957 (22/G); Kings Meads, 1956 (31/M), *Hb. H.M.*; Millwards Park, 1960 (20/N); Rowley Green, 1957 (29/H), v.c. 20 [G.L.].

Cyclamen hederifolium Ait., a garden relic, was recorded from Totteridge in *Pryor*, 343 and more recently from a derelict garden at Smaley Wood, Meesden, 1959 (43/L), *J. C. Gardiner*!, *Hb. H.M.*

Lysimachia L.
L. nemorum L.   (Map 32k)   *Wood Pimpernel* Franks, 1819
Woodland rides   Native
Occasional in woods on the London Clay and Clay-with-Flints, rare on the Boulder Clay and river gravels and absent on the Chalk. H.S. 42, 44, 60, 62, 77, 88, 93, 94, 104, 105, 107.

L. nummularia L.   (Map 32 l)   *Creeping Jenny*
Blake, c. 1820
Sides of ditches, woodland rides, etc.   Native
Frequent on the Boulder Clay and occasional elsewhere except on the Clay-with-Flints where it is rare. H.S. 27, 33–35, 42, 44, 46, 47, 74–78, 88, 90, 107.

L. vulgaris L.   *Yellow Loosestrife*   How, 1650
Riversides   Native
Rare and apparently limited to the lower parts of the Colne Valley. Recorded during the period of the present survey from below Moor Park (09/R), *G. Day*; Maple Cross, 1959 (09/G); West Hyde, 1959 (09/L); wet meadow, Bishop's Wood, 1963 (09/Q). It has been recorded as a garden escape e.g. Westland Green (42/F) but may have been confused with the following species.

L. punctata L.   (Map 32n)   *Dotted Loosestrife*   Uncertain
Waste places, sites of old gardens, etc.   Garden escape
Rare and not often established in natural habitats.

Anagallis L.
A. arvensis L. subsp. **arvensis**   (Map 32n)   *Scarlet Pimpernel*   Franks, 1823
Arable fields, gardens, etc.   Native
Very common. H.S. 6, 35, 52, 53, 77. Colour forms have been recorded but not in recent years.
subsp. **foemina** (Mill.) Schinz & Thell. (*A. caerulea* Schreb.)
Blue Pimpernel
This has been recorded but could have been confused with a colour form of subsp. *arvensis*. It is abundant in gardens at Ware and Chorley Wood but in both places it was originally introduced. Salisbury (1933) doubted whether subsp. *foemina* occurs naturally in the county and with this opinion I agree.

A. tenella (L.) L., *Bog Pimpernel*, first recorded by L. Manser, 1835, was known as a native from a few bogs on the edge of the London Clay but in all of these it was presumably extinct when Pryor began his work on the Flora. It was also known from Oughton Head Common and Pollard collected a specimen there in 1868, *Hb. H.M.*, but it may have survived later than this. In 1965 P. M. Benoit rediscovered it in a meadow by Wilstone Reservoir from where it had originally been recorded by H. H. Crewe, c. 1875, *Hb. H.M.*

A. minima (L.) E. H. L. Krause (*Centunculus minimus* L.), *Chaffweed*, a native of wet sandy heaths, was first recorded by Webb and Coleman (1843) and known to them from Colney Heath and Moor Park. It was apparently extinct at both of these by the turn of the century but A. W. Graveson knew it in one station in Broxbourne Woods and saw it there at least until 1931, *Hb. Gr.*

Samolus L.
S. valerandi L.   *Brookweed*   Webb and Coleman, 1843
A very rare native of marshy places and known only from Ashwell Common (a site no longer there) and Oughton Head Common (13/Q). It was found at the latter by E. B. Bangerter in 1956 but I have not seen it there.

Buddleja davidii Franch. (BUDDLEJACEAE) occurs occasionally in waste places as a garden escape or throw-out.

OLEACEAE
Fraxinus L.
F. excelsior L.   (Map 32o)   *Ash*   Coles, 1657
Woods, hedgerows, etc.   Native
Probably the most common Hertfordshire tree. H.S. 14–17, 26, 32–37, 39–49, 54, 56, 60, 61, 63, 67, 78–80, 84, 88, 93–95, 100, 104–107.

Syringa vulgaris L., *Lilac*, was recorded by Little as a garden escape.

Ligustrum L.

L. vulgare L. (Map 33a) *Privet* Coleman, 1838
Hedgerows, wood borders, etc.   Native
Common on the Chalk and occurring also, but less frequently, on chalk exposures, etc. H.S. 4, 33.

L. ovalifolium Hassk., *Garden Privet*, is much planted around houses but does not appear as a wild plant.

APOCYNACEAE
Vinca L.

V. minor L. (Map 33b) *Lesser Periwinkle* Sabine, 1815
Roadsides, wood borders, etc.   Naturalized
Scattered over the county and established because of its shrubby nature.

V. major L.   *Greater Periwinkle* Coles, 1657
Hedgerows and waste places usually near houses
    Garden escape
Less common than *V. minor* and rarely established.

GENTIANACEAE
Centaurium Hill

C. erythraea Rafn (Map 33c) *Centaury* Steele MS.,
Erythraea centaurium auct.   c. 1730
Pastures, woodland rides, etc.   Native
Occasional but well distributed. H.S. 33, 39, 42, 51, 52. 62, 67, 69, 71, 77, 99, 100, 105.

C. pulchellum (Sw.) Druce (*Erythraea pulchella* (Sw.) Fr.), first recorded by Woods in 1805 was rare in clearings in the Broxbourne Woods area. A. W. Graveson knew it there until about 1935 but I have not seen it in the county.

Blackstonia Huds.

B. perfoliata (L.) Huds. (Map 33d) *Yellow-wort*
    Woods, 1805
Bare places on calcareous soils   Native
Rare but most often on the Chalk. It is apparently not able to withstand competition. H.S. 6, 67.

Gentianella Moench

G. amarella (L.) Börner (Map 33e) *Felwort*
Gentiana amarella L.   Parkinson, 1640
Chalk hills   Native
Occasional on the chalk downs and on chalky exposures elsewhere. H.S. 3, 4, 15, 49, 56.

G. germanica (Willd.) Börner (Map 33f) *Chiltern Gentian* Tilden, c. 1700 but more certainly
Gentiana germanica Willd.   Anderson, 1812
This, one of the most attractive plants entering into the Flora, is a native on the western part of the Chalk in places where the soil has been previously disturbed. At Oddy Hill (H.S. 15) it grows with hybrids with *G. amarella*. See also Salisbury (1914). H.S. 15, 50.

G. anglica (Pugsl.) E. F. Warb. (*Gentiana amarella* var. *praecox* of Pryor's Flora, 274) was recorded from Tring, 1849, by E. Forster, *Hb. B.M.* It was also recorded by Charles Oldham but with no station given (*Salisbury, Trans. Herts. N.H.S.* 16 (1916), 77). It is well known on Pitstone Hill, immediately over the county boundary in Buckinghamshire, and we await a more satisfactory record for Hertfordshire.

G. campestris (L.) Börner (*Gentiana campestris* L.) a native of wet gravelly pastures was first recorded for the county by Gerard, 1597. It was known to nineteenth-century botanists from Colney Heath (spec. 1859, *H. Peirson, Hb. Gr.*) and Nomansland. It was last recorded in the county by Crespigny, 1877.

MENYANTHACEAE
Menyanthes L.

M. trifoliata L.   *Bogbean* Steele MS., c. 1730
This was recorded by nineteenth-century botanists as frequent as a native species in peaty marshes and upland ponds but it was probably introduced into a number of the latter. During the period of the present survey it has gone from ponds at Bovingdon (00/B) and Bayford (30/E) into each of which it may have been introduced. I have not seen it at Oughton Head Common (13/Q) – a native station – since 1956. It is still at Sarratt Bottom (09/J) and may survive at Noake Mill (00/P), a station which was shown to me by R. B. Benson.

Nymphoides peltata (S. G. Gmel.) Kuntze (*Limnanthemum peltatum* S. G. Gmel.) was recorded by Webb (1857) as an introduced plant on Totteridge Green. See also *Pryor, 277.*

Polemonium caeruleum L. (POLEMONIACEAE) was recorded as a garden escape in *Pryor, 278,* and from Hertford Heath by J. W. Higgens in *B.E.C. 1916 Rep.* 495.

BORAGINACEAE
Cynoglossum L.

C. officinale L.   *Hound's-tongue* Alchorne, 1751
Rough pastures   Native
Rare as it always has been. Current records are: edge of Tingley Wood (13/F), first recorded by Little, *Hb. H.M.*; Anchusa Pit (31/M)!, first recorded by A. W. Graveson; Bayfordbury (31/A), A. G. Brown and H. Williams; gravel pit, Bunker's Hill (30/E); gravel pit near Broxbourne Station, 1965 (30/T), *Hb. H.M.*

C. germanicum Jacq. (*C. montanum* auct.) was recorded as a native in *Pryor, 291,* but not since. Its only certain record was from Cassiobury Park, 1857, by Pidcock.

Anchusa L.

A number of species of Anchusa were discovered in 1907 in a disused gravel pit near Ware Park. These persisted for a number of years and the site became known to local botanists as the Anchusa Pit. Many names were applied to these plants: *A. officinalis* L., *Hb. Gr.*; *A. undulata* L., *Hb. Gr.*; *A. italica* Retz., *Hb. Gr.*; *A. hybrida* Ten. (*A. barrelerii* Vitm.), *Hb. Gr.*; *A. azurea* Mill., *Hb. Gr.*; *A. ochroleuca* Bieb. and *A. procera* Bess. ex Link; but interesting as the colony may have been it is doubtful if so many species were involved. One, which I take to be **A. azurea**, *Hb. H.M.*, is still there.

A. officinalis may be naturalized near old gardens e.g. Hitchin, c. 1952, *G. L. Evans, Hb. H.M.*

Lycopsis L.

L. arvensis L. (Map 33i) *Bugloss* Coleman, 1838
Rough ground, field borders, etc.   Colonist
Mainly on the Lea Gravels where it is occasional.

Pulmonaria officinalis L., *Lungwort*, has appeared only as a garden escape, see *Pryor, 284.*

Myosotis L.

M. scorpioides L. (Map 33j) *Water Forget-me-not*
M. palustris (L.) Hill   Blake, c. 1820
Riversides, ditches, ponds, etc.   Native
Frequent in the lower-lying areas. H.S. 8, 66, 76, 91, 108.

M. secunda A. Murr. (*M. repens* auct.) was first recorded by Coleman in 1844, *Hb. Druce,* as a rare native and was known to Webb and him from a few bogs between Bell Bar and Little Berkhampstead. Its last certain record was by Pryor, c. 1880.

M. caespitosa K. F. Schultz (Map 33k) *Tufted Forget-me-not* Franks, 1820
Ponds and wet marshy places   Native
Frequent on the London Clay and occasional on the Boulder Clay. Rare or absent by rivers.
M. caespitosa × scorpioides. Braughing, 1965 (32/X), *P. M. Benoit, Hb. H.M.*

M. sylvatica Hoffm.   (Map 33 l)   *Wood Forget-me-not* Pryor, 1875
Woods and shady places by rivers, damp woods, etc.   Native
Locally plentiful by the Ash just as Pryor found it to be. H.S. 45. Otherwise it appears occasionally as a garden escape but it does not become established.

M. arvensis (L.) Hill   (Map 33m)   *Field Forget-me-not*
M. intermedia Link ex K. F. Schultz   Coleman, 1838
Edges of arable fields, woodland rides, waste places, etc.   Native
Common and growing in a variety of habitats in none of which can it survive competition. Pryor was interested in its variability which is apparently mainly in its size. H.S. 22, 25, 33, 35, 37, 39, 41, 46, 52, 56, 77, 80, 100, 105.

M. discolor Pers. (Map 33n)   *Changing Forget-me-not*
M. versicolor Sm.   Coleman, 1838
Bare gravelly ground   Native
Occasional and found mainly on the Lea Gravels. H.S. 22, 69, 96.

M. ramosissima Rochel (Map 33o) *Early Forget-me-not*
M. collina auct.   Coleman, 1838
Bare gravelly ground   Native
Having a similar distribution to *M. discolor* but found most often on railway banks.

Omphalodes verna Moench, *Blue-eyed Mary*, was recorded, presumably as a garden escape, in *Pryor*, 291, see also *B.E.C. 1920 Rep.* 135. **Asperugo procumbens** L., has been recorded as a casual e.g. Hertford, 1878, *R. T. Andrews, Hb. B.M.*; Cole Green, 1922, *A. W. Graveson, Hb. Gr.* See also *Pryor*, 291.

Symphytum L.
S. officinale L.   (Map 33g)   *Comfrey*   Blake, 1819
Sides of rivers, wet places, etc.   Native
Occasional and found mainly near the larger rivers.

S. asperum Lepech. (*S. asperrimum* Donn ex Sims) is naturalized by the side of Easneye Park (31/RW)!, *D. McClintock, Hb. H.M.*

S. × uplandicum Nyman (Map 33h) *Russian Comfrey*
S. asperum × officinale, S. peregrinum auct.   Little, 1909
This was introduced as a fodder crop towards the end of the nineteenth century and is now found occasionally and well distributed in the county on roadsides and in waste places.

S. tuberosum L.   *Tuberous Comfrey*
    Webb and Coleman, 1843
This is probably of garden origin but persists for many years, as in Coleman's original station at Thundridge old church (31/T)!, *Hb. H.M.* Other current records are: Symondshyde Great Wood (11/V)!, *T. G. Skinner*; Newfield Hill, 1965 (23/L), *J. Adams and B. Clay, Hb. H.M.*; roadside, Sawbridgeworth, 1966 (41/X), *J. L. Fielding.*

S. orientale L. was recorded as a naturalized plant at Hitchin by Little, 1927, *Hb. B.M.* and still persists in a few places in the town.

Borago officinalis L., *Borage*, first recorded by Coleman, 1839, occurs occasionally on rubbish heaps, sites of old gardens, etc. but rarely persists. **Pentaglottis sempervirens** (L.) Tausch (*Anchusa sempervirens* L.) a garden escape first recorded by Webb and Coleman, 1843, may become established as around the village of Barley (33/Z, 43/E).

Lithospermum L.
L. arvense L.   (Map 34a)   *Corn Gromwell*   Franks, 1822
Arable fields   Colonist
Frequent in cornfields on the Chalk and Boulder Clay.

L. officinale L.   *Common Gromwell*   Maria Ransom, c. 1839
Hedges, field borders, etc.   Native
Rare and recorded during the survey from near Pirton Hall, 1966 (13/G), *F. Bentley*; Easneye, one of Coleman's original stations, 1955 (31/R); near Manor Farm, Hinxworth, 1963 (24/F), *Hb. H.M.*

Echium L.
E. vulgare L.   (Map 34b)   *Viper's Bugloss*   Ellis, 1750
Rough gravelly ground   Native
Rare but to be found on both the river and glacial gravels.

E. italicum L. was recorded from Ware, 1907, by C. G. Trower in *B.E.C. 1917 Rep.* 39, *Hb. Druce, Hb. Gr.*

The following are recorded as casuals: **Amsinckia lycopsioides** (Lehm.) Lehm. (*Benthamia lycopsioides* Lehm.), Ware, Hayllar, *B.E.C. 1915 Rep.* 274: **A. intermedia** Fisch. & Mey. (*Benthamia intermedia* (Fisch. & Mey.) Druce) Ware, *Trower and Druce, B.E.C. 1915 Rep.* 274: **A. angustifolia** Lehm., St. Albans, *A. Dickinson, Trans. Herts. N.H.S.* 17 (1921), 248: **Cerinthe gymnandra** Gasp., garden, Great Amwell, 1943, *Mr. Stevens, Hb. B.M.*: **Heliotropium europaeum** L., Ware, *Mrs. Wedgwood, B.E.C. 1921 Rep.* 389: **Lappula myosotis** Moench (*L. echinata* Gilib., *Echinospermum lappula* (L.) Lehm.) records include, near Hertford, 1875, *T. B. Blow, Hb. B.M.*; Limbrick Hall, Harpenden, 1917, *Salisbury, Trans. Herts. N.H.S.* 17 (1919), 145; Totteridge, v.c. 20 [G.L.], 1925, *J. E. Cooper in Kent and Lousley,* 191.

CONVOLVULACEAE
Convolvulus L.
C. arvensis L.   (Map 34c)   *Bindweed*   Blake, 1824
Arable land, roadsides, etc.   Colonist
A very common and persistent weed. H.S. 5, 6, 24, 50, 59, 67, 83. A form with a dissected corolla c.f. var. *stonestreetii* Druce persisted for many years near Baldock!, *R. Morse, Hb. H.M.*

Calystegia R. Br.
C. sepium (L.) R. Br.   (Map 34d)   *Great Bindweed* Ellis, 1750
Hedgerows   Native
Common in the south of the county and frequent elsewhere.

C. silvatica (Kit.) Griseb. (Map 34e) *American Bindweed* A. W. Graveson, 1916
Hedgerows, waste places, etc.   Colonist
Occasional and found most often near to towns and on rubbish dumps. It presents many difficulties as it hybridizes freely with *C. sepium* giving rise to a wide range of intermediates.

C. dahurica (Herbert) G. Don is of recent introduction and has been seen in the following tetrads: 23/A, 22/GQ*, 32/G, 21/P*, 41/J, 00/RS, 20/A, 30/LS, 19/Z*, 29/HI; * indicates a specimen in Herb. Hitchin Museum determined by Dr. S. M. Walters.

Cuscuta L.
C. epithymum (L.) L. *Common Dodder* Coales, c. 1836
C. trifolii Bab.
Parasite on various plants including *Ulex* and clovers. Native
Earlier botanists found this rarely on *Ulex* and more often
on clover the seed of which they thought had been imported. The only recent record is from Chorley Wood, 1961,
(09/I), *Hb. H.M.* where R. F. Turney found it as a parasite
mainly on *Medicago lupulina*.

C. europaea L., *Greater Dodder*, a parasite on stinging
nettle and hops, was first recorded by J. Coales in 1839.
It was reported a few times in the mid-nineteenth century
but usually wrongly identified (see *Pryor*, 279).

C. epilinum Weihe, *Flax Dodder*, was first recorded from
Hertford by L. Manser, c. 1835, *Hb. H.M.* and known in
the nineteenth century as a rare parasite. It was last recorded
in 1921 by J. E. Little from Ashwell, *Hb. B.M.*, *Hb. Camb.*
C. suaveolens was recorded in *Pryor*, 281, but there is
doubt as to what was intended.

Ipomoea batatas (L.) Lam., *Sweet Potato*, *Yam*, was found
on Hitchin U.D.C. Dump, 1964 (13/V), *Hb. H.M.*

SOLANACEAE
Lycium L.
L. halimifolium Mill. *Duke of Argyll's Tea Tree*
Little, 1917
Hedgerows Originally planted
Occasional. To this should be referred the early records of
L. chinense Mill. which itself awaits record in the county.

Nicandra physalodes (L.) Gaertn. is a rare casual of waste
places e.g. Garston (10/A), *W. F. Buckle*; near Digswell,
1966 (21/M), *B. E. Jennings*; dump, Hilfield Lane, 1961
(19/N), *B. Sheasby*; Cock Lane Dump, 1965 (30/U); Park
Street Dump, 1965 (10/L).

Atropa L.
A. bella-donna L. (Map 34f) *Deadly Nightshade*
Blackstone, 1737
Old chalk pits and waste places on the Chalk Colonist
Occasional and often well established on the Chalk in the
west of the county. Until recently it was cultivated at
Hitchin which may account for its present frequency in the
immediate neighbourhood.

Hyoscyamus L.
H. niger L. (Map 34g) *Henbane* Franks, 1820
Waste ground, roadsides, etc. Colonist
More widely distributed than *Atropa bella-donna* but rarely
established for any length of time.

H. albus L., a casual, was recorded from Hitchin by Little
in *B.E.C. 1934 Rep.* 833.

Physalis alkekengi L. occurs only as a garden escape e.g.
waste ground near Aldenham, 1955 (19/I): **P. peruviana**
L. was recorded from Radlett by N. E. G. Cruttwell in
B.E.C. 1939–40 Rep. 286 and **P. angulata** L. from Great
Wymondley as a wool adventive in *B.E.C. 1929 Rep.* 127.

Solanum L.
S. dulcamara L. (Map 34h) *Woody Nightshade*, *Bittersweet*
Blake, 1818
Hedges, damp and shady places Native
Very common. H.S. 17, 20, 36, 37, 77, 95, 99, 107, 108.

S. nigrum L. (Map 34i) *Black Nightshade* Coleman, 1838
Gardens, cultivated land, waste places, etc. Colonist
Well distributed and to be found most frequently in town
gardens or in root crops. A distinct form cf. var. *chloro-*

carpon (Spenn.) Boiss. is well established on Blackbridge
Dump (11/X), *Hb. H.M.*

S. triflorum Nutt. was recorded from Hertford by A.
W. Graveson in *B.E.C. 1919 Rep*, 668 *Hb. Gr.*: **S.
sisymbrifolium** Lam. from Harpenden by H. F. Barnes
in *B.E.C. 1941–2 Rep.* 497, *Hb. B.M.*; Pocock's Farm,
Bishop's Stortford, *C. S. Coleman*, 1951, *Hb. J. F. Fielding*:
S. sarrachoides Sendtn. and **S. americanum** Mill. are
found regularly on Blackbridge Dump (11/X), *Hb. H.M.*

Datura L.
D. stramonium L. (Map 34j) *Thorn Apple*
D. inermis Juss. ex Jacq. Webb and Coleman, 1843
A plant which never fails to attract attention when found.
It has been recorded occasionally but follows no distribution
pattern.

SCROPHULARIACEAE
Verbascum L.
V. thapsus L. (Map 34k) *Aaron's Rod, Mullein*
Ellis, 1736
Waste ground, cleared woodland, etc. Native
Occasional and although well distributed it occurs too
frequently in artificial habitats to be claimed as a certain
native species.

V. nigrum L. (Map 34l) *Dark Mullein* Hill, 1756
Waste ground, cleared woodland, roadsides, etc. Native
Occasional on the Chalk and river gravels.

Verbascums set seed freely and may become established for
a number of years when introduced into a favourable
habitat. It is a critical genus and I wish to thank Mr. J. E.
Lousley for his assistance in naming my material. The
following are recorded: **V. blattaria** L., *Moth Mullein*,
Ware, *Hayllar*, *Trans. Herts. N.H.S.* 16 (1916), 78; Park
Street Dump, 1965 (10/L), *Hb. H.M.*; see also *Pryor*, 296:
V. chaixii Vill., Ware, *J. W. Higgens*, *B.E.C. 1919 Rep.*
669: **V. lychnitis** L., *White Mullein*, chalkpit, Hitchin
Station, *Little*, *B.E.C. 1916 Rep.* 495, *Hb. Camb.*; Ware,
Trower and Druce, *B.E.C. 1917 Rep.* 118; disused station, St.
Albans, 1957 (10/N); see also *Pryor*, 296: **V. pulverulentum**
Vill., *Hoary Mullein*, Hertford, 1908, *A. W. Graveson*, *Hb.
Gr.*; Ware, *Trower and Druce*, *B.E.C. 1916 Rep.* 495: **V.
phlomoides** L. was recorded occasionally by Little e.g.
Hitchin, *B.E.C. 1926 Rep.* 126, *Hb. Camb.*; current records
are Theobalds Lane, Cheshunt, 1953, *C. H. Morgan*, *Hb.
Camb.*; Baldock rubbish dump, 1960 (23/H); Cole Green
Dump, 1962 (21/Q); Rickmansworth U.D.C. Dump,
1965 (09/M), *Hb. H.M.*: **V. speciosum** Schrad., Hitchin,
Little, *W.E.C. 1930–31 Rep.* 79: **V. × thapsi** L. (*V. lychnitis*
× *thapsus*), Hitchin, *Little*, *W.E.C. 1931–32 Rep.* 132: **V.
virgatum** Stokes, *Twiggy Mullein*, Engineer's sidings,
Hitchin, 1964 (22/E), *Hb. H.M.*; see also *Pryor*, 296.

Misopates orontium (L.) Raf. (*Antirrhinum orontium* L.),
Lesser Snapdragon, first recorded by Webb, 1838, was in the
nineteenth century a rare colonist of gravelly fields. The
only current record is from Bayfordbury, 1957, by A. G.
Brown and H. Williams. **Antirrhinum majus** L., *Common Snapdragon*, was first recorded by L. Manser, 1838,
and is still a wall denizen at Hertford Castle and Rickmansworth.

Linaria Mill.
L. vulgaris Mill. (Map 34m) *Common Toadflax*
Franks, 1822
Roadsides, rough grassland, railway sidings, etc. Native
Common on the Chalk and river gravels but very rare on
the Boulder Clay. H.S. 4, 6, 83.

L. repens (L.) Mill. (Map 34n) *Pale Toadflax* Eales, 1696,
L. decumbens Moench   more certainly T. B. Blow, 1873
Railway ballast, waste ground on chalk, etc.   Colonist
Locally frequent on railway tracks and especially so on the
line between Luton and Welwyn Garden City.

L. repens × vulgaris occurs with both parents e.g. railway, Letchworth, 1963 (23/G); railway, Boreham Wood,
1965 (19/Y).

L. purpurea (L.) Mill. was first recorded in Pryor's Flora
and is now frequent as a garden escape on rubbish dumps.

Chaenorhinum (DC.) Reichb.

C. minus (L.) Lange   (Map 34o)   *Small Toadflax*
Linaria minor (L.) Desf.,   Woodward, 1787
L. viscida Moench
Arable fields, railway tracks, etc.   Colonist
Occasional as a weed in chalky fields and common on the
permanent way on railways. H.S. 52, 53.

Kickxia Dumort.

K. spuria (L.) Dumort. (Map 35a) *Round-leaved Fluellen*
Linaria spuria (L.) Mill.   J. Woods, 1805
Arable fields, mainly those under root crops   Colonist
Frequent on the Chalk and Boulder Clay. H.S. 35, 52, 53.

K. elatine (L.) Dumort. (Map 35b) *Sharp-leaved Fluellen*
Linaria elatine (L.) Mill.   Franks, 1820
In similar habitats to and often growing with *K. spuria*.
                                                          Colonist
This was considered by Coleman to be more common than
K. spuria but it appears now to be less common but more
widely distributed. H.S. 52.

Cymbalaria Hill

C. muralis Gaertn., Mey. & Scherb.   (Map 35c) *Ivy-*
Linaria cymbalaria (L.) Mill.   *leaved Toadflax*
                                                        Parkinson, 1640
Walls, also rarely on waste ground   Colonist
Occasional except in the more rural areas.

Scrophularia L.

S. nodosa L. (Map 35d) *Common Figwort* Blake, c. 1820
Woods, shady hedgerows, etc.   Native
Frequent in the more wooded parts of the county. H.S.
34, 35, 39, 41, 42, 45, 80, 88, 105.

S. auriculata L. (Map 35e) *Water Figwort* Blake, 1819
S. aquatica auct.
Riversides, ditches, etc.   Native
Frequent by water throughout the county. H.S. 8, 9, 18, 30,
31, 65, 66, 74, 76, 100.

S. vernalis L., *Yellow Figwort*, first recorded by Webb
and Coleman (1843) was known to them from Hertford
and Hatfield Park. It has persisted at the latter and is still
there in a few shady places. In other places it has not become
established e.g. near Mardley Heath, c. 1960, *D. Stanbridge*;
Harpenden Common, 1963 (11/L), *Mrs. Clark.*

Mimulus L.

M. guttatus DC. *(Map 35f)* *Monkey Flower* I. Brown,
M. luteus sensu Pryor   c. 1843
Riversides, sides of artificial lakes, etc.   Colonist
Occasional by some of the larger rivers but very rarely
established for more than a few years.

M. moschatus Dougl. ex Lindl. was recorded, from mud
dredged from the river at Hertford, by A. W. Graveson in
B.E.C. 1920 Rep. 138, *Hb. Gr.*

Limosella L.

L. aquatica L., *Mudwort*, a rare native of margins of
ponds, etc. was first recorded by Webb and Coleman (1843).
It is now known only from Tring Reservoirs (91/B)!
H.S. 20, *Hb. H.M.* where it was first found by Salisbury –
see *Trans. Herts. N.H.S.* 17 (1919), 143.

Digitalis L.

D. purpurea L.   (Map 35g)   *Foxglove*   Coles, 1657
Woods and scrub on heathy soils   Native
Frequent on the Clay-with-Flints, river gravels and London
Clay but rare on the Chalk and Boulder Clay.

Veronica L.

V. beccabunga L. (Map 35h) *Brooklime* Coleman, 1838
Wet places   Native
Frequent in suitable habitats. H.S. 9, 18, 19, 29, 33, 34, 65,
66, 74, 76, 77, 91.

V. anagallis-aquatica L. (Map 35i) *Blue Water Speedwell*
                                                    Coleman, 1838
Running water and also rarely in ponds and wet woodland
rides   Native
Occasional but widely distributed. Little considered it to be
variable and named a number of forms. H.S. 20, 66.

V. anagallis-aquatica × catenata was recorded from
Tringford Reservoir (91/B) by I. A. Williams in *J. Bot. 1929*,
24, and is still there. It is plentiful in the Gade between
Great Gaddesden and Hemel Hempstead and occurs also
by the Ash near Wareside, 1964 (31/X), *P. M. Benoit*!,
Hb. H.M.

V. catenata Pennell   (Map 35j)   *Pink Water Speedwell*
V. aquatica Bernh.   Little, 1911
By sides of ponds rather than rivers but often growing with
V. anagallis-aquatica   Native
Rare and found usually in the east of the county.

V. scutellata L. (Map 35k) *Marsh Speedwell* Franks, 1820
Sides of ponds in heathy areas   Native
Rare and probably diminished with the filling in of ponds.
It has now an unusual distribution as it survives in some
of the less heathy areas. H.S. 108.

V. officinalis L. (Map 35 l) *Heath Speedwell* Coles, 1657
Dry banks, clearings in woods, etc.   Native
Occasional in the more heathy parts of the county. H.S.
26, 41, 62, 69, 70, 72, 80, 100, 105.

V. montana L.   (Map 35m)   *Wood Speedwell*
                                                    Coleman, 1838
Woodland rides   Native
Frequent but avoiding the Chalk and the more calcareous
parts of the Boulder Clay. It is interesting to note that it is
rare in Cambridgeshire and north Bedfordshire. H.S. 43,
44, 77, 94, 95.

V. chamaedrys L.   (Map 35n)   *Germander Speedwell*
                                                    Blake, 1818
Pastures, wood borders, banks, etc.   Native
Very common. H.S. 5, 11, 14, 17, 21, 22, 24, 25, 28, 32,
33, 35, 39, 41, 42, 44, 45, 47, 52–56, 59, 60, 62, 63, 65–67,
69, 70, 77, 78, 80, 82, 88, 95, 103–105, 107.

V. serpyllifolia L.   (Map 35o)   *Thyme-leaved Speedwell*
                                                    Blake, 1820, Franks, 1820
Lawns, edges of cultivated fields, banks, etc.   Native
Frequent and well distributed. H.S. 33, 37, 41, 42, 44, 45, 69,
77, 80, 100.

V. arvensis L. (Map 36a) *Wall Speedwell* Blake, 1820
Bare ground, gravelly pastures, edges of cultivated fields, etc. Native
Common. H.S. 4, 19, 22, 52, 55, 65, 69, 83.

V. hederifolia L. (Map 36b) *Ivy-leaved Speedwell*
Coleman, 1838
Arable fields, bare banks by roadsides and edges of woods.
Colonist
Very common. H.S. 22.

V. persica Poir. (Map 36c) *Common Field Speedwell*
V. buxbaumii Ten., non Schmidt Webb and Coleman, 1843
Cultivated land, waste places, etc. Colonist
This was a recent introduction when Webb and Coleman first recorded it. H.S. 35, 52, 53.

V. polita Fr. (Map 36d) *Grey Field Speedwell*
V. didyma auct. Blake (as V. agrestis), 1820
In similar situations to *V. persica* Colonist
Occasional but well distributed and tending to be more common on the poorer soils. H.S. 53.

V. agrestis L. (*Map 36e*) *Green Field Speedwell*
Kalm, 1748; but more certainly Coleman, 1843
Cultivated ground Colonist
Occasional and more plentiful in the south of the county than elsewhere. Little asserted that it is 'limited to gardens and never found in arable fields', *W.E.C. 1927–8 Rep.* 437. I have found it frequently in gardens but also in other well-worked and heavily manured soils.

V. filiformis Sm. (Map 36f) *Slender Speedwell*
H. D. Garside, 1952.
Lawns, pastures with short grass, garden plots, etc.
Colonist
This had already become a noxious weed in Hertfordshire when I became interested in the Flora in 1955. It appears to be still increasing.

Pedicularis L.
P. sylvatica L. (Map 36g) *Lousewort* Woodward, 1787
Wet heathy pastures Native
Probably a little more rare than it was a century ago but still surviving in a number of places. H.S. 72, 98.

P. palustris L. *Red Rattle* Coleman, 1838
A rare native of marshes which was known to earlier workers from a number of stations in the Lea and Colne Valleys but from these sites I have no recent records. It survived at Walsworth Common, Hitchin, until at least 1927, *Hb. Ph.*, *Hb. H.M.* The only place I have seen it is Sarratt Bottom (09/J) where it was shown to me by R. B. Benson.

Rhinanthus L.
R. minor L. (Map 36h) *Yellow Rattle* Ellis, 1733
Pastures Native
Occasional but well distributed. It has probably decreased as Coleman and Pryor considered it to be common. H.S. 73, 76.

R. major Ehrh. was recorded by Salisbury from Radlett in *B.E.C. 1921 Rep.* 392 and by Little from Pirton, 1925. A specimen collected by Blake from Crocket (sic) Hall, 1822, *Hb. Druce* was referred to R. apterus (Fr.) Ostenf. in *B.E.C. 1912 Rep.* 214. A specimen of Blake's from Brocket Hall, 1822, Hb. Druce appears to be *R. minor*. It is possible that a close examination of herbarium material and of colonies in the field may establish the Greater Yellow Rattle (R. serotinus (Schönh.) Oborny), which is now considered to be synonymous with R. major and R. apterus, as an unquestioned Hertfordshire species.

Melampyrum L.
M. pratense L. (Map 36i) *Common Cow-wheat*
Coleman, 1838
Woods and shady places on heathy soils Native
Occasional and very local. H.S. 97, 103.

M. cristatum L. *Crested Cow-wheat* I. Brown, 1838
Roadside verges and woodland borders Native
Rare and limited to the Boulder Clay where it has decreased no doubt in part due to changing policies with regard to the maintenance of roadside verges. An early record from woods near Northchurch Common by Chambers (1838) may have been in error. Current records are: roadside between Great Hormead and Brent Pelham, 1954 (33/F)!, *G. L. Evans*; waste heap near Hare Street, 1961 (33/Z), *Lloyd-Evans*!; roadside near Philpotts Wood, (33/H), *Lloyd-Evans*.

M. arvense L. may be claimed as a Hertfordshire plant only on the evidence of H. Fordham's record from near Ashwell, 1840, see *Webb and Coleman*, 212; *Pryor*, 314.

Euphrasia L.
E. nemorosa (Pers.) Wallr. (Map 36j) *Eyebright* Blake, 1820, for the aggregate, Little, 1914, for the restricted species
Pastures Native
This is the common Hertfordshire eyebright and it is to be found most frequently in calcareous pastures. H.S. 3, 4.

E. pseudokerneri Pugsl. (Map 36k) Little, 1922
Chalk hills Native
Locally plentiful on chalk downland. H.S. 15, 49.

E. borealis Wettst. was recorded from a meadow near Welbury Farm, 1911, det. C. Bucknall by Little (see *Little MS.*)

Odontites Ludw.
O. verna (Bellardi) Dumort. (Map 36 l) *Red Bartsia*
Rudge, c. 1810
Rough grassy places, edges of arable fields, etc. Native
Frequent on the more calcareous soils but rare on the river gravels H.S. 11, 42, 71, 78–80, 91. This is a variable species and the distribution of the two subspecies has not been fully worked out but it appears that subsp. **serotina** Corb. is the common form in Hertfordshire and that subsp. **verna** is occasional.

Parentucellia viscosa (L.) Caruel (*Bartsia viscosa* L.), *Yellow Bartsia*, was recorded by E. J. Salisbury from the Node, Codicote, (22/A) in *J. Bot. 1938*, 68, but the means of its introduction was not known.

OROBANCHACEAE
Lathraea L.
L. squamaria L. (Map 36m) *Toothwort*
Woods (see Pryor, 317), 1813
Woods, hedges, etc. Parasite on the roots of hazel and elm
Native
Rare and mainly on the Clay-with-Flints.

L. clandestina L., *Purple Toothwort*, a parasite on roots of poplar in wet wooded places is recorded as naturalized in Knebworth House garden, 1935, *Hb. Letch. Mus.* and in Whitney Wood, 1954 (22/I)!, *M. J. Clarke, Hb. B.M., Hb. H.M.*

Orobanche L.
O rapum-genistae Thuill. *Greater Broomrape*
O. major sensu Webb and Coleman L. Manser, 1838
A parasite on broom Native
Very rare and formerly known at Colney Heath and a number of places in the Hertford–Hatfield area. I have

seen it only by the side of Burleigh Meadow (22/G), *Hb. B.M.*, a well known station. It disappeared after the severe winter of 1962–3 but it may come back again.

O. elatior Sutton　　(Map 36n)　　*Tall Broomrape*
O. major sensu Pryor　　　　　　　　　Sabine, 1815
A parasite on *Centaurea scabiosa*　　　　　　Native
Frequent on the Chalk and chalky Boulder Clay to the east of the Hitchin Gap: rare elsewhere. H.S. 4.

O. minor Sm.　(Map 36o)　*Lesser Broomrape*　Blake, 1822
Parasite on a number of plants but mainly on clover. Native Occasional and more widely distributed than *O. elatior*. H.S. 6.

O. purpurea Jacq. (*Phelypaea caerulea* (Vill.) C. A. Mey.), *Purple Broomrape*, a parasite on *Achillea millefolium*, was first recorded by Coleman from Hoddesdon in 1839. It was a feature of a small area here and Hayllar watched its gradual disappearance. He did not see it after 1938.

A specimen collected by Blake at the Hoo, Welwyn, 1822, *Hb. Druce* was referred to O. picridis F. W. Schultz ex Koch in *B.E.C. 1912 Rep.* 215. A close examination shows that it is *O. minor* as Blake had considered it to be.

LENTIBULARIACEAE
Pinguicula L.
P. vulgaris L.　　　*Butterwort*　　　Gerard, 1597
Boggy places　　　　　　　　　　　　　　Native
Previously recorded for a few moorish places scattered over the county and apparently last seen about 1880.

Utricularia L.
U. vulgaris L.　　*Greater Bladderwort*　　Franks, 1820
A very rare native of deep pools on heathy ground. It persisted in a pond on Broxbourne Common and Hayllar has seen it here within the past five years. In 1965 B. P. Pickess found it in a vegetative state in a pond on Batchworth Heath where it may have been introduced by birds.

VERBENACEAE
Verbena L.
V. officinalis L.　　(Map 37a)　　*Vervain*　　Blake, 1819
Roadsides, rough grassland, etc.　　　　　　　Colonist
Occasional but well distributed.

LABIATAE
Mentha L.
Mentha is one of the more difficult genera entering into the flora owing to the hybrid nature of cultivated mints. This is further complicated by an imperfect knowledge of the morphological limits of the species responsible for the hybrids. Most of my early gatherings were examined by the late R. A. Graham and the more recent ones by Dr. R. M. Harley whom I wish also to thank for his advice on the treatment of the genus.

M. pulegium L., *Pennyroyal*, first recorded by Coleman in 1839 was rare on wet ground in various parts of the county in the nineteenth century. It was last recorded in 1926 from Brickendon by Hayllar.

M. arvensis L.　(Map 37b)　*Field Mint*　Coleman, 1838
Arable fields and also frequently in woodland rides
　　　　　　　　　　　　　　　　　　　　Native
Frequent and well distributed. H.S. 33, 34, 38, 39, 42, 77, 78, 80, 94, 105, 108.
M. × gentilis L. (*M. arvensis* × *spicata*)
This is of garden origin and found as a rare plant on rubbish dumps. Current records are: Reed End, 1962 (33/N), *Hb. H.M.*; Bishop's Stortford, 1961 (42/V)!,

J. L. Fielding, Hb. H.M.; dump at Calais Wood, 1965, *Hb. H.M.* These were all referred to var. *gracilis* (Sole) Fraser.

M. aquatica L.　　(Map 37c)　　*Water Mint*　Blake, 1819
M. hirsuta Huds.
Riversides, ponds, etc.　　　　　　　　　　Native
Frequent and well distributed. H.S. 8, 10, 18–20, 27, 29–31, 37, 65, 66, 74, 76, 99, 100.
M. × verticillata L. (*M. aquatica* × *arvensis*)　(Map 37d)
M. sativa L.　　　　　　　　　　　　　Rudge, c. 1810
In similar situations to *M. aquatica* and probably more common than the map records show.
M. × smithiana R. A. Graham (*M. aquatica* × *arvensis* × *spicata*)
Very rare. Royston, as *M. rubra*, 1843, *W. H. Coleman, Hb. H.M.*; Woodside, as *M. rubra*, 1926, *A. W. Graveson, Hb. Gr.*; near Bricket Wood, 1955 (10/F), *Hb. H.M.* All of these specimens were determined by R. A. Graham.
M. × piperita L. (*M. aquatica* × *spicata*)　*Peppermint*
　　　　　　　　　　　　　　　　　　　Ray, 1690
A very rare plant of waste places. The current records are: canal bank, Tring, 1956 (91/G), *Hb. H.M.*; Bishop's Stortford, var. *citrata* (Ehrh.) Briq., 1961 (41/V), *J. L. Fielding, Hb. H.M.*

M. spicata L.　(Map 37e)　*Horse Mint*　Forster (see Pryor,
M. viridis L., *M. longifolia* auct. angl.　　335), c. 1806
Waste places, rubbish dumps, etc.　　Of garden origin
Occasional but the distribution of the species is not fully known owing to the difficulty of distinguishing it from its hybrids with *M. suaveolens* and *M. longifolia* (L.) Huds. The latter species, which does not occur in Britain, has been much confused in the past with hairy forms of *M. spicata*.
M. × villosa Huds. var. **alopecuroides** (Hull) Briq.
　Apple Mint　　　　　　　　A. W. Graveson, 1922
M. spicata × *suaveolens*, *M. niliaca* auct.
Rare: current records are: Therfield Heath, 1957 (34/V), *Hb. H.M.*; Gaddesden Row, 1960 (01/L), *Hb. H.M.*; Cock Lane, 1964 (30/U), *Hb. H.M.*

M. suaveolens Ehrh. (*M. rotundifolia* auct.), first recorded by Webb and Coleman, 1843, was recorded a number of times subsequently. The only record supported by a satisfactory specimen is from near Hertford, 1933, *J. E. Lousley, Hb. Lousley.*

Lycopus L.
L. europaeus L.　(Map 37f)　*Gipsywort*　Franks, 1820
Wet places　　　　　　　　　　　　　　Native
Frequent by rivers and ponds. H.S. 19, 20, 76, 77, 108.

Origanum L.
O. vulgare L.　(Map 37g)　*Marjoram*　Coles, 1657
Banks, roadsides, wood borders, etc.　　　　Native
Frequent on the Chalk. H.S. 11, 14, 21, 51, 53, 67, 83.

Thymus L.
T. pulegioides L.　(Map 37h)　*Thyme*　Kalm, 1748
T. chamaedrys Fr., *T. ovatus* Mill.　(for the aggregate)
Pastures　　　　　　　　　　　　　　　Native
Occasional on the Chalk and chalky exposures. H.S. 3, 14, 15, 22, 48, 49, 56, 84.

T. drucei Ronn. (*T. serpyllum* auct.) is a rare native of similar habitats to *T. pulegioides* and was first recorded by Prof. C. D. Pigott in 1950. Its known distribution is Therfield Heath, 1950 (33/J)!, *C. D. Pigott, Hb. H.M.*; chalkpit near Ashwell, 1951, *C. D. Pigott*; Patmore Heath, 1956 (42/M) det. *C. D. Pigott, Hb. H.M.* It no doubt awaits record elsewhere.

Calamintha Mill.

C. ascendens Jord. (Map 37i) *Common Calamint*
C. menthaefolia auct. Coleman, 1838
Banks, rough ground, etc. Native
Rare and limited to the north-east of the county.

C. nepeta (L.) Savi *Lesser Calamint* Blackstone, 1737
A very rare native of dry banks and known to the earlier
botanists from a few stations including the roadside near
to Maple Cross where it still survives, *Hb. H.M.*

Acinos Mill.

A. arvensis (Lam.) Dandy (Map 37j) *Basil Thyme*
Calamintha acinos (L.) Clairv. Blake, c. 1820
Bare exposed ground Native
Occasional on the Chalk.

Clinopodium L.

C. vulgare L. (Map 37k) *Wild Basil* Blake, c. 1820
Pastures, hedgebanks, etc. Native
Frequent on all but the most acid soils. H.S. 4, 11, 14, 21,
24, 51–54, 67, 80.

Melissa officinalis L. is rare as a naturalized plant of garden
origin.

Salvia L.

S. horminoides Pourr. *Wild Clary* Coleman, 1838
S. verbenaca auct.
Rough pastures Colonist
Rare as it has been always. Recent records are: Windmill
Hill, 1923, *Little*, *Hb. Camb.*, refound 1952 (12/Z)!, *G. L.
Evans*, *Hb. H.M.*; Bayfordbury, 1957 (31/A), *A. G. Brown
and H. Williams*; slope by Sawtrees Wood, 1956 (31/Z),
H.S. 22, *Hb. H.M*; between Sandon and Roe Green, 1959
(33/G).

S. verticillata L. D. Peirson, 1857
Railway banks and rough ground usually by the railway
Colonist
Rare. Recent records are: Mardley Heath, 1911, *Little*,
Hb. Camb.; Ickleford, 1965 (13/W), *H. Bowry*, *Hb. H.M.*;
near Todds Green, 1964 (22/D), *H. Bowry*; Hitchin railway
sidings, 1963 (12/Z), *Hb. H.M.*; by Spirella Bridge, Letch-
worth, 1963 (23/B); railway bank south of Carpenders
Park, 1965 (19/G), *Hb. H.M.*; St. Ippolyts, 1966 (12/Y),
H. Bowry.

The following Salvias have been recorded as garden escapes
or casuals. **S. sylvestris** L., Ware Park Mill, 1875, *T. B.
Blow*, *Hb. B.M.*; Ware, *Druce*, *B.E.C. 1917 Rep.* 121:
S. virgata Jacq., Ware, *Trower and Druce*, *B.E.C. 1914
Rep.* 73: **S. horminum** L., Riddy Lane, Hitchin, *Little*,
B.E.C. 1922 Rep. 851, *Hb. Camb.*: **S. sclarea** L., Upper
Icknield Way, Tring, 1945, *J. E. Dandy*, *Hb. B.M.*: **S.
bertolonii** Vis., *Druce,B.E.C. 1919 Rep.* 573: **S. amplexi-
caulis** Lam., between Waterford and Bull's Mill, 1920,
A. W. Graveson, *Hb. Gr.*: **S. reflexa** Hornem. has appeared
recently on rubbish dumps as a bird-seed alien, e.g. Pye
Corner, 1964 (41/L), *Hb. H.M.*

Prunella L.

P. vulgaris L. (Map 37 l) *Self-heal* Kalm, 1748
Meadows, pastures, etc. Native
Common. H.S. 1–6, 8, 11, 13–15, 19, 21, 23, 24, 27–29,
33–38, 41–44, 46, 48–53, 56, 57, 59, 60, 62, 69–73, 75,
77–80, 84, 90, 91, 93–95, 99, 100, 105.

P. laciniata (L.) L., an introduced plant of pastures, was
first recorded for the county from Royston Heath by C. E.
Moss in *B.E.C. 1912 Rep.* 216. There were a few subsequent
records from other places but it has not become established.
P. laciniata × vulgaris, Royston Heath, *C. E. Moss*,
as above.

Betonica L.

B. officinalis L. (Map 37m) *Betony* Woodward, 1787
Heathy places, wood borders, etc. Native
Occasional. H.S. 28, 55, 69, 78, 103.

Stachys L.

S. sylvatica L. (Map 37n) *Hedge Woundwort*
Blake, c. 1820
Hedgerows, rough pastures, etc. Native
Very common. H.S. 17, 35, 36, 46, 47, 54, 60, 63, 77, 80,
82, 84, 93–95, 100, 103, 106.

S. palustris L. (Map 37o) *Marsh Woundwort*
Coleman, 1838
Riversides canals, etc. Native
Occasional and found mainly by the sides of the larger
rivers.
S. palustris × sylvatica (*S. × ambigua* Sm.), Cave Gate,
W. W. Newbould, *Webb and Coleman Supplement*, 16;
Norton, 1932, *H. M. Dymes*, *Hb. Letchworth Mus.*; below
Moor Park, *F. M. Day*.

S. arvensis (L.) L. *Field Woundwort* Coleman, 1838
A rare colonist of arable fields found during the present
survey at Therfield, 1958 (32/N), *Lloyd-Evans*, *Hb. H.M.*;
Harmer Green, 1959 (21/N), *J. C. Gardiner*; Barber's Close,
1963 (21/Y), *Lloyd-Evans*!, *Hb. H.M.*; Wood End, Ardeley,
1961 (32/H); Moor Green, 1963 (32/I).

S. annua (L.) L., a very rare casual of arable fields, was first
recorded from High Down by J. Pollard in 1896, *Hb. H.M.*
Little found it a few times and Salisbury reported it from
Limbrick Hall, Harpenden, 1917, *Trans. Herts. N.H.S.*
17 (1919), 145. I have seen it only once: in field below Sawtrees Wood, 1956 (31/Z), *Hb. H.M.*

Ballota L.

B. nigra L. (Map 38a) *Black Horehound* Blake, c. 1820
Roadsides, waste ground, etc. Native
Common and widely distributed. White-flowered forms
have been recorded but I have not seen any.

Galeobdolon Adans.

G. luteum Huds. (Map 38b) *Yellow Archangel*
Lamium galeobdolon (L.) L. Gerard, 1597
Woods Native
Common in woods on the Clay-with-Flints, occasional
elsewhere except on the Chalk and Boulder Clay where it is
rare. H.S. 12, 34, 41, 46, 60, 61, 63, 82.

Lamium L.

L. amplexicaule L. (Map 38c) *Henbit* Coleman, 1838
Arable fields, gardens, etc. Colonist
Common on the Chalk and occasional on gravelly soils.

L. hybridum Vill. (Map 38d) *Cut-leaved Dead-nettle*
L. dissectum With. I. Brown, 1840
Arable fields Colonist
Occasional on the Boulder Clay, rare elsewhere. A paper by
J. E. Little (1953) published posthumously dismisses sug-
gestions that *L. hybridum* may be of hybrid origin.

L. purpureum L. (Map 38e) *Red Dead-nettle* Kalm, 1748
Arable fields, waste places, etc. Colonist
Very common. H.S. 22, 83.

L. album L. (Map 38f) *White Dead-nettle* Blake, c. 1820
Roadsides, waste places, etc. Native
Very common. H.S. 24.

L. **maculatum** L., *Spotted Dead-nettle*, is a rare garden out-cast which was first recorded by Little in *W.E.C. 1912–13 Rep.* 378.

Galeopsis L.

G. tetrahit L.   (Map 38g)   *Common Hemp-nettle*
                                                       Blake, 1824
Rough grassland, wood borders, etc.   Native
Common on all but the most calcareous soils. H.S. 55, 58, 61, 62, 68, 77.

G. bifida Boenn.   Pryor, c. 1880
Found in similar situations to the above and from which it is scarcely distinguishable. P. M. Benoit has referred a number of my gatherings to this but its distribution in the county is not yet known.

G. angustifolia Ehrh. ex Hoffm.   (Map 38h)   *Narrow-*
G. ladanum sensu Pryor   *leaved Hemp-nettle*   Blake, 1819
Arable fields   Colonist
Occasional and found mainly on the Chalk.

G. speciosa Mill.   *Variegated Hemp-nettle*
                                          Webb and Coleman, 1843
This occurs only as a casual and was seen during the survey in tetrads 33/T, 10/AHV, 09/H.

Nepeta L.

N. cataria L.   (Map 38i)   *Cat-mint*   Cockfield, 1813
Field borders, roadsides, etc.   Native
Occasional and found mainly on the Chalk.

Glechoma L.

G. hederacea L.   (Map 38j)   *Ground Ivy*   Blake, 1820
Shady banks, woodland rides, etc.   Native
Very common. H.S. 11, 16, 20, 21, 32, 35–37, 39, 41, 42, 44, 53, 60, 62, 63, 69, 77, 80, 82, 93, 106.

Marrubium vulgare L., *White Horehound*, first recorded by Blake, c. 1820, was possibly a native of gravelly banks a century ago. Little found it as a wool adventive but did not realise that it was. I have seen it only as a casual at Slip End (23/Y).

Scutellaria L.

S. galericulata L.   (Map 38k)   *Skull-cap*   Blake, 1819
Banks of rivers and sides of wet ditches and ponds Native
Occasional in the south of the county.

S. minor Huds.   *Lesser Skull-cap*   Webb and Coleman,
                                                            1843
Recorded by Coleman and Pryor as a rare native of a few bogs and heathy places between Colney Heath and Northaw and in the extreme south of the county. It is relatively common in Bishop's Wood, 1956 (09/X), H.S. 105, *Hb. H.M.* and occurs rarely in Great Wood, 1964 (20/X).

Teucrium L.

T. scorodonia L.   (Map 38 l)   *Wood Sage*   Forster, 1789
Woods, shady tracks and banks   Native
Frequent on the London Clay and river gravels. H.S. 89, 103–105.

Ajuga L.

A. reptans L.   (Map 38m)   *Bugle*   Blake, 1821
Woodland rides and damp shady places   Native
Common and well distributed. H.S. 11, 16, 21, 28, 32, 34–36, 38, 39, 41, 42, 44, 60, 62, 73, 75, 77, 78, 82, 88, 90, 94, 95, 99, 100, 104, 105.

A. chamaepitys (L.) Schreb.   *Ground Pine* J. Woods, 1805
Disturbed soils   Colonist
One of the more interesting plants entering into the flora and limited to perpetually disturbed places such as field borders on the Chalk. Given suitable conditions it may be locally abundant in favourable years. Records have been numerous in the neighbourhood of Hexton, Pirton, Baldock and Ashwell but during the period of the survey I have seen it only in the fields below Tingley Wood.

The following casuals have been recorded: **Sideritis romana** L., **S. lanata** L. and **Ziziphora taurica** Bieb. all from Hoddesdon by Hayllar in *B.E.C. 1915 Rep.* 207 and **Dracocephalum parviflorum** Nutt. by A. W. Graveson from Mead Lane, 1920; Cole Green, 1924, *Hb. Gr.*

PLANTAGINACEAE
Plantago L.

P. major L.   (Map 38n)   *Great Plantain* Knowlton, 1724
Roadsides, pastures, waste ground, etc.   Native
Abundant. H.S. 8, 11, 13, 19, 20, 33, 35, 38, 39, 41–43, 46, 47, 50, 53, 59, 60, 66, 69, 74, 77–80, 82, 84, 88, 90, 94, 100, 105, 108.

P. media L.   (Map 38o)   *Hoary Plantain*   Kalm, 1748
Calcareous pastures   Native
Common on the Chalk and Boulder Clay and found also frequently in churchyards. H.S. 1, 2, 5, 7, 11, 13–15, 23, 28, 29, 48, 49, 56, 71, 84.

P. lanceolata L.   (Map 39a)   *Ribwort Plantain* Franks, 1823
Pastures, waste ground, etc.   Native
Ubiquitous. A variable species but none of its forms is constant. H.S. 1–8, 11, 13–15, 18, 21–24, 26, 28, 29, 44, 48, 49, 51–53, 55–59, 62, 65–67, 69–73, 75, 79, 83, 84, 90–92, 96, 100, 105.

P. coronopus L.   (Map 39b)   *Buck's-horn Plantain*
                                                   Coleman, 1838
Bare gravelly ground   Native
Rare and limited mainly to the Lea Gravels.

P. indica L., a casual, was first recorded by Hayllar from Ware in *B.E.C. 1916 Rep.* 499, *Hb. Gr.* It now occurs rarely as a bird-seed alien: e.g. Little Dudswell, 1965 (90/U), *R. I. Sworder, Hb. H.M.*

Littorella uniflora (L.) Aschers. (*L. lacustris* L.), *Shore-weed*, was recorded by Coleman in 1843 from Berkhamsted Common but has not been seen since.

CAMPANULACEAE
Campanula L.

C. latifolia L.   (Map 39c)   *Giant Bellflower*
                                          Webb and Coleman, 1843
Woods and shady places   Native
Locally frequent in a small area near to Buntingford and scattered in woods in the west of the county.

C. trachelium L.   (Map 39d)   *Nettle-leaved Bellflower*
                                                   Gerard, 1597
Woods   Native
Occasional in clay woods overlying the Chalk and rare otherwise.

C. rapunculoides L.   (Map 39e)   *Creeping Bellflower*
                                                   Pollard, 1868
Established in hedgerows and rough pastures   Of garden
                                                      origin
This has increased in recent years and is now occasional.

C. glomerata L. (Map 39f) *Clustered Bellflower*
Gerard, 1597
Chalk pastures   Native
A feature of the chalk downs and chalk exposures throughout the county. H.S. 2, 3, 5.

C. rotundifolia L. (Map 39g) *Harebell* Plukenet, 1696
Pastures, dry banks, etc.   Native
Occasional in suitably exposed pastures on the Chalk and on heathy and gravelly soils. H.S. 1–3, 7, 14, 15, 26, 48, 49, 55, 56, 58, 68, 86, 101.

C. patula L., one plant in cornfield, Pirton Cross, 1874, *J. Pollard, Hb. H.M.* (see also *Pryor*, 266): **C. rapunculus** L., *Rampion*, was recorded as a colonist in the earlier floras but there has been no record for nearly a hundred years. **C. medium** L. was recorded from a railway cutting at Berkhamsted, *Pryor*, 262 and **C. persicifolia** L. from a wood at Welwyn Garden City, *H. D. Garside*, 1946, *Hb. B.M.* The latter seems to be well established on the canal bank near Bulbourne (91/G).

Legousia Durande
L. hybrida (L.) Delarb. (Map 39h) *Venus's Looking-glass*
Parkinson, 1640
Arable fields   Colonist
Frequent on the Chalk and the more calcareous parts of the Boulder Clay. H.S. 53.

L. speculum-veneris (L.) Fisch. ex Druce was recorded from Lilley Hoo, 1907, by J. Vaughan, see *B.E.C. 1924 Rep.* 664, *Hb. Druce*.

Jasione montana L., *Sheep's-bit*, was a rare native of bare gravelly pastures in the Lea and Colne Valleys. It was first recorded by Blake from Welwyn, c. 1820, *Hb. Druce* and was last seen in the county about 1914.

RUBIACEAE
Sherardia L.
S. arvensis L. (Map 39i) *Field Madder* Franks, 1823
Arable fields, bare ground, etc.   Native
Frequent and well distributed. H.S. 52, 53.

Asperula L.
A. cynanchica L. (Map 39j) *Squinancywort* Blake, 1820
Chalk hills and chalk exposures   Native
Rare but constant in well established chalk turf. H.S. 2, 3, 14, 15, 56.

A. arvensis L. has been recorded as a rare casual e.g. *Pryor*, 207, and more recently as a bird-seed alien, Little Dudswell, 1965 (90/U), *R. I. Sworder!, Hb. H.M.*

Cruciata Mill.
C. laevipes Opiz (Map 39k) *Crosswort* Steele MS.,
Galium cruciata (L.) Scop.   c. 1730
Rough ground, wood borders, etc.   Native
Common in a small area of gravelly soils between Colney Heath and Potters Bar and otherwise thinly scattered over the county.

Galium L.
G. odoratum (L). Scop. (Map 39 l) *Sweet Woodruff*
Asperula odorata L.   Blake, c. 1820
Woods and shady places   Native
This has a western distribution in the county and although more common on the Clay-with-Flints than elsewhere it is probably so restricted by climatic rather than edaphic factors. H.S. 16, 17, 54, 61, 63, 95.

G. mollugo L. subsp. **mollugo** (Map 39m) *Hedge Bedstraw* Coles, 1657
Hedges, wood borders, rough pastures, etc.   Native
Generally common but becoming rare on the London Clay. H.S. 3–5, 11, 14, 18, 21, 24, 31, 50–54, 79, 80, 84.
subsp. **erectum** Syme (*G. erectum* Huds.) (Map 39n)
Pryor, 1875
This is found either in improved pastures or by the side of railway tracks. Its status appears to be that of a colonist rather than a native species.

G. verum L. (Map 39o) *Lady's Bedstraw* Ellis, 1750
Pastures, hedgerows, etc.   Native
Common and especially so on the more calcareous soils. H.S. 2–5, 7, 8, 11, 14, 22, 25, 26, 28, 48, 56, 58, 84, 92.

G. saxatile L. (Map 40a) *Heath Bedstraw* Coleman, 1838
Heaths   Native
Frequent on the more acid soils. H.S. 26, 57, 58, 64, 68, 70, 81, 85–87, 97, 98, 101, 105.

G. pumilum Murr. (*G. sylvestre* Poll., non Scop.) a rare colonist of chalk grassland was first recorded by E. Milne-Redhead from Blows Downs, v.c. 20 [Beds.] in *B.E.C. 1943–4 Rep.* 728 but it seems to have disappeared from there. A large patch was found in 1964 in Royston Churchyard (34/K), *Hb. H.M.*

G. palustre L. (Map 40b) *Marsh Bedstraw* Franks, 1820
Marshy and wet places   Native
Occasional but well distributed. This is a very variable species which was examined critically in the county by Pryor and it would now repay a fresh examination. H.S. 20, 29, 34, 42, 44, 65, 76–78, 90, 91, 94, 103, 108.

G. uliginosum L. (Map 40c) *Fen Bedstraw* Franks, 1820
Boggy places   Native
Occasional but well distributed. H.S. 9, 10, 18, 19, 30, 31, 76, 90, 91.

G. tricornutum Dandy *Corn Bedstraw* Coleman, 1838
G. tricorne auct.
Until recently a frequent colonist in arable fields on the Chalk and Boulder Clay. In 1956 and 1957 I saw it in three tetrads (33/FR, 43/F) and in 1960 Lloyd-Evans found it near Hamels (32/S) but there appear to be no subsequent records. I am at a complete loss to explain why it should have disappeared not only in Hertfordshire but simultaneously in Bedfordshire.

G. aparine L. (Map 40d) *Goosegrass* Ellis, 1750
Hedges, arable fields, waste places, etc.   Native
Abundant. H.S. 5, 7, 11, 22, 25, 35–37, 40, 42, 45–47, 53, 63, 77, 78, 82, 84, 94, 95, 107.

G. parisiense L. (*G. anglicum* Huds.), *Wall Bedstraw*, was recorded as a colonist on the walls of Brocket Park by Edwards in 1857 and there is a specimen in *Hb. Gr.* collected there in 1860. I know of no more recent record.

CAPRIFOLIACEAE
Sambucus L.
S. nigra L. (Map 40e) *Elder* Ellis, 1733
Woods, hedgerows, etc.   Native
Common. In addition to the usual form with black berries Ellis noted an introduced form with white berries which he described at great length. This was noted subsequently, see *Pryor*, 199, but I have seen no such forms. H.S. 5, 12, 22, 40, 41, 43, 53, 55, 82, 106.

S. ebulus L.   *Danewort*   Coles, 1657
A very rare denizen of hedgerows as it apparently has always been. I have seen it near to Symond's Green (22/CH) where it was shown to me in 1958 by H. and D. Meyer and on the roadside south of Barkway (33/WX), *H. B. Souster.*

S. racemosa L. has been recorded as a naturalized shrub, e.g. Berkhamsted Common, *J.A.* (? I.A.) *Williams, B.E.C. 1928 Rep. 913.*

Viburnum L.
V. lantana L. (Map 40f) *Wayfaring Tree*
                                    Woodward, 1787
Hedgerows, wood borders and occasionally in scrub Native Common on the Chalk and chalk exposures and on the more calcareous parts of the Boulder Clay. H.S. 3, 17, 21, 49, 54.

V. opulus L. (*Map 40g*) *Guelder Rose* Coleman, 1838
Wood borders, hedgerows, etc.   Native
Occasional but widely distributed. H.S. 42, 46, 61, 78, 80, 89.

Symphoricarpos rivularis Suksd. (*S. racemosus* auct.), *Snowberry*, first recorded by Pryor, is now occasional as a garden escape.

Lonicera L.
L. periclymenum L. (Map 40h) *Honeysuckle*
                                    Knowlton, 1724
Hedgerows, woods, etc.   Native
Frequent on all but the most calcareous soils. H.S. 26, 30, 33, 36, 39, 42, 45–47, 58, 61, 77, 78, 80, 81, 88, 89, 93–95, 103, 104, 106.

L. xylosteum L. and **L. caprifolium** L., both of garden origin, were recorded by earlier workers (see *Pryor*, 200–1) at a time when it was thought possible that they might be native.

ADOXACEAE
Adoxa L.
A. moschatellina L. (Map 40i) *Moschatel, Town Hall*
                                    Clock Blake, 1821
Woods and shady places   Native
Frequent in woods in the Aldenham area and to the west of Berkhamsted but rare elsewhere.

VALERIANACEAE
Valerianella Mill.
V. locusta (L.) Betcke (Map 40j) *Lamb's Lettuce*
V. olitoria (L.) Poll.   Blake, 1824
Arable fields, bare ground, etc.   Colonist
Occasional and found most frequently on railway banks. H.S. 83.

V. carinata Lois. was recorded as a casual from Watford by 'J. M.', 1847, *Hb. B.M.* and there were subsequent records from Hertford and Chorley Wood. The only current record is from West Leith, c. 1958 (91/A)!, *C. Leach Hb. H.M.* and it appears to be well established here.

V. rimosa Bast. was recorded as a rare colonist, see *Pryor*, 211. Its recent records are Benington, 1927, *A. W. Graveson, Hb. Gr.* and Old Sarratt, 1951 (09/J)!, *R. A. Graham.*
V. eriocarpa Desv. was recorded in *Pryor*, 210, on the authority of a specimen from Hatfield in *Hb. B.M.* which I cannot find.

V. dentata (L.) Poll. (Map 40k) *Sharp-fruited Corn Salad*
                                    Webb, 1839
Arable fields   Colonist
Occasional on the edges of fields on the more calcareous parts of the Boulder Clay.

Valeriana L.
V. officinalis L. (Map 40 l) *Valerian* Coleman, 1838
V. sambucifolia Mikan f.
Rough grassland, wood borders, etc.   Native
Occasional in a few scattered and unrelated areas. H.S. 75, 76. It is very variable and Pryor thought that there were two species to be considered.

V. dioica L. (Map 40m) *Marsh Valerian* Blake, 1820
Marshy places   Native
Rare but usually to be found in the few truly marshy places left in the county. H.S. 9, 10, 18, 30, 31, 76, 90, 99.

Centranthus ruber (L.) DC., *Wall Valerian*, first recorded by J. Pollard (see *Pryor*, 209) is found occasionally as a garden escape on old walls, etc. but is not established.
Cephalaria gigantea (Ledeb.) Bobrov (*C. tatarica* Schrad.) was recorded as a garden escape at Wareside by J. W. Higgens in *B.E.C. 1918 Rep. 285.*

DIPSACACEAE
Dipsacus L.
D. fullonum L. subsp. **fullonum** (Map 40n) *Teasel*
                                    Franks MS., 1819
Sides of streams and ditches, waste places, etc.   Native
Frequent on the Boulder Clay and occasional elsewhere in the wetter parts of the county. H.S. 39.
subsp. **sativus** (L.) Thell.   *Fuller's Teasel* Pryor, 1874
A rare casual of waste places e.g. Standon, 1957 (32/V), *Lloyd-Evans, Hb. H.M.*; Bishop's Stortford (42/V), *J. L. Fielding*; Kinsbourne Green, 1966 (11/C), *H. B. Souster*; Hitchin U.D.C. Dump, 1964 (31/V); Cock Lane, 1966 (30/N).

D. pilosus L. (Map 40o) *Small Teasel* Coles, 1657
Damp woods, riversides, etc.   Native
Occasional in a limited area on the Boulder Clay. Known also to earlier botanists from the Colne Valley but I have not seen it there. H.S. 82.

Knautia L.
K. arvensis (L.) Coult. (Map 41a) *Field Scabious*
Trichera arvensis (L.) Schrad.   Blake, 1819
Arable fields, rough pastures, etc.   Native
Common on the more calcareous soils and becoming rare only on the London Clay. H.S. 3–5, 11, 24, 50–53, 67.

Scabiosa L.
S. columbaria L. (Map 41b) *Small Scabious*
                                    Coleman, 1838
Pastures   Native
Common on the Chalk and chalk exposures. H.S. 1–3, 5, 7, 14, 15, 48, 49, 67.

S. atropurpurea L. (*S. maritima* L.) was recorded as a casual from Buckland by A. W. Graveson in *B.E.C. 1922 Rep. 729, Hb. Gr.*

Succisa Haller
S. pratensis Moench (Map 41c) *Devil's-bit Scabious*
                                    Blake, 1820
Damp woods and pastures   Native
Frequent on the London Clay and occasional elsewhere. H.S. 28, 55, 75, 87, 89, 91, 98, 99.

COMPOSITAE
Bidens L.
B. cernua L. (Map 41d) *Nodding Bur-marigold*
Coleman, 1838
Riversides, ponds, ditches, etc.   Native
Occasional. H.S. 66, 76, 88, 89.

B. tripartita L. (May 41e) *Bur-marigold* Blake, c. 1820
Sides of ponds, ditches, etc.
Occasional and found in similar situations to *B. cernua*.
It seems generally to grow by more shallow water. H.S. 20.

B. frondosa L. appears as a colonist by the river at Dobbs
Weir (30/Z) and **B. bipinnata** L., as a wool adventive e.g.
Wymondley, 1961 (22/D), *Hb. H.M.*

Galinsoga Ruiz & Pav.
G. parviflora Cav. (Map 41f) *Gallant Soldier*
R. Gimingham (J. Bot. 1912, 228) 1912
A recent introduction which appears to have reached the
limit of its frequency.

G. ciliata (Raf.) Blake (Map 41g) *Shaggy Soldier*
A. W. Graveson, 1921
In similar situations to *G. parviflora*
Occasional and found more generally in the south of the
county.

Ambrosia artemisiifolia L., a garden escape, was first
recorded by Sir Edward Salisbury from Harpenden Common in 1911 and still occurs on rubbish dumps as at
Pye Corner, 1965 (41/L) and Park Street, 1966 (10/L):
A. trifida L. was recorded from Hitchin by Little in *B.E.C.
1923 Rep.* 375 and from Stansteadbury by A. Trower in
B.E.C. 1925 Rep. 878, *Hb. Druce*.

Xanthium spinosum L., *Spiny Cocklebur*, first recorded
by Ansell in 1846, is occasional as a wool adventive near
to Hitchin and is rare on rubbish dumps e.g. Cock Lane,
1965 (30/U).

Senecio L.
S. jacobaea L. (Map 41h) *Common Ragwort* Ellis, 1750
Pastures, waste places, etc.   Native
Generally common but becoming rare on the intensively
cultivated Boulder Clay where it no doubt has been
exterminated in quite considerable areas. H.S. 2, 4, 7, 11, 14,
17, 21–23, 48, 50, 51, 53, 56, 62, 65, 77, 80, 83, 84, 100.

S. aquaticus Hill (Map 41i) *Marsh Ragwort*
Coleman, 1838
Marshes, water meadows, etc.   Native
Occasional but well distributed. H.S. 29, 65, 66, 90, 91.
S. aquaticus × jacobaea occurs with both parents in wet
meadows e.g. Marford, 1964 (11/X), *P. M. Benoit*!;
Waterford, 1964 (31/C), *P. M. Benoit*!; Water End, 1966
(11/A). It is probably more common than these records
indicate.

S. erucifolius L. (Map 41j) *Hoary Ragwort* Blake, 1820
Rough pastures, field borders, etc.   Native
Well distributed but more common on the Chalk than
elsewhere. H.S. 4, 6, 20, 24–28, 33, 35, 39, 52, 53, 66, 67,
79, 96.

S. squalidus L. (Map 41k) *Oxford Ragwort*
A. W. Graveson, 1921
Waste places, rough ground, etc.   Colonist
Common in the built-up areas in the south of the county
and around the larger towns. It spread into Hertfordshire

along the railways before the Second World War but its
rapid increase did not come until after 1945.
S. squalidus × viscosus (*S. × londinensis* Lousley)
First observed by the author in company with A. W.
Graveson at Hertford, 1957 (31/G), *Hb. H.M.* Recorded
also for the following tetrads: 21/J (*Hb. H.M.*), 31/M
(*Hb. H.M.*) V (*Hb. H.M.*), 30/P (*Hb. H.M.*) R (*Hb. H.M.*)
S T, 29/S.

S. sylvaticus L. (Map 41 l) *Heath Groundsel*
J. A. Hankey, 1833
Heathy places especially in cleared woodland   Native
Occasional on the more gravelly soils.

S. viscosus L. (Map 41m) *Sticky Groundsel*
Andrews, 1874
Waste ground, railway tracks, etc.   Colonist
A rare casual until about 1914 since when it has spread
rapidly all over the county.

S. vulgaris L. (Map 41n) *Groundsel* Coleman, 1838
Cultivated ground, waste places, etc.   Colonist
Ubiquitous. Forms with rayed florets are found rarely and
usually on railway ballast. H.S. 7, 9, 34, 65, 83, 103.

S. fluviatilis Wallr. (*S. sarracenicus* auct.), *Saracen's
Woundwort*, was planted at Wilstone Reservoir (91/B)
by H. H. Crewe about 1870. It is still there.

S. integrifolius (L.) Clairv. *Field Fleawort*
Cineraria campestris Retz.   W. Anderson, 1812
Chalk hills   Native
Very rare as it has always been. Therfield Heath (34/K,
33/J), H.S. 2; Aldbury Nowers (91/L.). Both of these
confirm old records.

Doronicum pardalianches L. *Leopard's Bane* is an intro-
duced plant with a few early records (see *Pryor*, 217).
Recent records include Whippendell Wood, 1964 (09/T),
P. J. Ellison, *Hb. H.M.* I know of no recent record of
D. plantagineum L. (see *Pryor*, 218).

Tussilago L.
T. farfara L. (Map 41o) *Coltsfoot* Kalm, 1748
Waste ground, roadsides, etc.   Native
Very common and found most abundantly on ground that
is wet in the winter. H.S. 6, 10, 17, 35, 41, 46, 50, 53, 56, 80,
99, 100.

Petasites Mill.
P. hybridus (L.) Gaertn., Mey. & Scherb.   (Map 42a)
P. officinalis Moench   *Butterbur* Blackstone, 1737
Wet hollows by the sides of rivers   Native
Occasional in places where the rivers are in comparatively
flat country. The 'male' plant is the one commonly met
with in Hertfordshire but the 'female' was recorded from
between Harlow and Sawbridgeworth, 1953, *J. C. Gardiner*,
Hb. H.M. and from Otterspool, 1966 (19/J).

P. fragrans (Vill.) C. Presl (*Nardosmia fragrans* (Vill.)
Reichb.), *Winter Heliotrope*, first recorded in Pryor's Flora
(1887) is occasional as a garden escape and **P. japonicus**
(Sieb. & Zucc.) F. Schmidt is found rarely as a garden relic.

Inula L.
I. conyza DC. (Map 42b) *Ploughman's Spikenard*
Blake, 1819
Rough grassland   Native
Occasional and found most frequently on chalky soils in
the west of the county.

I. helenium L., *Elecampane*, a garden relic, was first recorded by Blake from Danesbury, 1820, *Hb. Druce*. It appears now on rough ground by the Spirella Bridge, Letchworth (23/B).

Pulicaria Gaertn.
P. dysenterica (L.) Bernh. (Map 42c) *Fleabane*
Blake, 1819
Roadsides, wet places, etc. Native
A species with an unusual distribution which compares very closely with that of *Dipsacus fullonum*. H.S. 18, 27, 28, 99, 100.

P. vulgaris Gaertn., *Small Fleabane*, was first recorded by Blake, c. 1820, and known to nineteenth-century botanists as a rare native of a few wet sandy heaths. In 1923 A. W. Graveson found two plants only at Colney Heath and I know of no more recent records. A record by Phillips from Wymondley in *B.E.C. 1931 Rep.* 654, *Hb. Druce* is for a wool adventive and may refer to a closely allied species.

Filago L.
F. germanica L. (Map 42d) *Cudweed* Blake, 1820
Bare ground on gravelly soils Native
Occasional and probably decreasing although its habitat has not diminished.

F. apiculata G. E. Sm., *Red-tipped Cudweed*, a colonist of gravelly fields, was first recorded by Webb and Coleman (1851). It was found in a few places in the neighbourhood of Hatfield and Hertford and was apparently last seen in the county by A. W. Graveson at Waterford in 1919, *Hb. Gr.*

F. spathulata C. Presl *Broad-leaved Cudweed*, first recorded by Backhouse c. 1828, is a rare colonist of chalky and gravelly fields. It has been recorded, often with long intervals of time, from near Hertford and in the area between Hitchin and Royston. I have seen it only on the edge of Cock Lane Dump, 1958 (30/U), *Hb. H.M.*, *Hb. B.M.*

F. gallica L., *Narrow Cudweed*, was first recorded independently by both Webb and Ansell (*Hb. Druce*) in 1847. It was a rare colonist of gravelly places near to Hertford and Welwyn and was last recorded for the county by H. Groves in 1878, *Hb. B.M.*

F. minima (Sm.) Pers. *Small Cudweed* Blake, 1821
Bare sandy and gravelly places Native
Rare and apparently diminishing. During the period of the present survey it has been recorded from Broxbournebury (30/NP)!, *Lloyd-Evans*; Westland Green (42/F)! *J. L. Fielding*; Codicote High Heath (21/E); Mardley Heath (21/P); Cole Green Dump (21/Q). It has been recorded from Letchworth, 1928, *H. Meyer, Hb. Letch. Mus.* but I have not seen it in this part of the county.

Gnaphalium L.
G. sylvaticum L. *Wood Cudweed* Blake, c. 1820
Rides in heathy woods Native
Rare but recorded for a number of stations by earlier workers. The only current records are from Whippendell Wood e.g. *A. W. Exell*, 1954, *Hb. B.M.* I have not seen it in the county.

G. uliginosum L. (Map 42e) *Marsh Cudweed*
Franks, 1820
Edges of marshes, cart-tracks, etc. Native
Frequent on the more acid soils in the south of the county. H.S. 20, 39, 77, 78, 87–89, 105.

Antennaria dioica (L.) Gaertn., *Mountain Everlasting*, was first recorded in 1841 by Fordham from Therfield Heath and this was the only place in the county from which it was known. It was apparently last seen by C. D. Pigott in 1947.

Solidago L.
S. virgaurea L. *Golden-rod* Coleman, 1838
This has been recorded as a rare native plant of woods on light gravelly soils mainly on the London Clay. Its last record was from Broxbourne Wood, 1952, *R. M. Payne*.

S. canadensis L. and **S. gigantea** Ait. are frequent as garden escapes.

Erigeron L.
E. acer L. (Map 42f) *Blue Fleabane* Coleman, 1838
Bare places, railway banks, etc. Colonist
Occasional on the more gravelly soils. H.S. 4, 51.

Conyza Less.
C. canadensis (L.) Cronq. (Map 42g) *Canadian Fleabane*
Erigeron canadensis L. D. Peirson, 1859
Waste places, roadsides, etc. Colonist
This appeared only as a casual until about forty years ago since when it has much increased.

Bellis L.
B. perennis L. (Map 42h) *Daisy* Kalm, 1748
Pastures, lawns etc. Native
Very common. H.S. 2, 8, 11, 13, 15, 21, 23, 24, 27, 29, 41, 49–53, 56, 65–67, 69, 71, 73, 79, 84, 91, 100.

Eupatorium L.
E. cannabinum L. (Map 42i) *Hemp Agrimony*
Blake, c. 1820
Riversides, ditches, etc. Native
Frequent by the larger rivers and in marshy places on the Chalk Marl. H.S. 99, 100.

Anthemis L.
A. cotula L. (Map 42j) *Stinking Mayweed* Blake, 1820
Arable fields, waste ground, etc. Colonist
Occasional and apparently limited to neutral soils.

A. arvensis L. *Corn Chamomile* Coleman, 1838
A rare colonist of grassy banks. Current records are: roadside verge, Rye Meads, 1962 (31/V)!, *Lloyd-Evans*; railway bank, Bragbury End, 1960 (22/KQ), *Hb. H.M.*

A. tinctoria L., *Yellow Chamomile*, occurs occasionally as a garden escape. **A. austriaca** Jacq., **A. ruthenica** Bieb. and **A. altissima** L. (*A. cota* L.) were recorded from Ware by Higgens in *B.E.C. 1919 Rep.* 661. There is a specimen of *A. altissima* in *Hb. Gr.* from Ware, 1916.

Chamaemelum Mill.
C. nobile (L.) All. *Chamomile* Blake (see Pryor, 221, but *Anthemis nobilis* L. there is no specimen in Herb. Druce), c. 1820
Sandy and gravelly pastures Native
Rare as it has always been. Current records are: Gustard Wood Common, 1959 (11/T)!, *Lloyd-Evans*; Totteridge Green, one of Webb and Coleman's stations, v.c. 20 [G.L.] 1964 (29/M).

Achillea L.
A. millefolium L. (Map 42k) *Yarrow, Milfoil*
Kalm, 1748
Pastures, rough ground, roadsides, etc. Native
Very common. H.S. 4–8, 11, 13, 14, 22, 24–26, 28, 29, 48, 52, 55–57, 59, 62, 65, 66, 68–70, 72, 73, 80, 83, 84, 92, 96, 100, 102.

A. ptarmica L. (Map 42 l) *Sneezewort* Blake, 1820
Ptarmica vulgaris DC.
Wet heathy pastures and more rarely in waste places Native
Frequent on the London Clay and scarce elsewhere. H.S.
72, 98, 101.

The following casuals are recorded: **A. decolorans**
Schrad. ex Willd., Ayot Green, 1857 (see *Pryor*, 223);
A. filipendulina Lam., Ware, *B.E.C. 1909 Rep.* 415:
A. nobilis L., Hertford, 1914, *Hb. Gr.*

Tripleurospermum Schultz Bip.
T. maritimum (L.) Koch subsp. **inodorum** Hyland. ex
Vaarama (Map 42m) *Scentless Mayweed* Blake (as
Matricaria inodora L. Matricaria chamomilla), 1820
Arable fields, waste land, etc. Colonist
Abundant. H.S. 7, 20, 38, 52, 53, 59, 77, 105.

Matricaria L.
M. recutita L. (Map 42n) *Wild Chamomile*
M. chamomilla auct. Coleman, 1838
Arable fields, waste places, etc. Colonist
Frequent and probably increasing on the Lea Gravels and
London Clay.

M. matricarioides (Less.) Porter (Map 42o) *Pineapple*
Weed Druce, 1907
Roadsides, farm tracks, etc. Colonist
A comparatively recent introduction which spread rapidly
in the county. H.S. 11.

Chrysanthemum L.
C. segetum L. (Map 43a) *Corn Marigold* Ellis, 1750
Arable fields Colonist
Rare and probably decreased with improved farming
methods. It occurs now generally as a casual rather than as a
regular colonist.

C. leucanthemum L. (Map 43b) *Ox-eye Daisy* Kalm, 1748
Leucanthemum vulgare Lam.
Pastures, railway banks, etc. Native
Common except in the more intensively farmed areas. H.S.
2, 3, 13, 23, 24, 49, 73, 79, 83, 84.

C. parthenium (L.) Bernh. (Map 43c) *Feverfew*
Pyrethrum parthenium (L.) Sm. Blake, 1820
This is occasional on rubbish dumps and on waste ground
near villages as a garden escape and is scarcely wild.

C. vulgare (L.) Bernh. (Map 43d) *Tansy* Blake, 1819
Tanacetum vulgare L.
Rough pastures, riversides, waste places, etc. Colonist
Occasional but well distributed and usually of garden
origin.

The following have been recorded as casuals: **C. coron-
arium** L., Hitchin, *Little, B.E.C. 1929 Rep.* 120; Welwyn,
Phillips, B.E.C. 1932 Rep. 104, *Hb. Ph.*: **C. serotinum** L.,
Hertford, *Druce, B.E.C. 1915 Rep.* 269.

Artemisia L.
A. vulgaris L. (Map 43e) *Mugwort* Blake, c. 1820
Roadsides, rough ground, etc. Native
Common. H.S. 83.

A. verlotorum Lamotte (Map 43f) *Chinese Mugwort*
Kent, 1953
A recent introduction found mainly in waste places and
which is increasing in the south of the county.

A. absinthium L. (Map 43g) *Wormwood* Blake, c. 1820
Rough pastures, waste ground, etc. Colonist
Local on gravelly soils but absent from much of the county.

The following are recorded as casuals: **A. annua** L., Ware,
Higgens, B.E.C. 1916 Rep. 491: **A. biennis** Willd., Hert-
ford, *Trower and Druce, B.E.C. 1915 Rep.* 270, *Hb. Gr.*:
A. dracunculus L., Watford, det. Kew, *F. M. Day.*

Carlina L.
C. vulgaris L. (Map 43h) *Carline Thistle* Blake, 1820
Franks, 1820
Chalky pastures Native
Frequent on the Chalk in short close turf and occurring
rarely in disued chalk pits. H.S. 2, 3, 15, 49, 56, 67.

Arctium L.
A. minus Bernh. (Map 43i) *Burdock* Franks MS., 1822
(for the aggregate), Pryor, 1874 (for the restricted species)
Waste places, scrub, etc. Native
This is the common burdock in the county. H.S. 45, 62, 80,
107 [*Arctium* species not determined. H.S. 12, 16, 17, 35, 36,
41, 63].

A. lappa L. (Map 43j) *Great Burdock* Pryor, 1874
A. majus Bernh.
Sides of ditches and rarely elsewhere Native
Frequent on the Boulder Clay.

A. pubens Bab. (Map 43k) Pryor, 1874
A. nemorosum sensu Pryor, *A. intermedium* sensu Pryor
Waste places, roadsides, etc. Native
More common on the river gravels than *A. minus* but I have
found it at times difficult to separate the two species.

A. tomentosum Mill., a casual, was found on waste
ground, Dobbs Weir, 1964 (30/Z).

Carduus L.
C. acanthoides L. (Map 43 l) *Welted Thistle*
C. crispus auct. Woodward, 1787
Roadsides, sides of streams, etc. Native
Common on the more calcareous soils but rare on the
London Clay. H.S. 22, 23.

C. nutans L. (Map 43m) *Musk Thistle* Blake, c. 1820
Rough pastures, waste ground, etc. Native
Occasional but with no apparent distribution pattern.
Coleman thought that it was especially common on the
Chalk but I have not found it so.

C. tenuiflorus Curt., *Slender Thistle*, was first recorded by
Pryor as being abundant by the canal at Boxmoor and I
found it still there in 1956, *Hb. H.M.* Otherwise it has
appeared by the side of Eastwick Wood, 1956 (41/H),
Hb. H.M. and it has been frequent as a wool adventive.

Cirsium Mill.
C. vulgare (Savi) Ten. (Map 43n) *Spear or Plume Thistle*
C. lanceolatum (L.) Scop., non Hill Ellis, 1750
Rough pastures, waste ground, etc. Native
Abundant. H.S. 4, 14, 22, 23, 35, 38, 50, 67, 69, 73, 77, 79,
80, 105.

C. palustre (L.) Scop. (Map 43o) *Marsh Thistle*
Blake, 1820
Marshes, damp woods, etc. Native
Frequent and well distributed. H.S. 8, 9, 18, 19, 27–31,
33–35, 37–39, 41, 42, 44–46, 62, 66, 73–77, 79, 80, 87,
89–91, 99, 100, 103–105.

C. arvense (L.) Scop.   (Map 44a)   *Field Thistle*
Blake, c. 1820
Arable land, waste places, roadsides, etc.   Colonist
Abundant. H.S. 5, 6, 8–10, 20, 25, 30, 32, 35, 37–39, 50, 52–54, 56, 62, 65, 69, 71, 73, 77, 79, 80, 82, 96, 99, 100, 102, 105.

C. acaulon (L.) Scop.   (Map 44b)   *Dwarf Thistle*
Blake, 1820
Dry calcareous pastures   Native
Frequent on the Chalk and chalky exposures. H.S. 1–3, 5, 7, 14, 15, 48, 49, 51, 52, 55, 56, 84.

C. eriophorum (L.) Scop.   *Woolly Thistle*
Franks MS., 1820
Rough grassland on the Chalk   Native
Very rare as it has always been. Current records are: Knott Wood, 1956 (11/B)!, *M. J. Richardson*; Coltsfoot Lane, Anstey, 1960 (43/B), *Lloyd-Evans*; Halls Green, 1964 (22/U), *H. Bowry*; chalkpit, Bandons, 1960 (33/W).

C. dissectum (L.) Hill   *Meadow Thistle*   Coleman, 1838
C. anglicum (Lam.) DC.
This rare native of boggy meadows was known from a few scattered stations by nineteenth-century botanists. Salisbury found it at Hertford Heath (*Trans. Herts. N.H.S.* 17 (1918), 60) but it is apparently not there now. It still survives, but has not flowered for many years, at Burleigh Meadow (22/G), *Hb. H.M.*, *Hb. Ph.*

Silybum marianum (L.) Gaertn., *Milk Thistle*, was first recorded from Sawbridgeworth, 1828, see Kent, D. H. (1957) and has always been a rare casual. The only recent record is from Hertingfordbury, 1951, *S. C. Mortis*:
Onopordum acanthium L., *Scotch Thistle*, first recorded by Coleman, 1838, occurs as a garden escape usually near houses but sometimes on rubbish dumps, e.g. Cock Lane, 1966 (30/N).

Centaurea L.
C. scabiosa L.   (Map 44c)   *Greater Knapweed*
Blake, c. 1820
Rough grassland, roadsides, etc.   Native
Frequent on the Chalk and chalk exposures. H.S. 4, 5, 7, 11, 51–53, 83.

C. nigra L.   (Map 44d)   *Hardheads, Lesser Knapweed*
Kalm, 1748
Pastures, roadsides, etc.   Native
Very common. H.S. 1–3, 5–11, 13, 14, 18, 22–29, 33, 48–50, 52, 53, 55, 58, 59, 67, 71–73, 75, 79, 83, 84, 90, 91, 100, 109. *C. nigra* is variable and there are in addition some closely allied species. A fresh study could well be made of the Hertfordshire knapweeds.

C. cyanus L.   (Map 44e)   *Cornflower*   Blake, c. 1820
In the nineteenth century this was apparently frequent as a cornfield weed especially on the Chalk. It still occurs regularly in a few fields to the east of Baldock, 1951 (23/MS), *Hb. H.M.* Otherwise it appears only as a casual in cornfields and on rubbish dumps.

C. solstitialis L., *St. Barnaby's Thistle*, first recorded by Blake in 1825, has occurred as a rare casual probably introduced with imported seed. Its last record is by Kellett from Lemsford in 1952: **C. calcitrapa** L., *Star Thistle*, first recorded by Coleman in 1843, has also been a rare casual: Park Street Dump 1966 (10/L), *B. Goater, Hb. B.M.*: **C. diluta** Ait., *Lesser Star Thistle*, first recorded by Phillips in *B.E.C. 1933 Rep.* 531, is occasional on rubbish dumps as a bird-seed alien: **C. melitensis** L. was recorded as a

casual from near Rye House by Trower and Druce in *B.E.C. 1916 Rep.* 492 and there are a few subsequent records: **C. montana** L. was recorded from Ware by Higgens in *B.E.C. 1916 Rep.* 492.

Serratula L.
S. tinctoria L.   *Saw-wort*   Kalm, 1748
Rough grassland   Native
Rare and now to be found occasionally in a few stations in the Barnet area. Otherwise I have seen it only on the disused airfield east of Barkway, 1958 (43/C) and on Therfield Heath, 1957 (33/J) where two plants appeared in one year only. It looked as if it might have been a misguided transplant experiment.

Cichorium L.
C. intybus L.   (Map 44f)   *Chicory*   Blake, c. 1820
Waste ground, field borders, etc.   Colonist
The earlier botanists noted this as being frequent especially on the Chalk and thought that it might be native. It appears now mainly as a relic of cultivation and with no marked frequency on any soil.

Lapsana L.
L. communis L.   (Map 44g)   *Nipplewort*   Blake, 1819
Pastures, roadsides, waste ground, etc.   Native
Abundant. H.S. 35, 53, 59, 61.

Arnoseris minima (L.) Schweigg. & Koete (*A. pusilla* Gaertn.), *Swine's Succory*, was apparently plentiful for a brief period at Easneye (see *Pryor*, 261). No information was given regarding its status.

Hypochoeris L.
H. radicata L.   (Map 44h)   *Common Cat's-ear*
Blake, c. 1820
Pastures, waste places, banks, etc.   Native
Very common on all but the most calcareous soils. H.S. 13, 23, 26, 28, 29, 50, 55, 57–59, 62, 69, 70–72, 81, 85, 86, 90, 92, 96, 101, 105.

H. maculata L., *Spotted Cat's-ear*, first recorded by B. F. C. Sennitt in 1954 from Therfield Heath (33/J)! has been seen there in limited quantity most years since. This is a welcome addition of a native species that may have escaped earlier discovery because of the close grazing of the hill. It is interesting to note that Henry Fordham thought he had seen it there – see Webb and Coleman (1843).

H. glabra L., *Smooth Cat's-ear*, was recorded by Coleman in 1840 from Bramfield no doubt as an introduced plant. It was probably as a wool adventive that Phillips recorded it from between Baldock and Clothall, 1927, *Hb. Ph.*

Leontodon L.
L. autumnalis L.   (Map 44i)   *Autumnal Hawkbit*
Blake, c. 1820
Pastures, roadsides, field borders, etc.   Native
Abundant. H.S. 6, 11, 13, 23, 24, 50–52, 57–59, 65, 66, 71–73, 84, 90–92, 102.

L. hispidus L.   (Map 44j)   *Rough Hawkbit*   Blake, 1820, Franks, 1820
Pastures, roadsides, railway banks, etc.   Native
Common on the more calcareous soils and especially so on the Chalk. H.S. 2–6, 11, 13–15, 23, 26, 28, 48–52, 54–56, 67, 73, 84, 100.

L. taraxacoides (Vill.) Mérat (Map 44k)   *Smooth Hawkbit*
L. leysseri G. Beck, *Thrincia hirta* Roth   Coleman, 1838
Pastures especially on base-rich soils   Native
Occasional in well-established turf and scattered over the county. H.S. 8, 13, 23, 27–29, 49, 56, 69, 71, 100.

Picris L.

P. echioides L. (Map 44 l) *Bristly Ox-tongue* Ellis, 1759
Helmintia echioides (L.) Gaertn.
Sides of ditches, rough pastures, roadsides etc. Native
Frequent on the Boulder Clay, rare elsewhere. H.S. 38, 50.

P. hieracioides L. (Map 44m) *Rough Ox-tongue*
P. spinulosa auct. Blake, 1821
Rough pastures, roadsides, field borders, etc. Native
Frequent on the Chalk and on chalky exposures. H.S. 2, 6, 50, 51, 67, 83, 84.

Tragopogon L.

T. pratensis L. (Map 44n) *Goat's-beard* Franks MS., 1823
Roadsides, railway banks, etc. Native
Common and well distributed. H.S. 24, 48, 51, 67, 84, 96.
The above applies to subsp. **minor** (Mill.) Wahlenb. which is the common form: subsp. **pratensis** is apparently a colonist or casual and is found regularly near to Hitchin and on some roadside verges in the east of the county.

T. porrifolius L., *Salsify*, a relic of cultivation, was first recorded from Hitchin by W. Ransom, 1838, *Hb. H.M.* Subsequent records were mainly from Hitchin and it was last recorded from there in 1951 by G. E. Evans, *Hb. H.M.*

Lactuca L.

L. virosa L. (*Map 44o*) *Greater Prickly Lettuce*
Coleman, 1841
Waste ground, rough pastures, etc. Colonist
Occasional and found most frequently in disused gravel pits. It persists around Hitchin where it is said by Little to have been grown as a medicinal herb.

L. serriola L. (Map 45a) *Prickly Lettuce*
A. W. Graveson, 1922
Waste places, disturbed ground, etc. Colonist
This increased rapidly after its introduction about fifty years ago but it now appears to be decreasing.

Mycelis Cass.

M. muralis (L.) Dumort. (Map 45b) *Wall Lettuce*
Lactuca muralis (L.) Gaertn. Blackstone, 1746
Woods and shady places on chalky soils, walls, etc. Native
Frequent in the west of the county. H.S. 17.

Sonchus L.

S. arvensis L. (Map 45c) *Corn Sow-thistle*
Coleman, 1839
Marshy places, arable fields, waste places, etc. Native
Abundant. H.S. 9, 10, 30, 31, 38, 39, 50, 52, 76, 105.

S. oleraceus L. (Map 45d) *Smooth Sow-thistle*
Coleman, 1838
Arable fields, waste ground, etc. Colonist
Abundant. H.S. 9, 14, 104.

S. asper (L.) Hill (Map 45e) *Prickly Sow-thistle*
Blake, c. 1820
Arable fields, waste ground, etc. Colonist
Abundant. H.S. 6, 20, 22, 25, 35.

Cicerbita Wallr.

C. macrophylla (Willd.) Wallr. (Map 45f) *Blue Sow-thistle* H. D. Garside, 1954
Lactuca macrophylla (Willd.) A. Gray
Roadsides, waste places, etc. Of garden origin
An attractive and increasing species.

Hieracium L.

A difficult genus presenting similar problems to the Brambles. There are, however, fewer microspecies of *Hieracium* present in the county than there are of *Rubus* and I have been fortunate in having my gatherings named either by P. D. Sell and C. West or by C. E. A. Andrews whom I wish to

thank for their assistance and advice. Except for *Hieracium pilosella* the records are not complete but the tetrads from which the various microspecies have been recorded are shown; * indicates that there is a specimen in Herb. Hitchin Museum.

H. murorum L. sensu lato *Hawkweed* Coleman, 1838
Wood borders, railway banks, roadsides, etc.
(Section Vulgata F. N. Williams).

H. exotericum Jord. ex. Bor. agg. Introduced. 41/Z*, 19/A.

H. grandidens Dahlst. Introduced. Roadside, Royston (34/Q), P. D. Sell, 1950. (see *Flora of Cambs*. 215).

H. maculatum Sm. Native. Weston Hills, Baldock, *J. E. Little, B.E.C. 1911 Rep.* 106 *Hb. Camb.* (for an earlier record see Pryor, 254).

H. diaphanum Fr. (*H. anglorum* (A. Ley) Pugsl.) Introduced. 12/Z*, 11/V*.

H. strumosum (W. R. Linton) A. Ley (*H. vulgatum* sensu Pryor) Native. 12/WZ, 91/A* Q*, 21/N*, 90/J*, 00/Y*, 10/LM*, 20/G, 30/ABD*, P*, S*, 09/T*, 19/G*, 29/ST*.

H. cheriense Jord. ex Bor. Introduced. 19/M*.

H. lepidulum (Stenstr.) Omang. Introduced. 20/K v.c. 21 [Herts.]*.

H. vulgatum Fr. Introduced. 19/Y*, 29/P*.
(Section Tridentata F. N. Williams).

H. trichocaulon (Dahlst.) Johans. Introduced. 19/S*.

H. calcaricola (F. J. Hanb.) Roffey Introduced. 19/Y*, 90/Z*.
(Section Sabauda F. N. Williams).

H. vagum Jord. Native. 20/L*, 30/S*, 09/S, 19/P*.

H. rigens Jord. Introduced. 29/S v.c. 20 [G.L.]*.

H. salticola (Sudre) Sell & West Introduced. 13/W*, 10/Y, 19/X* Y*.

H. virgultorum Jord. Native. 09/E*, 1955, *C. J. Bruxner.*

H. perpropinquum (Zahn) Druce (*H. sabaudum* auct., *H. boreale* sensu Pryor) Native. 22/G*, 81/Y, 01/G*, 21/G* J, 41/Y, 90/J, 00/K, 10/C* F*, 30/N*, 29/I* M*. H.S. 89.

H. pilosella L. sensu lato

H. pilosella L. sensu stricto (Map 45g) *Mouse-ear Hawkweed* Plukenet, 1690
Banks and pastures with short turf Native
Frequent in all but the most intensively cultivated parts of the county. H.S. 2–4, 6, 7, 14, 15, 22, 26, 49, 51–53, 55, 56, 58, 62, 65, 67, 69, 70, 83, 85, 92, 96.

H. brunneocroceum Pugsl. *Fox and Cubs*
H. C. Littlebury, 1912
A garden escape which may become easily established in similar situations to *H. pilosella*. 13/R, 23/BH, 42/V, 21/M, 41/Y, 00/U, 10/AL, 30/B, 09/R, 19/EXY.

H. praealtum Vill. ex Gochnat.
Introduced. Railway bank, north of Boreham Wood, 1965 (19/X), *Hb. H.M.*

H. spraguei Pugsl.
Introduced. Chorley Wood, c. 1955 (09/H), *R. H. Turney, Proc. Bot. Soc. Brit. Isles*, 2 (1956), 80.

Taraxacum Weber

T. officinale Weber (Map 45k) *Dandelion* Kalm, 1748
Pastures, waste ground, etc. Native
Ubiquitous. H.S. 3, 6, 7, 8, 11, 13, 14, 17–20, 22–25, 27–29, 35, 39, 46–53, 55, 56, 59, 62, 63, 65–67, 71–73, 75, 77, 82–84, 90, 96, 99, 100, 102, 105, 107.

T. palustre (Lyons) DC. *Marsh Dandelion* Coleman, 1838
(for the aggregate)
Marshy places Native
Very rare: Hitchin, 1933, *Hb. B.M.*, det. *T. lissocarpum* (Dahlst.) Dahlst., *H. Phillips* (see *B.E.C. 1936 Rep.* 224). I wish to thank Mr. D. E. Allen for his assistance in the account given here of this and the following species.

T. spectabile Dahlst.   *Marsh Dandelion*   Phillips, 1933
Marshy places   Native
No doubt more frequent than the records given below
would indicate. Hitchin, 1933, *Hb. B.M.*, det. *T. serratilobum*
Dahlst., *H. Phillips* (see *B.E.C. 1936 Rep.* 265); Rickmansworth Park, 1955, *A. H. G. Alston*, *Hb. B.M.*; Loudwater,
1955, *A. H. G. Alston*, *Hb. B.M.*; Rushy Meadow, 1966
(91/B), *D. E. Allen!*, *Hb. B.M.*; Burleigh Meadow, 1966
(22/S), *Hb. H.M.*; meadow, Boxmoor, 1966 (00/N),
Hb. H.M.; Sandon Green End, 1966 (33/G), *Hb. H.M.*

T. laevigatum (Willd.) DC.   (Map 45 l)   *Red-fruited*
T. erythrospermum Andrz. ex Bess.   *Dandelion*
                                                 Bentley, 1858
Dry pastures   Native
Frequent in short turf especially on the Chalk. H.S. 69, 84.

Carthamus tinctorius L. first recorded by A. W. Graveson
from Ware, 1911, *Hb. B.M.*, now occurs on rubbish dumps
probably as a bird-seed alien e.g. Pye Corner, 1964 (41/L);
Park Street, 1965 (10/L): **C. lanatus** L. was recorded from
Hitchin, no doubt as a wool adventive, by Phillips in *B.E.C.*
1929 Rep. 121.

Tagetes minuta L., a wool adventive, was recorded by
Little from Great Wymondley, 1928, *Hb. B.M.* and was
found at Little Wymondley, 1959 (22/D), *Hb. H.M.*:
T. patula L., a garden escape, was recorded from Welwyn
by H. Phillips in *B.E.C. 1933 Rep.* 471.

Guizotia abyssinica (L.f.) Cass., first recorded by A. W.
Graveson from Hertford, 1926, *Hb. Gr.*, occurs now as a
bird-seed alien e.g. Cock Lane, 1958 (30/U); Bulls Mill,
1958 (31/C); Hitchin, 1959 (12/V), etc.

Crepis L.
C. vesicaria L. subsp. **taraxacifolia** (Thuill.) Thell.
C. taraxacifolia Thuill.   (Map 45h)   *Beaked Hawksbeard*
                                 Herb. Haileybury, 1874
Roadsides, waste places, etc.   Colonist
A comparatively recent introduction which is now com-

mon and well distributed in the county. H.S. 7, 96.

C. biennis L.   (Map 45i)   *Rough Hawksbeard*
                                             Samuel Dale, 1724
Rough pastures, roadsides, etc.   Native
Rare but locally frequent in a few places in the south-west
of the county and a feature of some chalky roadside verges
near to Therfield.

C. capillaris (L.) Wallr.   (Map 45j)   *Smooth Hawksbeard*
C. virens L.   Blake, 1821
Pastures, roadsides, waste places, etc.   Native
Abundant. H.S. 7, 22, 50, 52, 56, 59, 62, 65, 66, 69, 80, 96.

C. setosa Haller f. was first recorded from Hitchin as a
casual by W. Dawson in the *Phytologist* 1: 997 (1844) and
there have been a few subsequent records. It has appeared
regularly at Dunstable, 1962–66 (02/B)!, v.c. 20 [Beds.],
G. Elwell, *Hb. Luton Mus.* The record of C. nicaeensis Balb.
in *Pryor*, 255, is to be doubted.

The following casuals have been recorded. **Centromadia
fitchii** (A. Gray) Greene, Hitchin (as *Hemizonia pungens*),
1924, *Little*, *Hb. Camb.*: **Cnicus benedictus** L., Hitchin, *H.
Phillips*, *B.E.C. 1928 Rep.* 744: **Galactites tomentosa**
Moench, Ware, 1910, *A. W. Graveson*, *Hb. Gr.*:**Grindelia
squarrosa** (Pursh) Dunal, Ware, *A. W. Graveson*, *B.E.C.*
1923 Rep. 188, *Hb. Gr.*: **Hemizonia kelloggii** Greene,
Ware, *Druce*, *B.E.C. 1917 Rep.* 111: **H. pungens** (Hook.
& Arn.) Torr. & Gray, Ware, *A. W. Graveson*, *B.E.C.*
1920 Rep. 129, *Hb. Gr.*: **Hedypnois cretica** (L.) Willd.
(*Rhagadiolus creticus* (L.) All.), Ware, *Higgens and Druce*,
B.E.C. 1917 Rep. 37. In addition the Compositae contain a
number of garden escapes and on rubbish dumps there are
to be found Sunflower (**Helianthus annuus** L., etc.),
Marigolds (*Calendula* spp.), Michaelmas Daisies (*Aster* spp.),
Cosmos, etc. but I have seen little purpose in studying
these.

ANGIOSPERMAE : MONOCOTYLEDONES

ALISMATACEAE
Alisma L.
A. plantago-aquatica L.   (Map 45m)   *Water-plantain*
                                             Franks, 1823
Ponds, flooded gravel pits, slow-flowing streams, etc.
                                                     Native
Frequent on the London Clay and occasional elsewhere.
H.S. 37, 108.

A. lanceolatum With.   (Map 45n)   *Narrow Water-plantain*
                                          Pryor, c. 1874
This is the common species in the Grand Union Canal and
otherwise found occasionally all over the county.

Baldellia ranunculoides (L.) Parl. (*Alisma ranunculoides*
L.) was recorded by Coleman from Ashwell Common,
1845. This is its only record for the county.

Damasonium alisma Mill. (*D. stellatum* Thuill.) is a rare
native of ponds on the London Clay. It was first recorded
by J. Woods from Totteridge Green, 1805, v.c. 20 [G.L.]
where it persisted for fifty years. It was reported from
Barnet Gate, 1928 by J. E. Cooper (see *Kent and Lousley*,
283) and it is said to grow on Hadley Green, v.c. 21 [Herts.
1904–65, G.L.] but I have looked for it here in vain.

Sagittaria L.
S. sagittifolia L.   (Map 45o)   *Arrow-head*   Coleman, 1838
Canals and slow-flowing rivers   Native
A feature of the Grand Union Canal and the Lea Naviga-
tion but otherwise rare.

BUTOMACEAE
Butomus L.
B. umbellatus L.   (Map 46a)   *Flowering Rush*
                                             Gerard, 1597
Slow-flowing rivers, reservoirs, etc.   Native
One of the most attractive species entering into the flora.
It is occasional in the south of the county and in the Tring
Reservoirs.

HYDROCHARITACEAE
Hydrocharis L.
H. morsus-ranae L.   *Frog-bit*   Coleman, 1841
A rare native of ponds and ditches which was known to
earlier workers from Watford, Waltham Cross and
Oughton Head. J. E. Little recorded it from Redcoats Green,
1921, where he thought it had been introduced by water
birds. During the period of the present survey it has been
found in disused gravel pits at Park Street, 1965 (10/L)!,

B. *Goater*, *Hb. H.M.* and below Cheshunt Lock, 1966 30/R in each case no doubt brought in by birds.

Elodea Michx.
E. canadensis Michx. (Map 46b)   *Canadian Waterweed*
Anacharis alsinastrum Bab.   Shute, 1856
Ponds, slow-flowing rivers, etc.   Colonist
A comparatively recent introduction that apparently reached its maximum frequency some time ago.

Stratiotes aloides L., *Water Soldier*, first recorded by John Ray, 1695, was known in the nineteenth century from Totteridge Green, v.c. 20 [G.L.] and Cadwell where in each case it was originally planted and has long been extinct.

Lagarosiphon major (Ridl.) Moss, a common aquarium plant, appeared in a pond at Potten End, 1966 (00/E) where it had been accidentally or intentionally introduced.

JUNCAGINACEAE
Triglochin L.
T. palustris L.   (Map 46c)   *Arrow grass*   Franks, 1820
Marshy ground usually near rivers   Native
Rare as it has apparently always been. H.S. 9, 76, 99.

POTAMOGETONACEAE
Potamogeton L.
I wish to thank Mr J. E. Dandy for giving me access to his very carefully collected records of the pondweeds and also for naming my specimens most of which have been added to the British Museum (Natural History) Herbarium (*Hb. B.M.*).

P. natans L.   (Map 46d)   *Broad-leaved Pondweed*
                                                              Blake, 1820
Ponds, flooded pits, reservoirs, etc.   Native
Occasional but well distributed.

P. polygonifolius Pourr.   *Bog Pondweed*
                                          Webb and Coleman, 1843
Bogs and ponds on acid heaths   Native
This has always been rare and the only recent records are Bricket Wood, *Salisbury*, *Trans. Herts. N.H.S.* 17 (1918) 62; pond, Danemead Wood (30/N)! *A. W. Graveson*; Hertford Heath, 1956 (31/K), *Lloyd-Evans*. In all of these stations it was known also to Coleman.

P. coloratus Hornem. was recorded by Coleman, 1838, from Ashwell Common, *Hb. B.M.* The only other record is from Hertford Heath by Higgens in *B.E.C. 1916 Rep.* 506 and is in error.

P. lucens L.   (Map 46e)   *Shining Pondweed*   Coleman,1839
Slow-flowing rivers, canals, flooded pits, reservoirs, etc.
                                                              Native
Frequent in suitable habitats but limited to deep water.

P. alpinus Balb.   *Reddish Pondweed*   Coleman, 1843
P. rufescens Schrad.
A rare native of ponds and rivers. The only recent records are: Marshmoor, 1926, *A. W. Graveson*, *Hb. Gr.*; Colne, Rickmansworth, 1939, confirming an earlier record by Crespigny, *G. Taylor*, *Hb. B.M.*; Stort Navigation, Hunsdon Mill, 1962 (41/F), *Hb. B.M.*

P. perfoliatus L.   (Map 46f)   *Perfoliate Pondweed*
                                                        Coleman, 1838
Rivers, canals, flooded pits, etc.   Native
Frequent in suitable habitats but requiring water of moderate depth for its growth.

P. friesii Rupr.   *Flat-stalked Pondweed*   Pryor, 1875
Reservoirs, slowly flowing water, etc.   Native
Known to Pryor only in Marsworth Reservoir and the adjoining canal system where it was refound by Dandy and Taylor, 1939–42, *Hb. B.M.* It was common in the Aylesbury branch of the canal (81/WX) in 1966 and otherwise I have found it only in the Lea Navigation at Stanstead St. Margarets, 1955 (31/V), *Hb. B.M.*

P. pusillus L.   *Lesser Pondweed*   Coleman, 1838 (more certainly Crespigny, 1881)
Ponds, flooded pits, reservoirs, etc.   Native
Rare. Dandy and Taylor recorded this from Wilstone Reservoir, 1939, *Hb. B.M.*, Little Tring, 1939, *Hb. B.M.* and Abbots Langley, 1939. I have found it at Colney Heath, 1958 (20/C), *Hb. B.M.*; Cole Green, 1956 (21/Q), *Hb. B.M.*; New Barnet, 1958 (29/M), v.c. 20 [G.L.].

P. obtusifolius Mert. & Koch, *Grassy Pondweed*, was collected by Coleman as *P. gramineus* at Colney Heath, 1840, *Hb. H.M.* and Coleman did in fact record *P. obtusifolius* from Colney Heath. I have found *P. obtusifolius* in a pond at Hook Wood, 1961 (20/Q), *Lloyd-Evans*! *Hb. H.M.* and at Aldenham Reservoir, 1960 (19/S).

P. berchtoldii Fieb.   (Map 46g)   *Small Pondweed*
                                          L. Manser (Hb. H.M.), 1836
Ponds, flooded pits, etc.   Native
More common than *P. pusillus* many of the early records of which should be referred to this.

P. trichoides Cham. & Schlecht.   *Hair-like Pondweed*
                                                           Taylor, 1939
This was recorded by Dandy and Taylor from Wilstone Reservoir: the old canal, Little Tring; the canal, Abbots Langley and the River Colne, West Hyde. It was shown to me by Dandy at Tring in 1956.

P. compressus L., a native, was collected at Little Tring, 1935, by A. H. Carter. It was found there up to 1944, *Hb. B.M.*, but has not been seen since.

P. acutifolius Link, a native, was found by Coleman in the river between London Colney and Colney Heath, 1844 (*Hb. B.M.*). There have been no subsequent records.

P. crispus L.   (Map 46h)   *Curled Pondweed*   Coleman, 1843
Ponds, slow-flowing rivers, etc.   Native
Occasional but well distributed.
P. × cooperi (Fryer) Fryer (*P. crispus × perfoliatus*)
This was first collected in Marsworth Reservoir by Druce in 1915 and identified by Dandy and Taylor twenty-five years later. It occurs now in the Grand Union Canal from the Reservoirs to Northchurch and probably still further south (*Hb. B.M.*, *Hb. H.M.*).

P. pectinatus L.   (Map 46i)   *Fennel-leaved Pondweed*
P. flabellatus Bab.   Webb and Coleman, 1843
Rivers, flooded pits, reservoirs, etc.   Native
Common in the Grand Union Canal and the Lea and Stort Navigations but only occasional elsewhere.

Groenlandia Gay
G. densa (L.) Fourr. (Map 46j)   *Opposite-leaved Pondweed*
Potamogeton densus L.   Coleman, 1838
Fast-flowing clear streams   Native
Occasional and apparently in no way diminished.

ZANNICHELLIACEAE
Zannichellia L.
Z. palustris L. (Map 46k) *Horned Pondweed*
Rudge, c. 1810
Ponds, ditches, etc. Native
Rare but often overlooked.

LILIACEAE
Convallaria L.
C. majalis L. *Lily-of-the-Valley* Gerard, 1597
A rare native of woodland known to Coleman from a few places in the Broxbourne Woods area. It was also found in Stubbings Wood in 1868 by T. B. Blow. Current records are: Wormley Wood, 1954, *R. M. Payne* in *Kent and Lousley*, 273; Thunderdell Wood, naturalized (91/R)!, *J. Wilson*.

Polygonatum multiflorum (L.) All., *Solomon's Seal*, was recorded from a few stations in the nineteenth century but it is doubtful whether it was ever native. **Asparagus officinalis** L. subsp. **officinalis** has appeared only as an escape from cultivation.

Ruscus L.
R. aculeatus L. *Butcher's Broom* Blackstone, 1737
Rare in woods and old parkland mainly in the south of the county. In all the places in which I have seen it e.g. Great Wood, Northaw; Priory Park, Ware; Chase Wood, Potters Bar; and Aldenham Park, there was some evidence of previous planting. Butcher's Broom may well have been native in Hertfordshire at some earlier time but it is doubtfully so now.

Lilium martagon L., *Martagon Lily*, is rare and has apparently always been originally planted e.g. Aconite Wood, Hertingfordbury, 1912, *Hb. Gr.*; Moor Place, Much Hadham c. 1955, *J. Hopkins*. For earlier records see *Pryor*, 415.

Fritillaria L.
F. meleagris L. *Snake's-head* Davies (see *Pryor*, 509), 1805
This was, until comparatively recently, probably a native plant of meadows in the neighbourhood of Totteridge and Barnet as at South Mimms (*South Mymms, the story of a parish*, F. Britain, 1931): see also *Kent and Lousley*, 276. In 1966 B. Wurzell found a number of plants in a disused garden adjoining a meadow at Darlands (29/L)!, v.c. 20 [G.L.] but there were unfortunately a number of cultivated plants growing in association with it. It is still a feature of meadows at Rothamsted (11/G) where it may have been originally introduced.

Tulipa sylvestris L., *Wild Tulip*, first recorded by Coleman, 1843, was established as a naturalized plant in a few stations as at Bayford, 1934, *D. Meyer, Hb. Letch. Mus.* and Wyddial, 1940, *H. W. Pugsley, Hb. B.M.* These were among the stations given in *Pryor*, 416.

Gagea lutea (L.) Ker-Gawl. (*G. fascicularis* Salisb.) was recorded once only from Easneye (see *Pryor*, 416). In 1954 a Ware Grammar School girl found it in 'Broxbourne Woods', *Hb. H.M.* but could not recall the exact location. Its status in the county is uncertain.

Ornithogalum L.
O. umbellatum L. (Map 46 l) *Star-of-Bethlehem*
Coleman, 1838
Sites of old gardens, roadsides, churchyards, etc.
Garden escape
Rare but often persisting when once established.

O. nutans L. (*Myogalum nutans* (L.) Kunth), *Drooping Star-of-Bethlehem*, was first recorded from Ashwell, 1862, *C. Bond Smith, Hb. Druce*. It is similar in status to *O. umbellatum* but is more rare. Pugsley found it in a coppice at Aspenden, 1940, *Hb. B.M.* which was one of the few stations given by Pryor.

Endymion Dumort.
E. non-scriptus (L.) Garcke (Map 46m) *Bluebell*
Scilla nutans Sm. Isaak Walton, 1653
Woods Native
Common generally but absent from the Chalk and much of the London Clay. H.S. 12, 16, 36, 39–41, 46, 60, 61, 63, 77, 80, 82, 87, 89, 95.

E. hispanicus (Mill.) Chouard (*Scilla hispanica* Mill.), two plants, Bull's Green, *Higgens* in *B.E.C. 1916 Rep.* 505, no doubt a garden escape.

Muscari atlanticum Boiss. & Reut. (*M. racemosum* auct.), a garden escape, was recorded in *Pryor*, 417, and by Little from Hitchin: **Colchicum autumnale** L. – J. Britten in *J. Bot. 1917*, 351, says that *Bot. Mag.* tab. 2673, 1826, was drawn from material collected in the neighbourhood of Hertford: **Asphodelus fistulosus** L. was recorded from Ware, 1916, *Hb. Gr.*

Paris L.
P. quadrifolia L. (Map 46n) *Herb Paris* Webb, 1838
Woods Native
Frequent on the Boulder Clay but very rare elsewhere. The nineteenth-century botanists recorded it from a number of woods in the west of the county but it is already apparently extinct in the only places in which I have seen it here, i.e. Howe Grove (00/P) where it was shown to me by R. B. Benson in 1955; Berrygrove Wood (19/J), destroyed by the M1 motorway. H.S. 36.

JUNCACEAE
Juncus L.
J. tenuis Willd. (Map 46o) *Slender Rush* R. D. Anstead
(Hb. Camb.), 1952
Heaths, disused gravel pits, bare ground, etc. Colonist
A recent introduction which is increasing.

J. squarrosus L., *Heath Rush*, was first recorded by Coleman in 1839 and was known as a native from a few wet heaths on the Colne Gravels. It was last recorded by Sir Edward Salisbury from Colney Heath about 1930.

J. compressus Jacq., a native species, has been well known for many years at Startops End Reservoir (91/BG)!, H.S. 20, but I do not know when it was first seen there. I found it by the roadside at Shaftenhoe End (43/B) in 1955 but have not been able to refind it.

J. bufonius L. (Map 47a) *Toad Rush* Coleman, 1838
Damp grassy places, woodland rides, etc. Native
Frequent on all but the most calcareous soils. H.S. 33–35, 39, 66, 77, 78, 87, 89.

J. inflexus L. (Map 47b) *Hard Rush* Coleman, 1838
J. glaucus Sibth.
Places which are wet at least in the winter Native
Common on all soils except the Clay-with-Flints. H.S. 8, 9, 18–20, 27–29, 33, 35, 37, 38, 65, 66, 74, 76, 77, 90, 91, 99, 100.

J. effusus L. (Map 47c) *Soft Rush* Blake, c. 1820
Wet places Native
Common on all soils except the Chalk. H.S. 18, 2 ', 33–35, 37, 39, 41, 42, 44, 45, 60, 62, 72, 75, 77, 78, 80, 81 87, 90, 91, 97, 99, 101, 102, 104, 105–109.

J. effusus × **inflexus** (*J.* × *diffusus* Hoppe)
First recorded by Webb and Coleman (1843) and there are specimens in *Herb. Cambridge* by Coleman from Hertingfordbury, 1844, and Darman's Green, 1846, and by J. E. Little from St. Ippolyts, 1921; Radwell, 1921; Norton Green, 1924, and Ickleford, 1925. I have seen no material in the field which I am satisfied is this.

J. subuliflorus Drej. (Map 47d) *Clustered Rush*
J. conglomeratus auct. Blake, c. 1820
Wet heathy places and also frequently in woods Native
Less common than *J. effusus* and found much less frequently on the calcareous soils. H.S. 35–39, 42, 44, 46, 55, 62, 64, 72, 75, 77, 78, 80, 81, 87, 89, 97–100, 104, 105.

J. subnodulosus Schrank (Map 47e) *Blunt-flowered Rush*
J. obtusiflorus Ehrh. ex Hoffm. Webb and Coleman, 1843
Marshes on calcareous soils Native
Considered to be rather rare by Coleman but the places in which it grows are remote from the parts of the county that he knew best. H.S. 9, 10, 18, 19, 27, 30, 31, 76.

J. acutiflorus Ehrh. ex Hoffm. (Map 47f) *Sharp-flowered*
J. sylvaticus auct. *Rush* Blake, 1820
Marshes on acid soils Native
Occasional on the London Clay and river gravels but rare elsewhere. H.S. 76, 87, 89, 99, 101, 105.
J. acutiflorus × **articulatus**
Rare in marshy places with both parents but possibly overlooked. Hadley Common, 1961 (29/N), v.c. 21 [Herts. 1904–65, G.L.], *P. M. Benoit*!, *Hb. H.M.*; Water End, 1966 (01/F), *P. M. Benoit*!

J. articulatus L. (Map 47g) *Jointed Rush* Coleman, 1838
J. lamprocarpus Ehrh. ex Hoffm.
Marshes, sides of ponds, etc. Native
Frequent and well distributed. H.S. 18, 19, 27, 29, 35, 38, 39, 66, 74, 78, 90, 91, 97, 99, 102, 108.

J. bulbosus L. sensu stricto (Map 47h) *Bulbous Rush*
J. supinus Moench Coleman, 1839
Boggy places on heathy soils Native
Rare and recorded mainly from the London Clay. H.S. 87, 89, 102.

J. kochii F. W. Schultz is found in similar situations to *J. bulbosus* e.g. Bricket Wood, 1964 (10/F), H.S. 87, *P. M. Benoit*!, *Hb. H.M.*

Luzula DC.
L. pilosa (L.) Willd. (Map 47i) *Hairy Woodrush*
L. vernalis (Reichard) DC. Blake, c. 1820
Woods on all but the most calcareous soils Native
Frequent. H.S. 45, 60, 64, 77, 78, 81, 103–105.

L. forsteri (Sm.) DC. *Forster's Woodrush* Coleman, 1838
This has always been rare in woods on gravelly soils and during the period of the present survey it has been found at Bishop's Wood (09/Q), *F. Rose*; Easneye Wood (one of Coleman's stations), 1956 (31/W), *Hb. H.M.*; wood by Shire Lane, 1956 (09/F), *Hb. H.M.*; Shire Lane by Phillipshill Wood, 1966 (09/C).

L. sylvatica (Huds.) Gaudin (Map 47j) *Greater Woodrush*
L. maxima (Reichard) DC. Webb and Coleman, 1843
Woods on gravelly soils Native
Occasional on the London Clay but rare elsewhere.

L campestris (L.) DC. (Map 47k) *Field Woodrush*
Coleman, 1838
Pastures Native
Frequent and well distributed. H.S. 11, 13, 18, 23, 25, 26, 29, 51, 55–58, 66, 68–73, 81, 85, 86, 90–92, 96–98, 100–102.

L. multiflora (Retz.) Lejeune (Map 47 l) *Heath Wood-*
L. erecta Desv. *rush* Blackstone, 1737
Heaths, woodland rides, etc. Native
Frequent on the more acid soils. H.S. 42, 78, 81, 87, 89, 104, 105.

AMARYLLIDACEAE
Allium L.
A. vineale L. (Map 47m) *Crow Garlic* Steele MS., c. 1730
Arable fields, roadside verges, etc. ? Native
Frequent on the Boulder Clay but rare elsewhere. H.S. 59.

A. oleraceum L., *Field Garlic*, was recorded from Welwyn by Blake, and Whempstead by A. W. Graveson in *B.E.C. 1920 Rep.* 150, *Hb. Gr.* The only recent record is from north of Ashwell, 1950, *J. C. Gardiner*, *Hb. H.M.*

A. ursinum L. (Map 47n) *Ramsons* Franks, 1823
Woods and shady dells Native
Occasional but well distributed, H.S. 63.

A. paradoxum (Bieb.) G. Don, *Few-flowered Leek*, a garden escape becoming naturalized, was recorded by F. M. Day from Moor Lane, Rickmansworth, 1957, *Hb. H.M.*, and P. Sheasby from near Tewin Mill. 1961, *Hb. B.M.* H. B. Souster has drawn my attention to its abundance on the roadsides at Poplars Green (21/R).

Leucojum aestivum L., a garden escape, is sometimes naturalized, e.g. at Totteridge Green, 1964 (29/L), v.c. 20 [G.L.], *D. J. Hinson*, as is **Galanthus nivalis** L., *Snowdrop*, which has been recorded often since Coleman's time.

Narcissus L.
N. pseudonarcissus L. (Map 47o) *Daffodil* Steele MS., c. 1730
Meadows, woods, etc. Native
Rare but no doubt diminished as it has been one of the main victims of the uprooting mania of some gardeners.

N. hispanicus Gouan (*N. major* Curt.), **N.** × **biflorus** Curt. and **N. majalis** Curt. (*N. poeticus* auct.) were recorded in *Pryor, 412*, as naturalized plants. There have been very few subsequent records.

IRIDACEAE
Iris L.
I. pseudacorus L. (Map 48a) *Yellow Flag* Franks, 1820
Marshes, riversides, etc. Native
Frequent and well distributed.

I. foetidissima L. (Map 48b) *Gladdon* J. E. Smith, 1799
Woods Native
Rare as it has always been and found most often in woods on calcareous soils.

Sisyrinchium bermudiana L. (*S. angustifolium* Mill.) was recorded from a waste heap, Welwyn, by Phillips in *B.E.C. 1932 Rep.* 111 and from canal bank, Rickmansworth, 1947, *O. M. Richards*, *Hb. B.M.*: **Crocus purpureus** Weston (*C. vernus* auct.) was recorded from Totteridge, v.c. 20 [G.L.], *New Botanist's Guide* (1835); near Colney Heath, 1840, 'R.S.H.,' *Hb.B.M.*; Brookman's Park, c. 1875, *T. B. Blow. Hb. B.M.* Both species were no doubt garden escapes.

DIOSCOREACEAE
Tamus L.
T. communis L. (Map 48c) *Black Bryony*
Blake, c. 1820
Hedges, wood borders, etc. Native
Common. H.S. 5, 10, 17, 32, 39, 40, 46, 47, 52, 54, 61, 67, 78–80, 84, 93, 95, 106.

ORCHIDACEAE
Cephalanthera Rich.

C. damasonium (Mill.) Druce   (Map 48d)   *Broad-leaved*
C. pallens Rich.   *White Helleborine* Eales, 1695
Beech woods   Native
Rare in beech woods on the Chalk and chalk exposures.
C. longifolia (L.) Fritsch (*C. ensifolia* (Schmidt) Rich.) has
been claimed as a Hertfordshire species only on the slender
authority of Eales in Camden's *Britannia* (1695).

Epipactis Zinn

E. palustris (L.) Crantz, *Marsh Helleborine*, first recorded
by Alchone c. 1752, has always been a very rare native of
perpetually wet ground. It appeared at Foulwells, (30/I)!,
H.S. 99, from 1850 to 1963, when the marsh was drained.
Otherwise it occurs only at Moor Green, Ardeley, 1959
(32/I), H.S. 27, *Lloyd-Evans*!, *Hb. H.M.*

E. helleborine (L.) Crantz   (Map 48e)   *Common Helle-*
E. latifolia (L). All.   *borine* Gerard, 1597, for the aggregate
Woods and shady places   Native
Occasional, especially on the London Clay.

E. purpurata Sm.   (Map 48f)   *Violet Helleborine*
    Webb and Coleman, 1843
Woods   Native
Occasional and found most frequently on the Clay-with-
Flints.

E. leptochila (Godfery) Godfery, *Narrow-lipped Helle-*
borine, is known only as a rare native of beech woods at
Stubbings Wood (91/A, 90/E)!, H.S.17, *Hb. H.M.* Pugsley
collected a specimen in 1943 (*Hb. B.M.*) but it may have
been known here earlier.

E. phyllanthes G. E. Sm., *Green-flowered Helleborine*,
has been recorded from a copse by Wilstone Reservoir,
1959 (91/B), det. D. P. Young, *R. I. Sworder*, and from an
orchard, Chorleywood, 1959 (09/H), det. V. S. Summerhayes, *R. F. Turney*.

Spiranthes Rich.
S. spiralis (L.) Chevall.   *Autumn Lady's Tresses*
S. autumnalis Rich.   Sabine, 1811
A very rare plant of close pastures which was known to
Coleman and Pryor from a number of widely distributed
stations. Little, on the other hand, did not know it from the
county and its only recent record is from a chalk slope near
Berkhamsted Common, 1956 (91/V)!, *E. A. Glennie*.

Listera R. Br.
L. ovata (L.) R. Br.   (Map 48g)   *Twayblade* Eales, 1695
Woods, pastures, etc.   Native
Frequent in woods on the Boulder Clay and occasional on
chalk downs and in other pastures. H.S. 10, 15, 33, 45, 78, 95.

Neottia Guett.
N. nidus-avis (L). Rich.   (Map 48h)   *Bird's-nest Orchid*
    Doody, c. 1700
Woods   Native
Occasional in beech woods and in deep shade in woods on
clay soils.

Hammarbya paludosa (L.) Kuntze (*Malaxis paludosa*
(L.) Sw.), *Bog Orchid*, has been claimed as a Hertfordshire
plant only on the authority of Parkinson's *Theatrum
Botanicum* (1640), 505.

Herminium Guett.
H. monorchis (L.) R. Br.   *Musk Orchid* Doody c. 1700
This was known from a few disused chalk pits to nine-
teenth-century botanists, see *Pryor*, 409. It was found in
Offley Park by Margaret Brown in 1923 and remained

there until at least 1928. The only other recent record is
from a chalk slope near Tingley Wood, 1966 (13/F)!,
F. Bentley, providing a welcome discovery of a plant feared
to have been lost to the county.

Coeloglossum Hartm.
C. viride (L.) Hartm.   *Frog Orchid*   How, 1650
This was apparently not infrequent as a native in well-
established pastures but it has diminished as pastures have
been improved. I know it only from Sheethanger Common
(00/H), H.S.48, where it is locally frequent.

Gymnadenia R. Br.
G. conopsea (L.) R.Br. subsp. **conopsea**   (Map 48i)
    Fragrant Orchid Dickson, 1815
Chalk Hills   Native
Occasional on well established chalk downland, H.S. 5.
subsp. **densiflora** (Wahlenb.) G. Camus, Bergon & A.
Camus.
This distinct plant of boggy places on calcareous soils was
recorded by W. W. Newbould from Barkway Moor in
Syme's edition of Smith's *English Botany*, 9 (1869), 103,
and this was apparently the first British record. Its current
records are Foulwells, 1955, site drained 1963 (30/I), H.S. 99,
Hb. H.M.; Bury Mead, 1959 (32/I).

Platanthera Rich.
P. chlorantha (Custer) Reichb.   (Map 48j)   *Greater*
    Butterfly Orchid Gerard, 1597
Woods   Native
Frequent in woods on the Boulder Clay. H.S.33, 36.

P. bifolia (L.) Rich., *Lesser Butterfly Orchid*, is a rare
native of wet heathy places and was recorded by Coleman
from two stations south of Tring. There are no later records.

Ophrys L.
O. apifera Huds.   (Map 48k)   *Bee Orchid* Johnson, 1633
Calcareous pastures   Native
Found most frequently on the Chalk but by no means
limited to it. It has a preference for previously disturbed
soils and is uncertain in its appearance. H.S. 2, 48, 50.

O. insectifera L.   (Map 48 l)   *Fly Orchid* Gerard, 1597
O. muscifera Huds.
Woods and shady places   Native
Rare and found usually on the Chalk. Unlike *O. apifera*
it is usually constant in its appearance. H.S. 54.

Himantoglossum hircinum (L.) Spreng., *Lizard Orchid*,
was found at Oxshott Hill, 1931, by K. R. Wooster. There
was one plant which was uprooted and grown on in
a garden where it later died. Flowers from the plant are in
Hb. Letchworth Mus.

Orchis L.
O. militaris L.   *Military Orchid*   Dickson, 1815
    (more certainly Coleman, 1841)
Edges of woods on the Chalk   Native
This was recorded from three Hertfordshire stations. 1,
Tring (Dickson's station). Chambers (1838) wrote of its
abundance on the hills to the south west of the town but
doubt has been expressed as to whether it was indeed in
Hertfordshire. 2, Aldbury, at the bottom of Timms Spring
Copse, at the foot of the hill under the Bridgewater column
(Coleman's station), *Webb and Coleman*, 286. Crewe found
it still there in 1867 and Blow took a specimen in 1878,
Hb. B.M. 3, near Rickmansworth, *Mr. Cory*, *Webb and
Coleman*, 286. This was no doubt Garett Wood, Springwell
(09/L), where the colony extended into Middlesex and
D. H. Kent has given me details of notes made on it by

John Benbow. Between 1889 and 1902 thirty-four plants were counted but none seen after 1902. Garett Wood, Middlesex (D. H. Kent says Herts.), 1900, *H. W. Pugsley, Hb. B.M.*

O. ustulata L.   *Burnt-tip Orchid*   Ray, 1670
A very rare native of chalk downs recorded at intervals of time and distance on the Chalk from Tring to Royston. It is still at Therfield Heath (33/J) plants having been seen there in 1965 by W. Darling.

O. morio L.   (Map 48m)   *Green-winged Orchid*
                                      Franks, 1823
Well-established pastures   Native
Occasional on the Boulder Clay but rare elsewhere. It is becoming more scarce because of changes in the maintenance of pastures. H.S. 71, 73.

O. mascula (L.) L.   (Map 48n)   *Early Purple Orchid*
                                      Franks, 1820
Woods   Native
Frequent in woods on the Boulder Clay and rare elsewhere. H.S. 36.

Dactylorhiza Nevski

D. fuchsii (Druce) Soó subsp. **fuchsii** (Map 48o) *Spotted
                      Orchid*   Franks MS., 1820 (for the
Orchis maculata auct.   aggregate)
Woods, calcareous pastures, etc.   Native
Frequent and well distributed. H.S. 27, 28, 31, 32, 34, 38, 39, 46, 50, 51, 62, 87, 99.
D. fuchsii subsp. **fuchsii × praetermissa**
Chalk pit, Grove Mill, 1953 (13/V)!, *Hb. H.M.*, with both parents, det. V.S. Summerhayes, *G. L. Evans.*

D. maculata (L.) Soó subsp. **ericetorum** (Linton) P. F.
Hunt & Summerh. *Heath Spotted Orchid* J. E. Little, 1910
Orchis ericetorum Linton
Wet heathy pastures   Native
Distribution not fully known. J. E. Little recorded it from Burleigh Meadow and Hertford Heath but I have seen it only at Bricket Wood, 1956 (10/F), *Hb. H.M.* conf V. S. Summerhayes; side of Bayford Wood, 1955 (30/E), *Hb. H.M.* conf. V. S. Summerhayes.

D. incarnata (L.) Soó   *Early Marsh Orchid*   Pryor, 1874
Orchis incarnata L.
Marshes on calcareous soils   Native
Very rare as it has always been: Bury Mead (32/I), *J. L. Fielding*; Green End, Sandon (33/G), H.S. 29, *Hb. H.M.*; Rushy Meadow, where it was also recorded by H. H. Crewe (91/B), H.S. 19.

D. praetermissa (Druce) Soó (*Map 49a*) *Southern Marsh
Orchis latifolia* auct.   *Orchid*   Coleman, 1838
Marshy places on a greater variety of soils than *D. incarnata*
                                      Native
Rare. H.S. 6, 10, 19, 76.

Aceras R. Br.

A. anthropophorum (L.) Ait. f.   *Man Orchid*
                              Dickson, 1815
Chalk hills   Native
Very rare. Dickson's record was from Tring and was doubtfully in Hertfordshire. Sir Edward Salisbury reported (*Trans. Herts. N.H.S.* 18 (1924), 61) a single specimen from near Tring just outside the county boundary. It is now known in the county only on a chalk bank near Offley (12/N)! where according to Little it was first seen by Miss Mears in 1931.

Anacamptis Rich.
A. pyramidalis (L.) Rich.   (Map 49b)   *Pyramidal Orchid*
                                   Coleman, 1838
Chalk downs and chalk exposures   Native
Occasional and found generally in places where the soil has been disturbed and in consequence widely distributed. H.S. 5, 49.

ARACEAE
Acorus L.
A. calamus L.   (Map 49c)   *Sweet Flag*   Irvine, 1838
Sides of artificial waterways, ornamental lakes, etc. Denizen
A comparatively recent introduction which appears to have spread slowly.

Arum L.
A. maculatum L.   (Map 49d)   *Cuckoo Pint, Lords-and-
                                Ladies*   Franks, 1821
Hedgerows, shady places, etc.   Native
Very common. H.S. 36, 40, 46, 47, 63, 82, 95.

LEMNACEAE
Lemna L.
L. polyrhiza L.   (Map 49e)   *Great Duckweed*
Spirodela polyrhiza (L.) Schleid.   Coleman, 1839
Ponds   Native
Occasional and found mainly in the south of the county.

L. trisulca L.   (Map 49f)   *Ivy Duckweed*   Coleman, 1838
Ponds and ditches   Native
Occasional but well distributed.

L. minor L.   (Map 49g)   *Common Duckweed*   Blake, 1824
Still water anywhere   Native
Common. H.S. 18, 65, 66, 76.

L. gibba L.   (Map 49h)   *Fat Duckweed*   Coleman, 1839
Ponds, ditches, etc.   Native
The least common of our duckweeds and rarely established in the same site for many years together.

SPARGANIACEAE
Sparganium L.
S. erectum L.   (Map 49i)   *Branched Bur-reed*   Blake, 1820
S. ramosum Huds.
Sides of ponds, ditches and slow-flowing rivers   Native
Frequent and well distributed. H.S. 76. I have not attempted to examine this critically but subsp. **erectum** appears to be the common form. The only record I have of subsp. **neglectum** (Beeby) Schinz & Thell. is from Brickendon Lane, 1919, *A. W. Graveson, Hb. Gr.*

S. emersum Rehm.   (Map 49j)   *Small Bur-reed*
S. simplex Huds. pro parte   Coleman, 1838
Rivers, ponds, etc.   Native
Frequent in the Grand Union Canal and the Lea and Stort Navigations where it often does not flower. It is otherwise found in ponds mainly in the south of the county.

S. minimum Wallr., *Least Bur-reed*, was recorded by Coleman as a rare native of ponds at Welwyn, 1842, *Hb. Bolton Mus.* There were no subsequent records.

TYPHACEAE
Typha L.
T. latifolia L. (Map 49k) *Bulrush, Reedmace* Rudge, c. 1810
Ponds, flooded pits, reservoirs, etc.   Native
Frequent in the south of the county and occasional elsewhere. H.S. 65.

T. angustifolia L. (Map 49 l) *Lesser Bulrush*
Webb and Coleman, 1843
Reservoirs, flooded pits, etc.   ? Native
Probably introduced. It flowers much less frequently than
T. latifolia.

CYPERACEAE
Eriophorum L.
E. angustifolium Honck. *Cotton-grass* Steele MS., c. 1730
Bogs and marshy places   Native
This was known to earlier botanists from a few sites in
various parts of the county. It survived at Oughton Head
until about 1939 but I knew it only at Foulwells, 1955
(30/I), H.S. 99, where it remained until the site was drained
in 1963.

E. latifolium Hoppe is a Hertfordshire plant only on the
evidence of Coleman's record from Barkway Moor, 1849.

Scirpus L.
S. lacustris L. (Map 49m) *Basket-rush* Coleman, 1838
Rivers, reservoirs, flooded pits, etc.   Native
Frequent in the Lea Navigation, occasional elsewhere.

S. setaceus L. (Map 49n) *Bristle Club-rush* Coleman, 1838
Isolepis setacea (L.) R. Br.
Damp grassy and muddy places affording little competition.
                    Native
Occasional but well distributed. H.S. 29, 77, 78.

S. fluitans L. (*Eleogiton fluitans* (L.) Link), *Floating Spike-rush*, first recorded by Webb and Coleman, 1843, has
always been a very rare native of heathy ponds. Current
records are: flooded pit on site of Cheshunt Marsh, 1956
(30/Q), *Hb. H.M.*; Arkley Manorial Lands, 1962 (29/D),
v.c. 20 [G.L.], *Hb. H.M.*

S. sylvaticus L., *Wood Club-rush*, a native species, was first
recorded by J. Woods,1805, and is still to be found by the
Spital Brook and similar wet places in neighbouring woods
much as Coleman knew it. Its tetrad distribution is
30/EIMP.

S. maritimus L., *Sea Club-rush*, was found in a pond on
Bovingdon Green, 1958 (00/B), *E. Milne-Redhead*!; disused
pit, London Colney, 1958 (10/R), *Hb. H.M.* It is not known
how it was introduced.

Eleocharis R. Br.
E. acicularis (L.) Roem. & Schult. *Needle Spike-rush*
Webb and Coleman, 1843
Muddy shores of reservoirs, etc.   Native
Rare. Aldenham Reservoir (Coleman's original station),
1958 (19/S), *Hb. H.M.*; Hilfield Reservoir, 1964; side of
canal, Hunton Bridge, 1964 (00/Q)! *P. J. Ellison*; Little
Tring Reservoir, 1917 (91/B), *E. J. Salisbury*, re-found,
1964, *J. C. Gardiner*! Also recorded from pond, Totteridge,
1906 v.c. 20 [G.L.], *J. E. Cooper*, *Hb. B.M.*

E. quinqueflora (F. X. Hartmann) Schwarz (*Scirpus
pauciflorus* Lightf.), *Few-flowered Spike-rush*, a rare native,
was first recorded by J. Woods, 1805, and known from a
few boggy places to nineteenth-century workers. Current
records are: Foulwells, 1955 (30/I), H.S. 99, *Hb. H.M.*;
Sandon Green End, 1962 (33/G), H.S. 29, *Hb. H.M.*

E. multicaulis (Sm.) Sm., *Many-stemmed Spike-rush*,
was first recorded by Coleman, 1839, and known to him
only from bogs at Bell Bar and Kentish Lane. There is a
specimen of Coleman's from Kentish Lane, 1843, *Hb.
Bolton Mus.* There have been no subsequent records.

E. palustris (L.) Roem. & Schult. subsp. **vulgaris** Walters
(Map 49o)   *Common Spike-rush* J. A. Hankey, 1838
Sides of ponds, wet places, etc.   Native
Occasional but well distributed. H.S. 20, 29, 74, 91, 108.
subsp. **microcarpa** Walters is found in similar habitats to
subsp. *vulgaris*. Sawbridgeworth Marsh, 1955 (41/X), det.
S. M. Walters, *Hb. H.M.*

Blysmus Panz.
B. compressus (L.) Panz. ex Link *Flat-headed Sedge*
Crespigny, 1877
A very rare native species of wet meadows which Crespigny
found on Rickmansworth Moor, 1877, *Hb. B.M.* Current
records are: meadow, Boxmoor, 1963 (00/N)!, *P. J.
Ellison*, *Hb. H.M.*; Sarratt Bottom, 1955 (09/J).

Schoenus nigricans L., a rare native of fens, was recorded
by Coleman from Barkway Moor, 1843, and there were
no subsequent records.

Cyperus longus L., *Galingale*, is plentiful beside the lake
in Aldenham Park (19/T), *Hb. H.M.*, where it was originally
planted, and in a disused garden, Smaley Wood, Meesden,
1959 (43/G), *Hb. H.M.* **C. eragrostis** Lam. (*C. declinatus*
Moench) was recorded from the border of 'Batchmore
Lake', Rickmansworth, *G. C. Machonchy*, *B.E.C. 1917 Rep.*
54.

Carex L.
C. distans L.   *Distant Sedge*   Coleman, 1838
A rare native known to the earlier botanists only from
marshes in the Hitchin area and Wilstone Reservoir. It
has been found during the period of the present survey at
Oughton Head (13/Q); Green End, Sandon (33/G); Rushy
Meadow, H.S. 18, 19 (91/B); marsh below Easneye (31/R);
Foulwells, H.S. 100 (30/I).

C. hostiana DC.   *Tawny Sedge*   Coleman, 1839
C. hornschuchiana Hoppe, *C. xanthocarpa* Degl.
A very rare native recorded for similar situations to *C.
distans* by nineteenth-century workers. Last record –
Knebworth (Burleigh Meadow), 1919, *A. W. Graveson*,
Hb. Gr.

C. binervis Sm.   *Moor Sedge*   Coleman, 1846
A rare native of wet heathy places which I have seen only at
Hertford Heath (one of Coleman's stations), 1955 (31/K),
Hb. H.M.; ride, Newton Wood, 1960 (22/G), *Hb. H.M.*

C. lepidocarpa Tausch *Long-stalked Yellow Sedge*
C. flava sensu Webb & Coleman   A. Wallis (Herb. Brit.
Mus.), 1841
A rare native of marshes on calcareous soils and confused
by Pryor and Little with the following species. I have seen
it only at Rushy Meadow, 1958 (91/B), H.S. 18, 19.

C. demissa Hornem. (Map 50a) *Common Yellow Sedge*
C. oederi sensu Webb & Coleman,   Coleman, 1838
included in *C. lepidocarpa* in Pryor's Flora.
Wet heathy places   Native
Rare and found most frequently on the London Clay.
H.S. 78, 87, 90.

C. sylvatica Huds. (Map 50b) *Wood Sedge*
Coleman, 1838
Woods   Native
Frequent and well distributed. H.S. 16, 32–40, 42, 44–47,
50, 51, 62, 63, 77, 78, 88, 93, 95, 100, 103, 104, 107.

C. pseudocyperus L. (Map 50c) *Hop Sedge*
Coleman, 1838
Ponds, sides of lakes, etc.   Native
Frequent in ponds on the London Clay as it was found to be
by Coleman and occasional elsewhere.

C. rostrata Stokes   *Bottle Sedge*   Coleman, 1838
Marshy places on acid soils   Native
Considered to be not uncommon by Webb and Coleman and by Pryor but I have not seen it in the county. It was recorded by Salisbury from Hertford Heath, 1918.

C. vesicaria L. (Map 50d) *Bladder Sedge* Coleman, 1838
Sides of ponds and marshy places   Native
Occasional but absent from considerable areas.

C. riparia Curt.   (Map 50e)   *Great Pond Sedge*
Blake, c. 1820
Sides of rivers, wet places, etc.   Native
Frequent by the larger rivers. Druce wrote in *B.E.C. 1920 Rep.* 154 that specimens in Ansell's herbarium (1846) from Franks Field, Brickendon, labelled '*C. vesicaria*' are **C. × csomadensis** Simonk. (*C. riparia × vesicaria*).

C. acutiformis Ehrh. (Map 50f) *Pond Sedge*
Coleman, 1838
Sides of rivers, ponds, ditches, etc.   Native
A little more widespread than *C. riparia.* H.S. 9, 19, 31, 74–76, 99.

C. pendula Huds. (Map 50g) *Drooping Sedge*
J. Woods, 1805
Damp woods   Native
Very common on the London Clay and almost as common in woods on the more sticky parts of the Boulder Clay. H.S. 32, 34–39, 82, 93, 103, 105.

C. strigosa Huds. (Map 50h) *Thin-spiked Wood Sedge*
Coleman, 1838
A native in woods and having the same distribution as *C. pendula* but more restricted. It is one of the more interesting plants of the county in view of its absence or great rarity in neighbouring counties. H.S. 34, 35, 43, 44.

C. pallescens L. (Map 50i) *Pale Sedge* Coleman, 1838
Woodland rides   Native
Occasional but well distributed. H.S. 62, 77, 78, 89, 104, 105.

C. panicea L. (Map 50j) *Carnation Sedge* Coleman, 1838
Marshes on calcareous or neutral soils   Native
Occasional but well distributed. H.S. 18, 27, 29, 31, 76, 87, 90, 91, 99.

C. flacca Schreb. (Map 50k) *Glaucous Sedge*
C. glauca Scop.   Coleman, 1838
Pastures, bare ground at some season waterlogged, etc.
Native
Common on chalk grassland and occasional elsewhere in a variety of habitats. H.S. 1–3, 5, 8, 13–15, 18, 19, 21, 27–29, 33, 38, 39, 48–52, 56, 67, 71, 73, 78, 84, 99, 100, 104.

C. hirta L. (Map 50 l) *Hairy Sedge* Coleman, 1838
More or less wet places   Native
Frequent and well distributed. H.S. 8, 9, 18, 27–29, 42, 65, 66, 73–75, 90, 91, 99, 109.

C. pilulifera L. (Map 50m) *Pill Sedge* Coleman, 1838
Heaths and heathy rides in woods   Native
Occasional in the south of the county. H.S. 26, 64, 81, 97, 98, 101, 105.

C. caryophyllea Latourr. (Map 50n) *Spring Sedge*
C. praecox auct.   Coleman, 1838
Pastures, chalk downland, etc.   Native
Occasional on the Chalk, chalk exposures and other calcareous soils. H.S. 2, 13–15, 48, 49, 84.

C. elata All. (*C. stricta* Gooden., non Lam., *C. hudsonii* A.Benn.), *Tufted Sedge*, a rare native, was recorded from Hitchin Common, i.e. Oughton Head, by Woods, c. 1840 (see *Pryor*, 440) and it was found here until 1928 by Little. The only other records are: 'near Broxbourne and in Gilstone Park', *Druce* in *B.E.C. 1922 Rep.* 752. I have seen it near West Mill, 1960 (32/T), *J. C. Gardiner!*, *Hb. H.M.*, *Hb. B.M.*

C. acuta L. (*C. gracilis* Curt.), *Graceful Sedge*, a rare native, was recorded by Coleman in 1838 from Hertford – Hoddesdon area. The only recent record is from between Ettridge Farm and Franksfield Cottages, 1955 (30/I), *F. Rose*, *Hb. H.M.*

C. nigra (L.) Reichard (Map 50o) *Common Sedge*
C. vulgaris Fr.   Coleman, 1838
Marshy places mainly on heathy ground   Native
Occasional but well distributed. H.S. 9, 29, 76, 87, 90, 91, 97, 98, 101, 102.

C. paniculata L. (Map 51a) *Tussock Sedge*
Coleman, 1838
Marshy places on calcareous soils   Native
Occasional and found often near to rivers. Little considered it to be variable and listed stations for some forms.
C. × boenninghausiana Weihe (*C. paniculata × remota*)
This was found by Coleman in 1843 in Balls Wood, *Hb. B.M.*, *Hb. Bolton Mus.* this being apparently its first recognition as a British plant. It was found in 1959 by a member of the Wild Flower Society during a Field Meeting at Easneye (31/W), *Hb. H.M.*

C. appropinquata Schumach. (*C. paradoxa* Willd., non J. F. Gmel.) was recorded by J. Benbow from meadows near Harefield, in Herts., in *J. Bot. 1885*, 339. As there are records supported by specimens for the neighbouring part of v.c. 21, Middlesex, there is no need to doubt Benbow's record.

C. diandra Schrank (*C. teretiuscula* Gooden.), a rare native of heathy ponds, was recorded by Coleman, 1843, for two stations in the Broxbourne Wood area but there were no subsequent records.

C. otrubae Podp. (Map 51b) *Fox Sedge* Rudge, c. 1810
C. vulpina auct.
Damp places, sides of ditches, etc.   Native
Frequent in those parts of the county where the soils hold water. H.S. 27, 29, 33, 35, 37–39, 77.
C. × pseudoaxillaris K. Richt. (*C. otrubae × remota*)
C. axillaris Gooden. non L.
This was first recorded by Coleman in 1838 and there are early specimens in *Hb. B.M.* and *Hb. Bolton Mus.* Current records are: High Wych, 1959 (41/S), *P. C. and J. Hall*, *Hb. H.M.*; Kettle Green, 1959 (41/E), *P. C. and J. Hall*; gravel pit, Colney Heath, 1958 (20/C), *Hb. H.M.*; Beeches Wood, 1962 (43/K); Hook Wood, 1961 (20/Q).

C. disticha Huds. (Map 51c) *Brown Sedge* Coleman, 1838
Marshy places   Native
Occasional but well distributed. H.S. 9, 19, 76, 90, 91.

C. divulsa Stokes (Map 51d) *Grey Sedge* Rudge, c. 1810
Dry hedge banks and grassy yet shady places   Native
Occasional but well distributed. H.S. 22, 38, 46, 107.

C. spicata Huds. (Map 51e) *Spiked Sedge* Coleman, 1838
C. contigua Hoppe, *C. muricata* auct.   (for the aggregate)
Pastures, hedgebanks, etc.   Native
Frequent and well distributed. H.S. 8, 11, 18, 62.

C. muricata L. (Map 51f) *Lesser Spiked Sedge*
C. pairaei F. W. Schultz   Little, 1924
In similar situations to *C. spicata* but on more acid soils.
Occasional and found mainly on the river gravels. H.S. 22.

C. echinata Murr.   *Star Sedge*   Coleman, 1838
Wet heathy places   Native
Rare as it has always been and recorded during the present
survey from: bog near Moor Park, 1953, *R. A. Boniface*
in *Kent and Lousley*, 298; Patmore Heath, 1956 (42/M),
Hb. H.M.; Foulwells, 1955 (30/I); Arkley Manorial Lands,
1957 (29/H), v.c. 20 [G.L.]. I have not seen it at either
Hertford Heath or Bricket Wood where it was known to
previous workers.

C. remota L. (Map 51 g) *Remote Sedge* Coleman, 1838
Wet shady places   Native
Common in the more wooded parts of the county. H.S. 34,
35, 37–39, 42, 45, 47, 77, 78, 88, 103, 106, 107.

C. ovalis Gooden. (Map 51h) *Oval Sedge* Coleman, 1838
C. leporina auct.
Wet heathy places   Native
Occasional and more frequent on the London Clay than
elsewhere. H.S. 26, 39, 42, 78, 87, 90, 91, 97, 98, 101, 105,
109.

C. pulicaris L., *Flea Sedge*, first recorded by Coleman in
1838 was known to him from a few scattered marshes as a
native species. Little did not know it in the county and during the present survey one solitary record was made –
Rushy Meadow, 1958 (91/B), *Trevor Lloyd-Evans*!

C. dioica L., a very rare native, was recorded from Hitchin
Common (i.e. Oughton Head) and Walsworth Common by
Isaac Brown, 1839. It was last recorded by H. Groves in
1878, *Hb. B.M.*

C. curta Gooden. recorded by Crespigny (1877) from
Totteridge and *C. laevigata* Sm. recorded from St. Albans,
1883 (see *Pryor*, 510) are almost certainly errors.

GRAMINEAE
Phragmites Adans.
P. communis Trin. (Map 51i) *Reed* Blake, 1820
Shallow water at sides of lakes, swampy places, etc. Native
Occasional but well distributed.

Molinia Schrank
M. caerulea (L.) Moench (Map 51j) *Purple Moor Grass*
M. varia Schrank   Coleman, 1838
Wet heathy pastures and marshes on acid soils   Native
At least as frequent as it was in Coleman's time. H.S. 10,
18, 87, 89, 97, 98.

Sieglingia Bernh.
S. decumbens (L.) Bernh. (Map 51k) *Heath Grass*
                                        Coleman, 1838
Heaths and acid pastures   Native
Occasional but absent in the north-east of the county.
H.S. 26, 55, 57, 58, 69, 70, 72, 84–87, 89, 97, 98, 102.

Glyceria R. Br.
G. fluitans (L.) R. Br. (Map 51 l) *Sweet-grass*
                                        Coleman, 1838
Ponds, ditches, etc.   Native
Frequent and well distributed. H.S. 42, 74, 78, 87–91, 102,
106, 109.
G. × pedicellata Townsend (*G. fluitans × plicata*)
                           (Map 51m)   Pryor, 1875
Occasional and not necessarily found with either or both
parents.

G. plicata Fr. (Map 51n) *Plicate Sweet-grass*
                           Webb and Coleman, 1849
Ponds, ditches, etc.   Native
Less common than *G. fluitans*. H.S. 18, 33, 34, 39, 66, 74,
76.

G. declinata Bréb. (Map 51o) *Glaucous Sweet-grass*
        Mrs. L. M. P. Small (Kent and Lousley, 314), 1905
Muddy margins of ponds   Native
Occasional and well distributed.

G. maxima (Hartm.) Holmberg (Map 52a) *Reed Sweet-
                                grass* Blake, 1824
G. aquatica (L.) Thunb., non J. & C. Presl.
Rivers, flooded pits, reservoirs, etc.   Native
Frequent in the areas with favourable habitats. H.S. 20, 108.

Festuca L.
F. pratensis Huds. (Map 52b) *Meadow Fescue*
F. elatior sensu Pryor   Kalm, 1748
Pastures   Native
Common and well distributed. H.S. 8, 9, 13, 27, 33, 66, 71,
73, 75, 76, 90, 91.

F. arundinacea Schreb. (Map 52c) *Tall Fescue*
F. elatior L.   H. Fordham, 1843
Rough pastures, roadside verges, etc.   Native
Frequent and well distributed. H.S. 10, 18, 19, 27, 28, 33,
76, 99.

F. gigantea (L.) Vill. (Map 52d) *Giant Fescue*
                                        Blake, 1824
Woods, shady ditches, etc.   Native
Common throughout the county. H.S. 16, 17, 32, 34–36,
39, 46, 47, 82, 88, 95, 103, 106, 107.

F. heterophylla Lam., *Various-leaved Fescue*, was probably
originally sown in woodlands and is now naturalized. Its
records are: by the side of New Pond, 1955 (43/C), H.S. 37,
Hb. H.M.; Plashes Wood, 1957 (32/V).

F. rubra L. (Map 52e) *Red Fescue* Coleman, 1838
F. duriuscula L.
Pastures, roadsides, railway banks, etc.   Native
Abundant. H.S. 4–7, 9–11, 14, 18, 19, 21–29, 42, 48, 49,
51–53, 55–58, 66–71, 75, 76, 78, 79, 83, 84, 86, 90–92,
96–98, 100–102, 109. This is a very variable species the
forms of which have not been studied in the county.

F. ovina L. (Map 52f) *Sheep's Fescue* Coleman, 1838
Pastures with a close turf   Native
Occasional and found on a great variety of soils from chalk
downland to heathy commons. H.S. 1–3, 7, 14, 15, 56, 67,
69, 70, 84–86, 92.

F. tenuifolia Sibth. (Map 52g) *Fine-leaved Sheep's Fescue*
                                        Little, 1909
Heaths and clearings in heathy woods   Native
Rare and limited to the more acid soils but its distribution
is not fully known.

F. longifolia Thuill., *Hard Fescue*, has been planted on
railway banks, golf courses, etc. and persists. It had not
been recorded before the present survey and its known
distribution now is: Hadham Mill (det. C. E. Hubbard),
c. 1960 (41/I), *J. L. Fielding*; golf course, Hertford, 1965
(31/K), *T. C. E. Wells*!, *Hb. H.M.*; railway bank, Hitchin,
1959 (12/Z), *Hb. H.M.*; railway bank, Watford, 1959
(19/C); railway bank, Northchurch, 1960 (90/U); Cock
Lane dump, 1966 (30/N).

× **Festulolium loliaceum** (Huds.) P. Fourn. (Map 52h)
Festuca pratensis × Lolium perenne,   *Hybrid Fescue*
Festuca loliacea Huds.   J. Woods, 1805
Water meadows, old established damp pastures, etc. Native
Occasional and often well established but not necessarily
with either parent also present.

Lolium L.

L. perenne L. (Map 52i) *Perennial Rye Grass* Kalm, 1748
Pastures, roadside verges, etc.   Native
Abundant. H.S. 1, 7, 8, 13, 14, 17, 19, 23, 24, 28, 29, 41, 44,
46, 49, 50, 52, 53, 55, 56, 58, 59, 62, 65, 66, 69, 71, 73, 77,
84, 102, 105.

L. multiflorum Lam.   (Map 52j)   *Italian Rye Grass*
                      Webb and Coleman, 1849
Pastures, waste places, etc.   Naturalized
Common in leys and persisting in all parts of the county.
H.S. 52.

L. temulentum L.   *Darnel*   Ellis, 1733
L. arvense With.
This was apparently a frequent and troublesome cornfield
weed a century ago. It now occurs from time to time as a
casual on most of our rubbish dumps.

Vulpia C. C. Gmel.

V. bromoides (L.) Gray (Map 52k) *Squirrel-tail Fescue*
                       Coleman, 1838
V. sciuroides (Roth) C. C. Gmel. ex Reichb.
Heaths, railway sidings, etc.   Native
Occasional on the more gravelly soils. H.S. 69, 105.

V. myuros (L.) C. C. Gmel. (Map 52 l) *Rat's-tail Fescue*
                       Coleman, 1838
Railway sidings, bare gravelly places, etc.   Colonist
Rare and probably less common that it was in Coleman's
time.

Puccinellia distans (Jacq.) Parl., normally a plant of seashores, was found in Ware brickfields, 1924, *A. W. Graveson, Hb. Gr.*

Catapodium Link

C. rigidum (L.) C. E. Hubbard (Map 52m) *Fern Grass*
Sclerochloa rigida (L.) Link   Coleman, 1838
Bare ground on the chalk, dry banks, etc.   Native
Occasional on the more calcareous soils. H.S. 22, 84.

Poa L.

P. annua L.   (Map 52n)   *Annual Meadow-grass*
                       Blake, c. 1820
Cultivated land, bare ground, waste places, etc. Native
Ubiquitous. H.S. 17, 33, 38, 39, 41, 42, 47, 53, 56–60, 65,
66, 69, 72, 77, 78, 80, 82, 84, 88, 93, 94, 104–106.

P. nemoralis L. (Map 52o) *Wood Meadow-grass*
                       Blake, 1824
Wood borders, shady places, etc.   Native
Common except on the most calcareous soils. H.S. 16, 17,
37, 54, 80, 94, 103, 105.

P. compressa L.   (Map 53a) *Flattened Meadow-grass*
                       Franks, 1819
Walls, bare chalk as in disused pits, etc.   Native
Occasional but well distributed. H.S. 6.

P. pratensis L.   (Map 53b) *Smooth Meadow-grass*
                       Kalm, 1748
Pastures, roadside verges, etc.   Native
Abundant. H.S. 4, 5, 7, 10, 18–22, 24, 25, 30, 33, 37, 38,
48, 50, 52, 58, 69, 71, 75, 79, 84, 90–92, 96, 109. A variable
species the forms of which have not been examined in the
county.

P. angustifolia L.   (Map 53c)   *Narrow-leaved Meadow-
          grass* F. Long (W.E.C 1910-11 Rep.), 1910
P. pratensis subsp. *angustifolia* (L.) Gaudin
Poor pastures, railway banks, etc.   Native
Occasional as a native in gravelly pastures but probably
originally planted on railway banks. H.S. 6, 48, 51, 67, 83.

P. trivialis L.   (Map 53d)   *Rough Meadow-grass*
                       Coleman, 1838
Meadows, cultivated land, waste places, etc.   Native
Abundant and equally as common as *P. pratensis*. H.S.
7–9, 11, 12, 18, 20, 21, 24, 25, 27–30, 33–42, 44–47, 52,
55, 90, 91, 93–95, 103–105, 107, 109.

P. chaixii Vill., *Broad-leaved Meadow-grass*, was originally
planted and is now naturalized in woods. Recorded from
Watford, 1955, *R. M. Harley* (see *Kent and Lousley,* 313);
Bramfield Park Wood, 1962 (21/W), *Hb. H.M.*

Catabrosa Beauv.

C. aquatica (L.) Beauv. (Map 53e) *Water Whorl-grass*
                       Coleman, 1838
Muddy places by slow-flowing rivers, etc.   Native
Occasional but well distributed. H.S. 65, 66, 76.

Dactylis L.

D. glomerata L.   (Map 53f)   *Cock's-foot* Kalm, 1748
Pastures, roadsides, open woodland (occasionally), etc.
                                Native
Abundant. It is very variable as selected strains are often
sown in leys. H.S. 1, 4–8, 10, 11, 13, 19, 21–25, 28, 33, 34,
37, 39, 46–50, 52–56, 58, 59, 62, 66, 67, 69, 71, 73, 75, 78–80,
83, 84, 94, 96, 100, 102, 105.

Cynosurus L.

C. cristatus L. (Map 53g) *Crested Dog's-tail* Kalm, 1748
Dry pastures, old grassland, etc.   Native
Very common. H.S. 6–8, 13, 23, 24, 27–29, 49–51, 55, 56,
59, 62, 65, 66, 69, 71, 73, 79, 84, 91, 100.

C. echinatus L., *Rough Dog's-tail*, a casual or colonist, was
first recorded by Salisbury from the canal bank between
Rickmansworth and Harefield, 1914, *Trans. Herts. N.H.S.*
16 (1916), 77, and found occasionally in the county between
then and 1939 much as it was in Bedfordshire. There are no
current records.

Briza L.

B. media L.   (Map 53h) *Quaking Grass* Kalm, 1748
Well established pastures on calcareous soils   Native
Frequent on the Chalk and occasional elsewhere. H.S. 1–3,
5, 8, 13–15, 23, 28, 29, 48–50, 55, 56, 67, 73, 75, 84, 99.

B. minor L. was recorded either as a casual or in error from
Berkhamsted in *Trans. Herts. N.H.S.* 2 (1883), 239.

Melica L.

M. uniflora Retz.   (Map 53i)   *Wood Melick*
                       Blackstone, 1735
Woods, shady banks, etc.   Native
Common on the Clay-with-Flints and only occasional
elsewhere. H.S. 16, 61.

Bromus L.

B. erectus Huds.   (Map 53j)   *Upright Brome*
                    Webb and Coleman, 1843
Chalk grassland   Native
Dominant on chalk downland and much increased since
sheep were taken off the hills about thirty years ago. Locally
frequent on chalk exposures. H.S. 1–3, 5, 7, 14, 56, 83 84.

B. ramosus Huds. (Map 53k) *Hairy Brome* Blake, 1824
Woods, hedgebanks, shady ditches, etc. Native
Common. H.S. 11, 17, 32–35, 37, 39, 46, 47, 54, 63, 78, 80, 107.

B. benekenii (Lange) Trimen (Map 53 l) Dandy and
Melderis, 1959
Beech woods Native
Limited to the west of the county where beech woodland is natural. H.S. 17.

B. inermis Leyss. (Map 53m) *Hungarian Brome*
Salisbury (Trans. Herts. N.H.S. 15: 172), 1914
An introduced plant and found mainly on railway banks where it was no doubt originally planted.

B. sterilis L. (Map 53n) *Barren Brome* Blake, 1824
Roadsides, waste ground, field borders, etc. Native
Very common. H.S. 7, 11, 14, 22.

B. mollis L. (Map 53o) *Soft Brome* Blake, 1824
Pastures, roadside verges, etc. Native
Common. H.S. 2, 7, 22, 50, 69, 100.

B. thominii Hardouin (Map 54a) has been found occasionally and well distributed during the period of the present survey. It has been probably introduced with grass mixtures.

B. lepidus Holmberg (Map 54b) is of similar origin, distribution and frequency to *B. thominii*.

B. racemosus L. *Smooth Brome* Webb and Coleman, 1849
Water meadows Native
This was considered to be frequent by Coleman but it is certainly not so now. Current records are: Boxmoor Common, 1963 (00/N), *Hb. H.M.*; water meadow, Stapleford, 1963 (31/D); meadows by R. Chess, (09/N).

B. commutatus Schrad. (Map 54c) *Meadow Brome*
Webb and Coleman, 1843
Meadows, arable fields, etc. Native
More common than *B. racemosus* and found as often in arable fields as in meadows. H.S. 73, 75.

B. interruptus (Hack.) Druce was first recorded as a cornfield weed in Britain by A. M. Barnard from 'Odsey, 1849', *Hb. B.M.* Odsey is in a narrow tongue of Cambridgeshire surrounded on three sides by Hertfordshire and it is possible that Miss Barnard's record may refer to Hertfordshire.

B. secalinus L. *Rye Brome* Ellis, 1736
This was recorded as an occasional but uncertain cornfield weed by Coleman and it was known also to Little. Current records are: railway, south of Brookman's Park, 1955 (20/L); disused pit, Chiswell Green, 1961 (10/H), *Hb. H.M.*; Cole Green Dump, 1963 (30/U).

B. arvensis L., recorded by Pryor and Little, was a weed introduced probably with sainfoin. There are no recent records.

The following are recorded as casuals: **B. carinatus** Hook. & Arn., Rickmansworth Aquadrome, 1961 (09/M), *Hb. H.M.*: **B. diandrus** Roth (*B. rigens* auct.) Ware, *A. W. Graveson, B.E.C. 1920 Rep.* 159: **B. macrostachys** Desf. det. A. Melderis, waste ground, Hitchin, 1912 (*B. patulus* Mert. & Koch), *J. E. Little, Hb. Camb.*: **B. squarrosus** L., Mead Lane, Hertford, 1927, *A. W. Graveson, Hb. Gr.*: **B. rigidus** Roth, Ware U.D.C. heaps, 1920, *A. W. Graveson, Hb. Gr.*: **B. tectorum** L., New Mill, Hoddesdon, 1847,

H. Williams, this was apparently its first occurrence in Britain (see *Webb and Coleman*, 339): **B. unioloides** Kunth (*B. schraderi* Kunth) Watford (see Pryor, 467); Ware U.D.C. heaps, 1920, *A. W. Graveson, Hb. Gr.*

Brachypodium Beauv.
B. sylvaticum (Huds.) Beauv. (Map 54d) *Wood False-brome* Blake, c. 1820
Woods, shady places, railway banks, chalk pits, etc. Native
Common. H.S. 3, 11, 14, 16, 17, 21, 24, 33, 37, 41, 45–47, 50–53, 56, 60, 62, 67, 79, 80, 84, 88, 94, 95, 103, 105.

B. pinnatum (L.) Beauv. *Chalk False-brome*
Coleman, 1843
A native of calcareous pastures which was considered rare by Coleman and known from only one station by Little. I have seen it in limited quantity at the foot of Therfield Heath, 1957 (34/K) and more abundantly on a railway bank, Standon, 1964 (32/V), *Hb. H.M.* It is also recorded from a railway bank, Letchworth, 1966 (23/B) *H. Bowry*.

Agropyron Gaertn.
A. caninum (L.) Beauv. (Map 54e) *Bearded Couch*
Triticum caninum L. Coleman, 1838
Wood borders, shady ditches, etc. Native
Frequent on the more calcareous soils.

A. repens (L.) Beauv. (Map 54f) *Couch, Twitch*
Triticum repens L. Blake, 1824
Rough grassland, a troublesome weed of cultivated land, etc. Colonist
Abundant. H.S. 5, 10, 20, 24, 35, 59, 96. Little made a thorough study of the named variants of this grass.

Hordeum L.
H. secalinum Schreb. (Map 54g) *Meadow Barley*
Coleman, 1838
Meadows Native
Frequent on calcareous soils only.

H. murinum L. (Map 54h) *Wall Barley* Blake, c. 1820
Roadsides, waste ground, etc. Colonist
Very common and found regularly near villages but it is absent from a few of the more uninhabited areas.

H. jubatum L., *Fox-tail Barley*, a rare casual, was first recorded from Ware by A. W. Graveson in *B.E.C. 1920 Rep.* 161, *Hb. Gr.* and found by him also on Cole Green Dump, 1924, *Hb. Gr.* where it was refound in 1955 (21/Q), *Hb. H.M.* Other current records are Oak Hill Park, 1964 (29/S), *J. Mason*; Welwyn Garden City, 1961 (21/L), *J. C. Gardiner!, Hb. H.M.*; Hitchin U.D.C. Dump, 1965 (13/V).

H. marinum Huds. was recorded by Little from Purwell Field, 1912, and Wymondley, 1930. It was more likely the wool adventive, *H. hystrix* Roth.

Hordelymus (Jessen) Harz
H. europaeus (L.) Harz (Map 54i)) *Wood Barley*
Elymus europaeus L. Woodward, 1787
A rare native of woods on the Chalk in the west of the county and having a distribution very similar to that of *Bromus benekenii*.

Koeleria Pers.
K. cristata (L.) Pers. (Map 54j) *Crested Hair-grass*
Coleman, 1838
Pastures Native
Frequent on the Chalk and on chalk exposures. H.S. 1–3, 7, 14, 15, 25, 26, 48, 49, 56, 67, 84, 92.

Trisetum Pers.

T. flavescens (L.) Beauv.   (Map 54k)   *Yellow Oat-grass*
Avena flavescens L.   Coleman, 1838
Dry pastures, roadsides, etc.   Native
Common and well distributed. H.S. 4, 5, 7, 8, 11, 13, 19, 21–25, 28, 37, 48, 49, 52, 53, 55, 56, 59, 67, 69, 71, 84, 96, 105.

Avena L.

A. fatua L.   (Map 54 l)   *Common Wild-oat*   Ellis, 1733
Arable fields, waste places, etc.   Colonist
A serious weed in cornfields on the Boulder Clay and occasional elsewhere. It is very variable and Dr. Hubbard has named specimens of mine var. **pilosissima** Gray, which seems to be the common form, var. **pilosa** Syme and var. **glabrata** Peterm.

A. ludoviciana Durieu   *Winter Wild-oat*
                                                J. M. Thurston, 1945
Arable fields, waste places, etc.   Colonist
A comparatively recent introduction which closely resembles *A. fatua* and in consequence its distribution in the county is not fully known. Miss Thurston found it first in the experimental plots at Rothamsted and I have seen it on Bishop's Stortford rubbish dump, 1956 (42/V), *Hb. H.M.* I have also recorded it from the following tetrads: 22/Q, 81/Y, 91/W, 31/V, 41/S, 10/L.

A. strigosa Schreb. was recorded as a casual by Coleman (specimen from Bayford, 1844, *Hb. Bolton Mus.*). There are no recent records.

Helictotrichon Bess.

H. pubescens (Huds.) Pilg.   (Map 54m)   *Hairy Oat-grass*
Avena pubescens Huds.   Coleman, 1838
Pastures, old grassland, etc.   Native
Frequent on the Chalk and other calcareous soils. H.S. 2, 7–9, 13–15, 48, 49, 52, 67, 84.

H. pratense (L.) Pilg.   (Map 54n)   *Meadow Oat-grass*
Avena pratensis L.   Kalm, 1748
Chalk pastures   Native
Much less common than *H. pubescens*. H.S. 1, 3, 7, 14, 15, 48, 49.

Arrhenatherum Beauv.

A. elatius (L.) Beauv. ex J. & C. Presl   (Map 54o)
A. avenaceum Beauv.   *False Oat-grass*   Ellis, 1750
Roadside verges, rough pastures, etc.   Native
Abundant. H.S. 4–11, 13, 17, 19, 21, 22, 24–26, 28, 31, 46, 48, 50, 53, 54, 56, 58, 59, 67, 75, 79, 80, 83, 84, 96, 99, 100, 106.

Holcus L.

H. lanatus L.   (Map 55a)   *Yorkshire Fog*   Blake, 1824
Roadside verges, rough pastures, etc.   Native
Abundant. H.S. 4–6, 8, 9, 11, 13, 18–21, 23–30, 33,–35, 37, 41, 42, 46, 48–50, 55–59, 62, 65–81, 84, 87–91, 94, 96, 98–103, 105–107, 109.

H. mollis L.   (Map 55b)   *Creeping Soft-grass*   Kalm, 1748
Woods, wood borders, margins of heaths, etc.   Native
Frequent except on calcareous soils where it is absent or rare. H.S. 44, 62, 64, 69, 78, 80, 81, 88, 97, 100, 101, 104, 105.

Deschampsia Beauv.

D. cespitosa (L.) Beauv.   (Map 55c)   *Tufted Hair-grass*
Aira cespitosa L.   Blake, 1821
Wet pastures, marshy places, etc.   Native
Common and well distributed. H.S. 8, 10, 13, 16–21,

26–28, 32–39, 41, 42, 44–47, 60, 62, 64, 73, 75, 77, 78, 87–89, 90, 93, 97, 98, 102, 103, 105, 106, 109.

D. flexuosa (L.) Trin.   (Map 55d)   *Wavy Hair-grass*
Aira flexuosa L.   Webb and Coleman, 1843
Heaths, wood borders, etc.   Native
Occasional on the more heathy soils especially in cleared woodland.

Aira L.

A. praecox L.   (Map 55e)   *Early Hair-grass*   Coleman, 1838
Avena praecox (L.) Beauv.
Heaths, bare gravelly ground, etc.   Native
Frequent on the river gravels and London Clay but rare elsewhere. H.S. 26, 57, 58, 81, 85, 92.

A. caryophyllea L.   (Map 55f)   *Silvery Hair-grass*
Avena caryophyllea (L.) Weber   Coleman, 1838
In similar situations to *A. praecox*   Native
Occasional on the river gravels and found particularly on railway embankments and edges of gravel pits. H.S. 105.

Calamagrostis Adans.

C. epigejos (L.) Roth   (Map 55g)   *Wood Small-reed*
                                                        Coleman, 1838
Wood borders, scrub, etc.   ? Native
Occasional and mainly in the north of the county where it has increased, for having been once introduced, it spreads vegetatively to form a clump which persists for a long period.

C. canescens (Weber) Roth (*C. lanceolata* Roth), a native species, was first recorded by Coleman, 1839, and was known to him from three woods in different parts of the county – specimen from Balls Wood, 1843, *E. Forster*, *Hb. B.M.* I know of no recent records.

Agrostis L.

A. canina L.   (Map 55h)   *Brown Bent*   Coleman, 1838
Wet heaths, borders of marshy areas, etc.   Native
Rare and scattered over the southern half of the county. H.S. 42, 57, 69, 70, 72, 78, 80, 81, 87, 89, 98, 102, 105.

A. tenuis Sibth.   (Map 55i)   *Common Bent*   Kalm, 1748
A. vulgaris With., *A. pumila* L.
Pastures, heaths, etc.   Native
Common except on the Chalk and much of the Boulder Clay. H.S. 13, 23, 25, 26, 42, 44, 55–59, 62, 64, 68, 69, 71, 72, 78–81, 84–87, 92, 96–98, 100–102, 104–106, 109.

A. gigantea Roth   (Map 55j)   *Black Bent*   Phillips, 1927
Rough grassland, edges of arable fields, etc.   Native
Frequent but its distribution is not fully known because of confusion with *A. tenuis*, from which it was not separated by earlier workers, including Little.

A. stolonifera L.   (Map 55k)   *Creeping Bent*
A. palustris Huds.   Coleman, 1838
Pastures, roadside verges, arable fields, etc.   Native
Ubiquitous. H.S. 1, 3, 4, 6–8, 11, 13, 15, 18–22, 24, 28, 29, 33, 37–39, 42, 44, 48, 50, 52, 53, 55, 56, 58, 59, 66, 67, 72, 74, 76–80, 84, 87, 88, 90, 91, 94. A very variable species the varieties of which have not been studied in the county.
A. stolonifera × tenuis. This has been observed by P. M. Benoit in the following tetrads: 33/H, 12/G (1962, *Hb. H.M.*) V (1962, *Hb. H.M.*), 91/L. It no doubt occurs elsewhere and may be frequent.

Apera Adans.

A. spica-venti (L.) Beauv. *Loose Silky-bent*
J. Woods, 1805
This was recorded as a colonist in arable fields by Coleman but it became subsequently only a casual. Current records are: Berkhamsted R.D.C. Dump, 1963 (00/D), *Hb. H.M.*; side of railway, Park Street, 1964 (10/L).

Polypogon monspeliensis (L.) Desf., a casual, was recorded from Ware, 1916, by A. W. Graveson, *Hb. Gr.* and from Hitchin, 1928, by Little. I have seen it only on a rubbish dump at Abbot's Langley, 1961 (00/V).

Gastridium ventricosum (Gouan) Schinz & Thell (*G. australe* (L.) Beauv.), a casual, was first recorded by Griffiths, 1831, see *Phytologist* 4: 94 (1851) and later by Webb and Coleman from a few stations in the south of the county. The only recent record is from an arable field near Cowheath Wood, Bayford (probably one of Coleman's original stations), 1946, S. Phelp, *Hb. Lousley* (see *Kent and Lousley*, 307).

Phleum L.

P. pratense L. (Map 55 l) *Timothy Grass, Cat's-tail*
Kalm, 1748 (for the aggregate)
Pastures, arable fields, etc. Colonist
Common being frequently sown in leys and persisting. H.S. 8, 75.

P. bertolonii DC. (Map 55m) *Smaller Cat's-tail*
P. praecox Jord., *P. nodosum* auct. Pryor, c. 1880
Established pastures, downland, etc. Native
Very common. H.S. 4, 7, 8, 11, 13, 18, 21, 22, 25, 28, 29, 33, 42, 46, 50, 52, 53, 59, 66, 78, 80, 90, 100.

P. phleoides (L.) Karst. *Purple-stalked Cat's-tail*
P. phalaroides Koel. Coleman, 1839
Gravelly banks overlying chalk Native
Very rare and now known only from Wilbury Hill (H.S. 7) but it was also found sparingly at Hertford by Coleman. It is one of the most interesting plants entering into the flora as Wilbury Hill is its western limit in Britain.

P. paniculatum Huds. (*P. asperum* (Retz.) Jacq.) was recorded from near Elstree, c. 1820, Rudge, *Hb. B.M.*:
P. exaratum Hochst. ex Griseb. (*P. graecum* Boiss. & Heldr.) Hertford, A. W. Graveson, *B.E.C. 1920 Rep.* 157, *Hb. Gr.*

Alopecurus L.

A. myosuroides Huds. (Map 55n) *Slender Foxtail*
Ellis, 1750
Arable fields, waste places, etc. Colonist
Very common on the more calcareous soils. H.S. 11, 52, 80.

A. pratensis L. (Map 55o) *Meadow Foxtail* Coleman, 1838
Pastures, roadside verges, etc. Native
Abundant. H.S. 13, 34, 66, 75, 96, 100, 109.

A. geniculatus L. (Map 56a) *Marsh Foxtail* Blake, 1824
Muddy margins of ponds, rivers and ditches Native
Frequent on the London Clay and occasional elsewhere. H.S. 9, 74, 91, 109.

A. aequalis Sobol. *Orange Foxtail*
A. fulvus Sm. Webb and Coleman, 1849
Muddy shores of ponds and reservoirs Native
Rare as it has always been. Current records are: pond, Hadham Hall, 1956 (42/L)!, E. J. Douglas, *Hb. H.M.*;

Startops End Reservoir, 1943 (91/B), *Dandy, Hb. B.M.* – it was recorded from Little Tring Reservoir by E. J. Salisbury in 1917; Aldenham Reservoir, one of Coleman's stations (19/S)!; Hilfield Reservoir, 1964 (19/M).

Milium L.

M. effusum L. (Map 56b) *Wood Millet*
Coleman, 1838
Woods Native
Frequent and absent only on the Chalk. H.S. 39, 60, 61, 63, 78, 103.

Anthoxanthum L.

A. odoratum L. (Map 56c) *Sweet Vernal-grass*
Kalm, 1748
Pastures, banks on verges of woods, etc. Native
Common on the more acid soils and rare or absent on the Chalk and Boulder Clay. H.S. 9, 13, 15, 18, 22, 23, 25, 26, 28, 29, 55, 57, 58, 60, 62, 70–73, 75, 78, 81, 87, 89–91, 96–98, 100, 101, 103, 104, 109.

A. puelii Lecoq & Lamotte, a colonist of arable fields, was recorded by H. C. Littlebury from Offley Holes, 1913, *W.E.C. 1914–15 Rep.* 514 and by J. E. Little from Purwell, *B.E.C. 1914 Rep.* 77. R. Morse found it at Offley Holes, 1930, *Hb. Letchworth Mus.* but it is not known whether it had persisted there since 1913 or was a separate introduction.

Phalaris L.

P. arundinacea L. (Map 56d) *Reed Canary-grass*
Baldingera colorata (Sibth.) Gaertn., Blake, 1820
Mey. & Scherb.
Sides of rivers, reservoirs and ponds, swampy places etc. Native
Frequent and well distributed. H.S. 19, 76.

P. canariensis L. (Map 56e) *Canary Grass* Blake, 1821
A casual which has much increased as a bird-seed alien.

The following casuals are also recorded: **P. minor** Retz. Hitchin, *Little, B.E.C. 1914 Rep.* 77, *Hb. Letch. Mus.*; Hertford, A. W. Graveson, *B.E.C. 1920 Rep.* 157; Maple Cross, 1958 (09/G), *Hb. H.M.*: **P. paradoxa** L., Hitchin, *Little, B.E.C. 1914 Rep.* 77; Ware, *Druce, B.E.C. 1917 Rep.* 133; Hertford, A. W. Graveson, *B.E.C. 1920 Rep.* 157, *Hb. Gr.*: **P. brachystachys** Link, Hilfield Lane rubbish tip, 1961 (19/M), *B.S.B.I. Field Meeting*: **P. angusta** Nees ex Trin., Mead Lane, 1923, A. W. Graveson, *Hb. Gr.*

Nardus L.

N. stricta L. (Map 56f) *Mat grass* Coleman, 1838
Wet heathy places Native
Considered to be rare by Coleman but it is now occasional at least on the London Clay. H.S. 26, 69, 92, 97, 98, 101, 102.

Echinochloa crus-galli (L.) Beauv., *Cockspur Grass*, first recorded by Ansell, 1846, has increased in recent years as a casual on rubbish dumps e.g. Cock Lane, 1958 (30/U); Bulls Mill, 1958 (31/C), etc. **E. frumentacea** Link has been recorded from Cock Lane, 1959 (30/U), *Lloyd-Evans*!; Bulls Mill, 1959 (31/C); Park Street, 1966 (10/L).

Setaria viridis (L.) Beauv., *Green Bristle-grass*, first recorded by Ansell, 1846 (*Hb. Druce*), has much increased on rubbish dumps as a bird-seed alien: **S. italica** (L.) Beauv., first recorded by A. W. Graveson, 1950, *Hb. Gr.* is even more common on rubbish dumps than *S. viridis*: **S. lutes-**

cens (Weigel) Hubbard (*S. glauca* auct.), *Yellow Bristle-grass*, first recorded by Ansell, 1846 (*Hb. Druce*) has been recently recorded from Cock Lane, 1965 (30/U), *Hb. H.M.*; Park Street, 1966 (10/L): **S. verticillata** (L.) Beauv. was recorded from Hertford by Ansell, 1846 (*Hb. Druce*).

Panicum miliaceum L., *Millet*, first recorded by Pryor, 1875 (*Hb. Brit. Mus.*) is now common on rubbish dumps as a bird-seed alien: the following are also recorded: **P. effusum** R. Br., Cock Lane, 1960 (30/U), *Hb. H.M.*: **P. laevifolium** Hack., Hertford, 1918, Druce, *Hb. Druce*; Cock Lane, 1965 (30/U), *Hb. H.M.*; Park Street, 1966 (10/L), *Hb. H.M.*: **P. capillare** L., Hatfield, *Pryor*, 1875, *Hb. B.M.*

Digitaria sanguinalis (L.) Scop. (*Panicum sanguinale* L.), *Hairy Finger-grass*, recorded by Webb and Coleman (1849) as a rare casual has been seen during the present survey only on Park Street Dump, 1964 (10/L), *Hb. H.M.*

The following casuals have also been recorded: **Monerma cylindrica** (Willd.) Coss. & Dur., Cock Lane Dump, 1965 (30/U), *B. Wurzell*, *Hb. H.M.*; Park Street Dump, 1966 (10/L), *Hb. H.M.*: **Eleusine indica** (L.) Gaertn., Cock Lane Dump, 1965 (30/U), *Hb. H.M.*: **Sorghum halepense** (L.) Pers., rubbish dump, Rickmansworth, 1965 (09/M), *Hb. H.M.* In addition the various species of wheat, oats, barley, rye and maize appear in waste places and 'bamboos' may run wild in derelict gardens.

The maps in the following section make use of the National Grid. The larger squares shown on a number of the maps are ten-kilometre grid squares (i.e. 100 square kilometres). These are numbered TL/00, TL/01, TL/02, etc.; see Inset Maps on M4, M5, M7 and M8.

The ten-kilometre grid squares are each further divided into twenty-five two-kilometre grid squares (i.e. four square kilometres), referred to in the text as tetrads. These are numbered, from the bottom left-hand corner of the ten-kilometre grid squares, from A to Z (O is omitted to save confusion with Q). See Inset Maps on M4, M5, M7 and M8.

The Distribution Maps on pages M10 to M56 relate to records made from 1951 to 1966 inclusive.

The maps are based upon the Ordnance Survey Map with the sanction of the Controller of H.M. Stationery Office, Crown Copyright reserved.

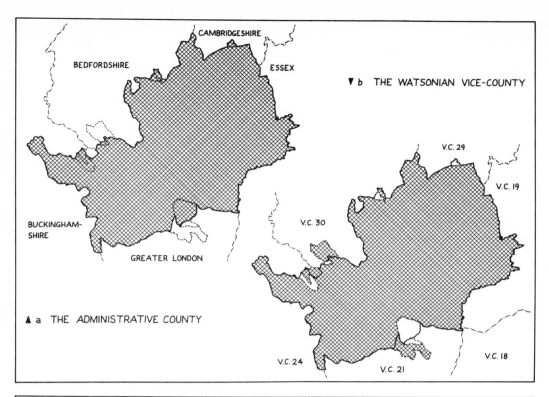

CAMBRIDGESHIRE

BEDFORDSHIRE

ESSEX

▼ b THE WATSONIAN VICE-COUNTY

V.C. 29

V.C. 19

V.C. 30

BUCKINGHAM-
SHIRE

GREATER LONDON

▲ a THE ADMINISTRATIVE COUNTY

V.C. 24

V.C. 21

V.C. 18

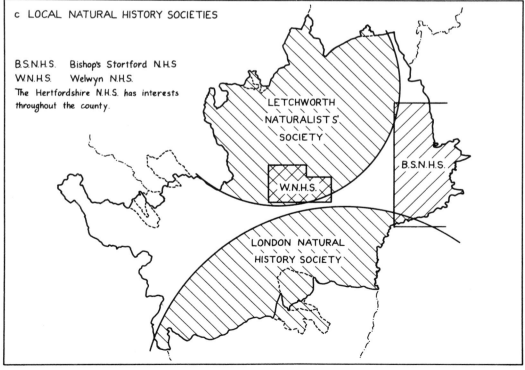

c LOCAL NATURAL HISTORY SOCIETIES

B.S.N.H.S. Bishop's Stortford N.H.S
W.N.H.S. Welwyn N.H.S.
The Hertfordshire N.H.S. has interests
throughout the county.

LETCHWORTH
NATURALISTS'
SOCIETY

B.S.N.H.S.

W.N.H.S.

LONDON NATURAL
HISTORY SOCIETY

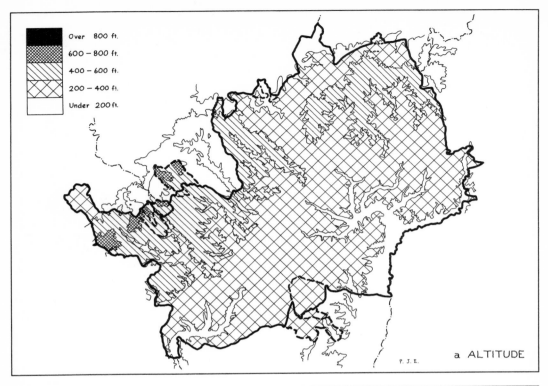

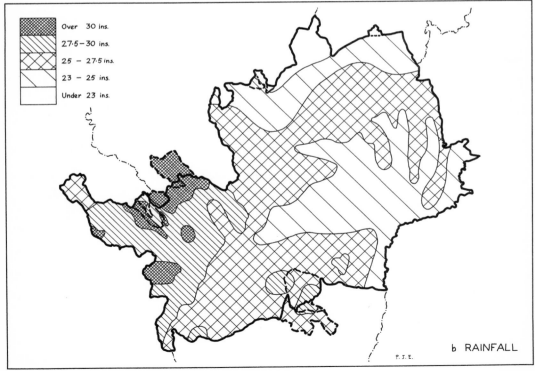

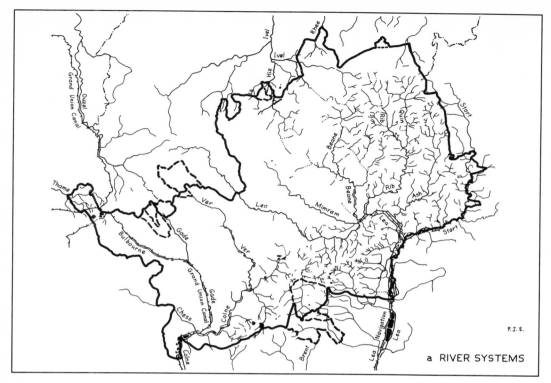

a RIVER SYSTEMS

P.J.E.

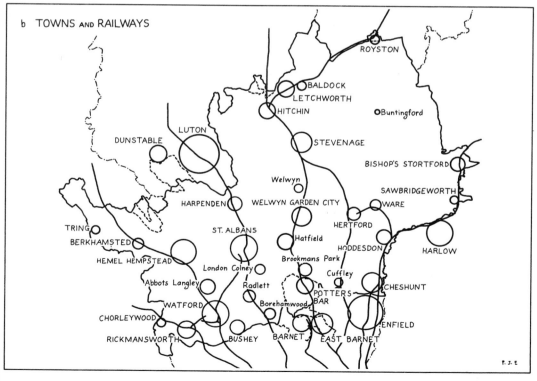

b TOWNS AND RAILWAYS

P.J.E.

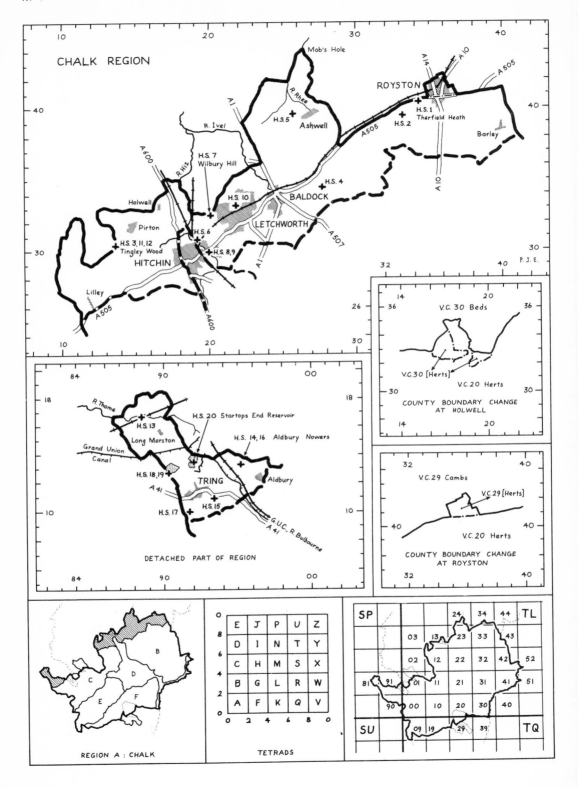

CHALK REGION

Mob's Hole

R.Rhee

ROYSTON

A14 A10

A505

R. Ivel

H.S.5
Ashwell

A1

A505

H.S.1
Therfield Heath

H.S.2

A10

Barley

A600

R.Hiz

H.S.7
Wilbury Hill

Holwell

Pirton

H.S.10

H.S.4

BALDOCK

LETCHWORTH

A507

H.S.6

H.S.3,11,12
Tingley Wood

H.S.8,9

HITCHIN

A1

Lilley

A505

A600

P.J.E.

COUNTY BOUNDARY CHANGE AT HOLWELL

V.C. 30 Beds

V.C.30 [Herts]

V.C. 20 Herts

DETACHED PART OF REGION

R.Thame

H.S.13
Long Marston

H.S.20 Startops End Reservoir

H.S. 14, 16 Aldbury Nowers

Grand Union Canal

H.S. 18,19

TRING

Aldbury

A 41

H.S.17

H.S.15

G.U.C., R.Bulbourne
A 41

COUNTY BOUNDARY CHANGE AT ROYSTON

V.C.29 Cambs

V.C.29 [Herts]

V.C. 20 Herts

REGION A : CHALK

B

C

D

E

F

TETRADS

E	J	P	U	Z
D	I	N	T	Y
C	H	M	S	X
B	G	L	R	W
A	F	K	Q	V

SP

TL

SU

TQ

		24	34	44	
03	13	23	33	43	
02	12	22	32	42	52
81	91	01	11	21	31	41	51
90	00	10	20	30	40
09	19	29	39	

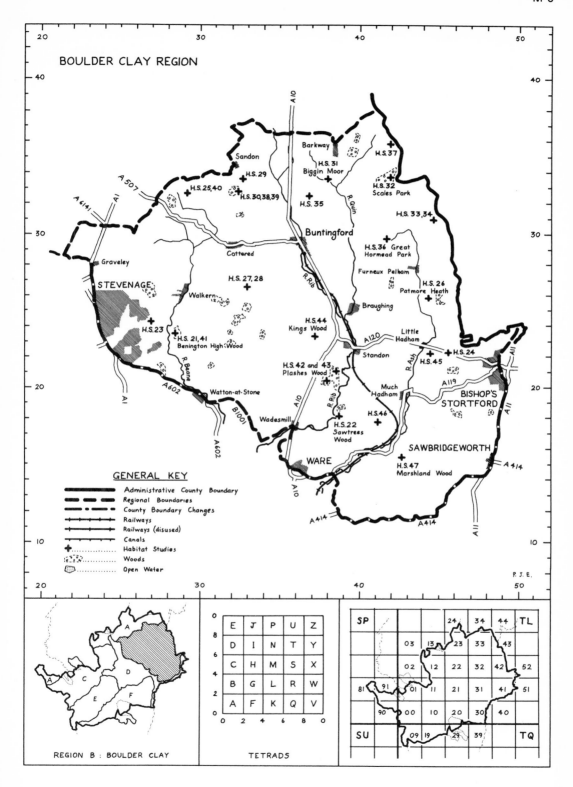

BOULDER CLAY REGION

Barkway
Sandon
H.S. 37
H.S. 29
H.S. 31
Biggin Moor
H.S. 32
Scales Park
H.S. 25,40
H.S. 30,38,39
H.S. 35
R. Quin
H.S. 33,34
Cottered
Buntingford
H.S. 36 Great
Hormead Park
Graveley
Furneux Pelham
STEVENAGE
H.S. 27, 28
H.S. 26
Walkern
Patmore Heath
R. Rib
H.S. 23
Braughing
H.S. 44
Kings Wood
Little
Hadham
H.S. 21,41
Benington High Wood
A120
H.S. 24
R. Ash
H.S. 45
Standon
R. Beane
H.S. 42 and 43
Plashes Wood
Much
Hadham
A119
BISHOP'S
STORTFORD
Watton-at-Stone
R. Rib
SAWBRIDGEWORTH
Wadesmill
H.S. 22
Sawtrees
Wood
H.S. 46
WARE
H.S. 47
Marshland Wood

GENERAL KEY

▬▬▬	Administrative County Boundary
▬ ▬ ▬	Regional Boundaries
▬ · ▬ ·	County Boundary Changes
┼┼┼┼	Railways
┼┼┼┼	Railways (disused)
═══	Canals
✛	Habitat Studies
	Woods
	Open Water

P. J. E.

REGION B : BOULDER CLAY

TETRADS

E	J	P	U	Z
D	I	N	T	Y
C	H	M	S	X
B	G	L	R	W
A	F	K	Q	V

SP | | | | 24 | 34 | 44 | TL
| | 03 | 13 | 23 | 33 | 43 |
| | 02 | 12 | 22 | 32 | 42 | 52 |
81 | 91 | 01 | 11 | 21 | 31 | 41 | 51 |
| 90 | 00 | 10 | 20 | 30 | 40 |
SU | 09 | 19 | 29 | 39 | TQ

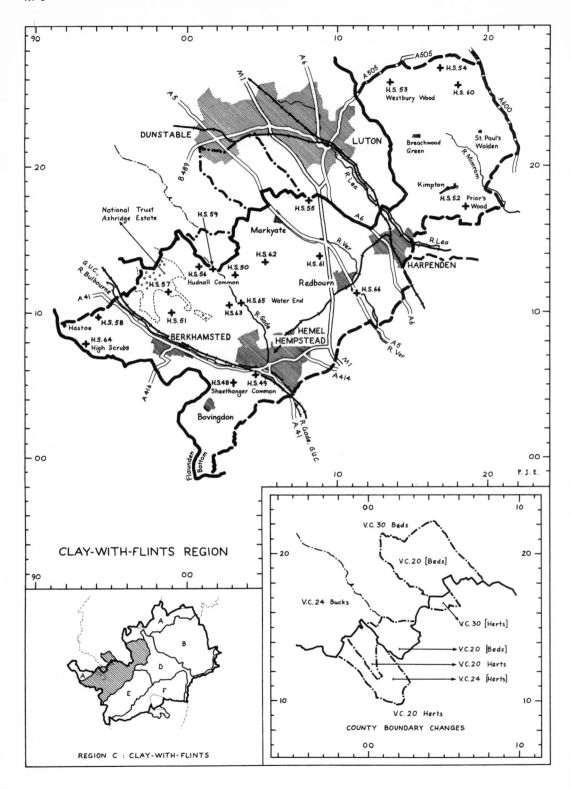

CLAY-WITH-FLINTS REGION

REGION C : CLAY-WITH-FLINTS

COUNTY BOUNDARY CHANGES

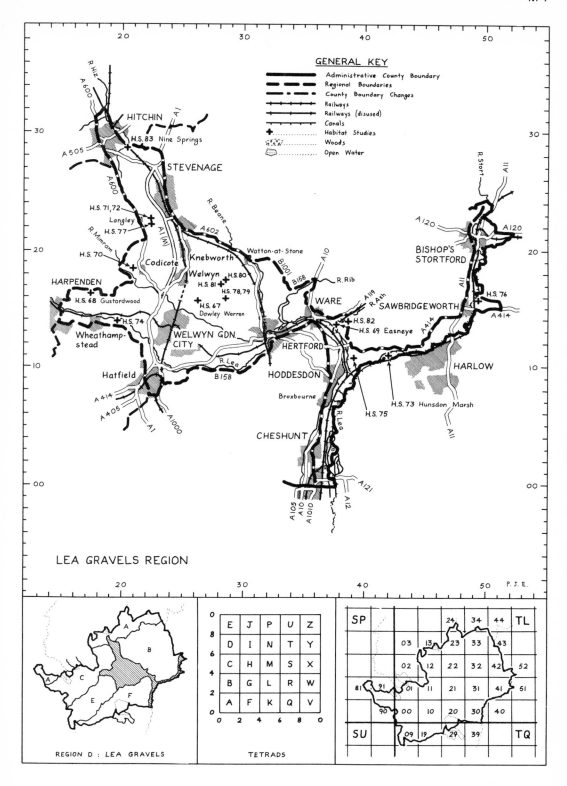

GENERAL KEY

Administrative County Boundary
Regional Boundaries
County Boundary Changes
Railways
Railways (disused)
Canals
Habitat Studies
Woods
Open Water

LEA GRAVELS REGION

P. J. E.

REGION D : LEA GRAVELS

TETRADS

8	E	J	P	U	Z
6	D	I	N	T	Y
4	C	H	M	S	X
2	B	G	L	R	W
0	A	F	K	Q	V

SP				24	34	44		TL
		03	13	23	33	43		
		02	12	22	32	42	52	
	81	91	01	11	21	31	41	51
		90	00	10	20	30	40	
SU		09	19	29	39			TQ

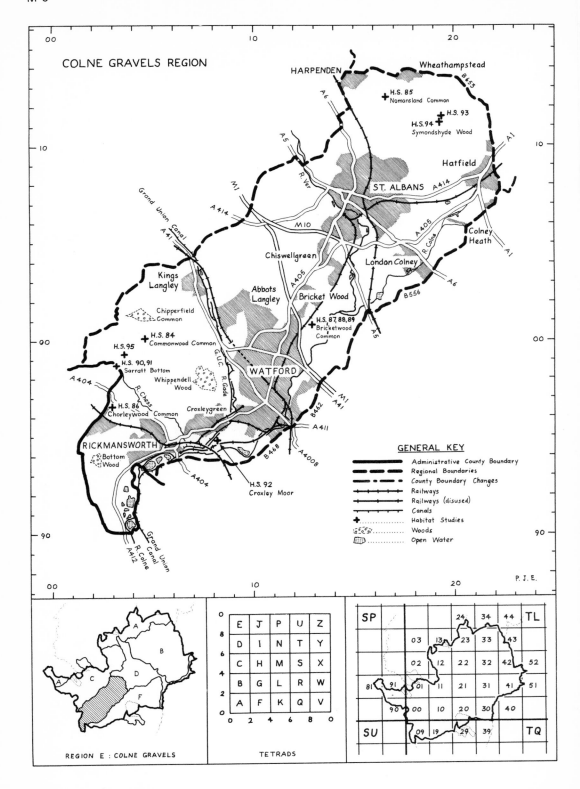

COLNE GRAVELS REGION

HARPENDEN

Wheathampstead

H.S. 85
Nomansland Common

H.S. 93

H.S. 94
Symondshyde Wood

Hatfield

ST. ALBANS

Colney
Heath

Chiswellgreen

London Colney

Kings
Langley

Abbots
Langley

Bricket Wood

Chipperfield
Common

H.S. 87, 88, 89
Bricketwood
Common

H.S. 84
Commonwood Common

H.S. 95

H.S. 90, 91
Sarratt Bottom

Whippendell
Wood

WATFORD

H.S. 86
Chorleywood Common

Croxleygreen

A 411

RICKMANSWORTH

Bottom
Wood

H.S. 92
Croxley Moor

Grand Union Canal

Grand
Union
Canal

R. Colne

GENERAL KEY

▬▬▬▬	Administrative County Boundary
▬ ▬ ▬	Regional Boundaries
·—·—·	County Boundary Changes
✜✜✜	Railways
┼┼┼	Railways (disused)
	Canals
✚	Habitat Studies
	Woods
	Open Water

P. J. E.

REGION E : COLNE GRAVELS

E	J	P	U	Z
D	I	N	T	Y
C	H	M	S	X
B	G	L	R	W
A	F	K	Q	V

TETRADS

SP					24	34	44	TL
		03	13	23	33	43		
		02	12	22	32	42	52	
81	91	01	11	21	31	41	51	
	90	00	10	20	30	40		
SU		09	19	29	39			TQ

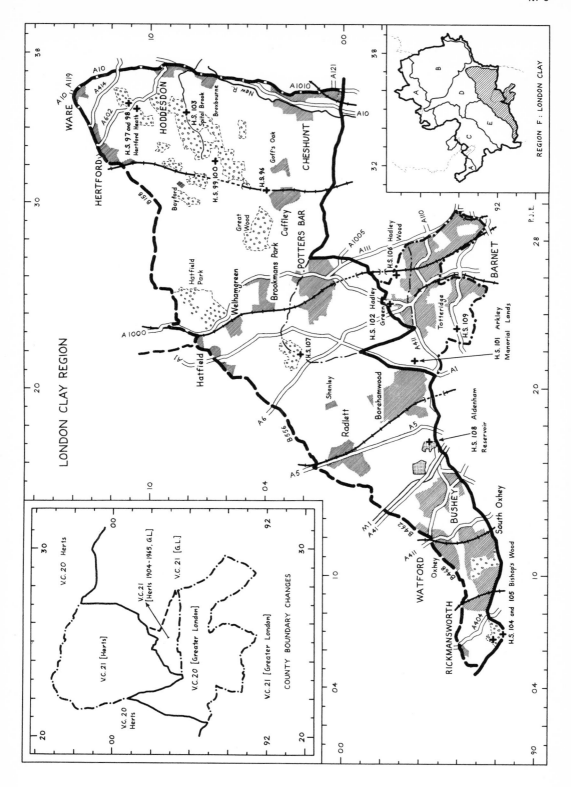

LONDON CLAY REGION

REGION F : LONDON CLAY

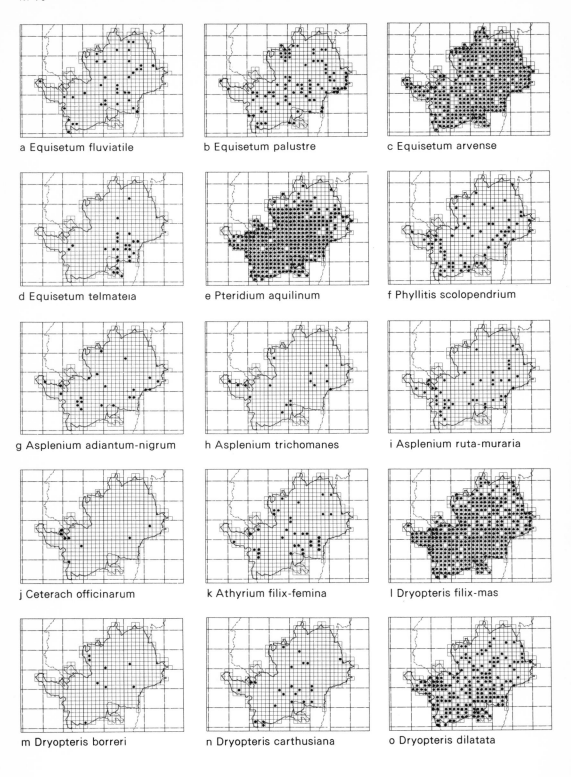

a Equisetum fluviatile

b Equisetum palustre

c Equisetum arvense

d Equisetum telmateıa

e Pteridium aquilinum

f Phyllitis scolopendrium

g Asplenium adiantum-nigrum

h Asplenium trichomanes

i Asplenium ruta-muraria

j Ceterach officinarum

k Athyrium filix-femina

l Dryopteris filix-mas

m Dryopteris borreri

n Dryopteris carthusiana

o Dryopteris dilatata

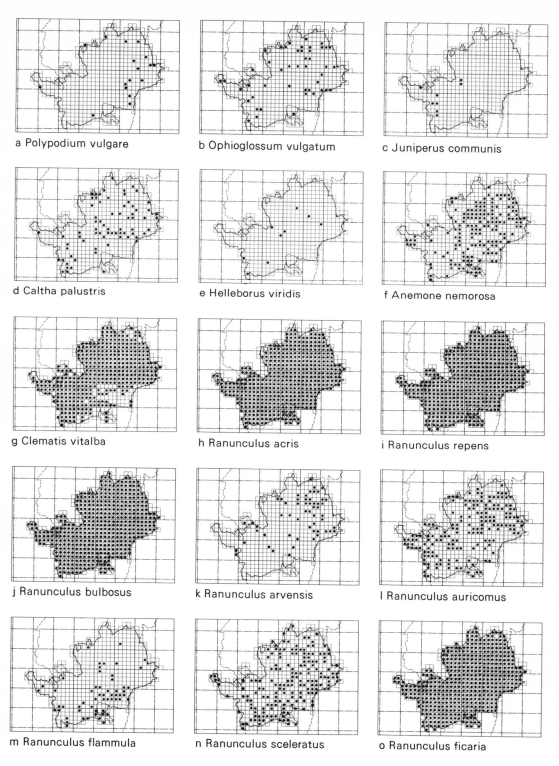

a Polypodium vulgare

b Ophioglossum vulgatum

c Juniperus communis

d Caltha palustris

e Helleborus viridis

f Anemone nemorosa

g Clematis vitalba

h Ranunculus acris

i Ranunculus repens

j Ranunculus bulbosus

k Ranunculus arvensis

l Ranunculus auricomus

m Ranunculus flammula

n Ranunculus sceleratus

o Ranunculus ficaria

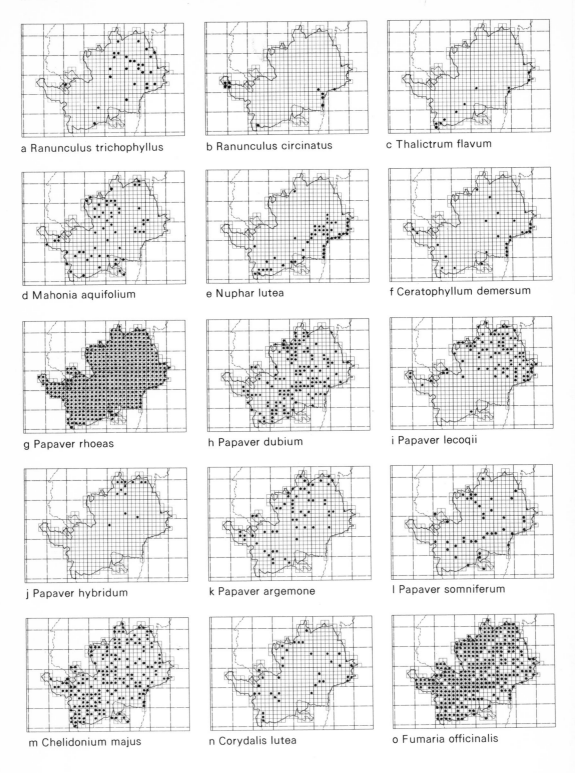

a Ranunculus trichophyllus

b Ranunculus circinatus

c Thalictrum flavum

d Mahonia aquifolium

e Nuphar lutea

f Ceratophyllum demersum

g Papaver rhoeas

h Papaver dubium

i Papaver lecoqii

j Papaver hybridum

k Papaver argemone

l Papaver somniferum

m Chelidonium majus

n Corydalis lutea

o Fumaria officinalis

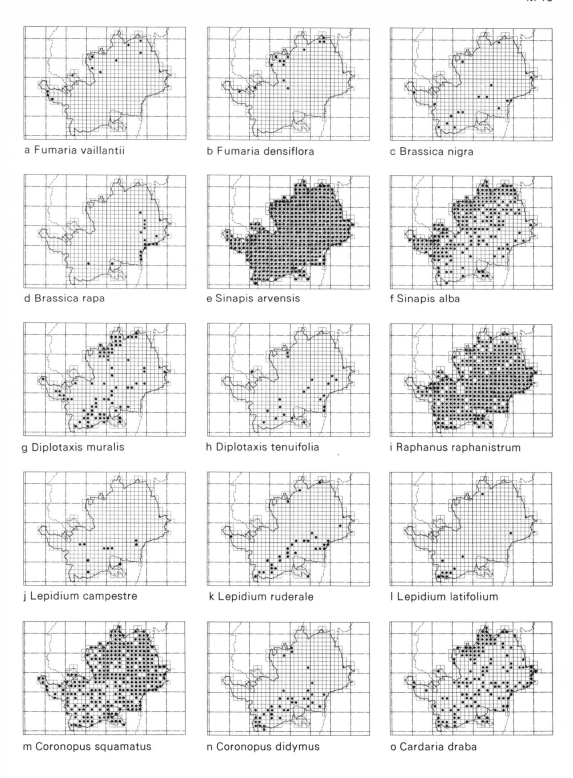

a Fumaria vaillantii

b Fumaria densiflora

c Brassica nigra

d Brassica rapa

e Sinapis arvensis

f Sinapis alba

g Diplotaxis muralis

h Diplotaxis tenuifolia

i Raphanus raphanistrum

j Lepidium campestre

k Lepidium ruderale

l Lepidium latifolium

m Coronopus squamatus

n Coronopus didymus

o Cardaria draba

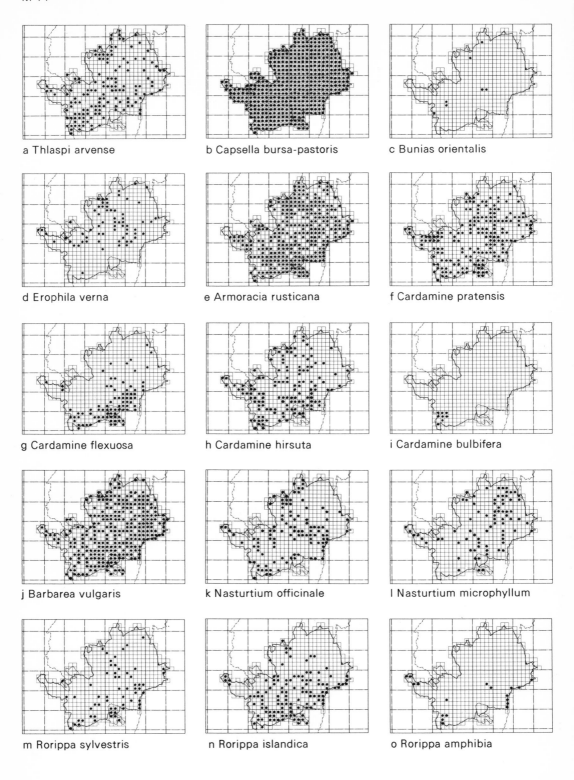

a Thlaspi arvense

b Capsella bursa-pastoris

c Bunias orientalis

d Erophila verna

e Armoracia rusticana

f Cardamine pratensis

g Cardamine flexuosa

h Cardamine hirsuta

i Cardamine bulbifera

j Barbarea vulgaris

k Nasturtium officinale

l Nasturtium microphyllum

m Rorippa sylvestris

n Rorippa islandica

o Rorippa amphibia

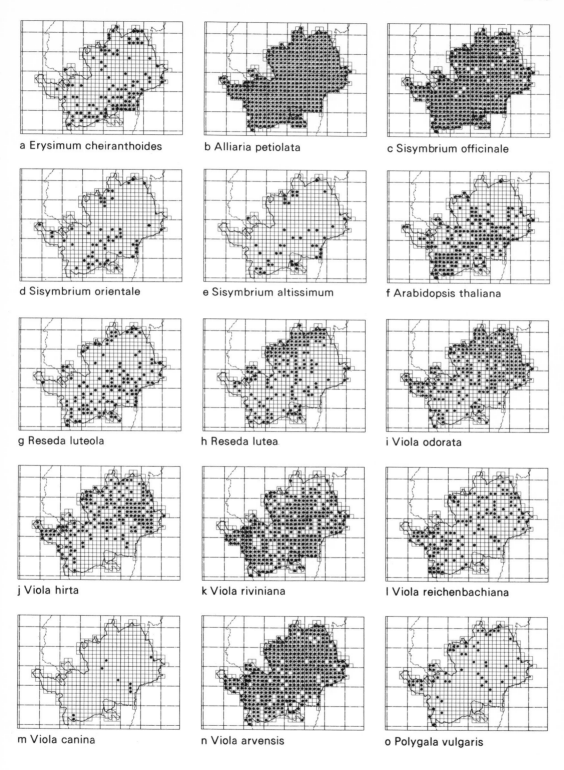

a Erysimum cheiranthoides

b Alliaria petiolata

c Sisymbrium officinale

d Sisymbrium orientale

e Sisymbrium altissimum

f Arabidopsis thaliana

g Reseda luteola

h Reseda lutea

i Viola odorata

j Viola hirta

k Viola riviniana

l Viola reichenbachiana

m Viola canina

n Viola arvensis

o Polygala vulgaris

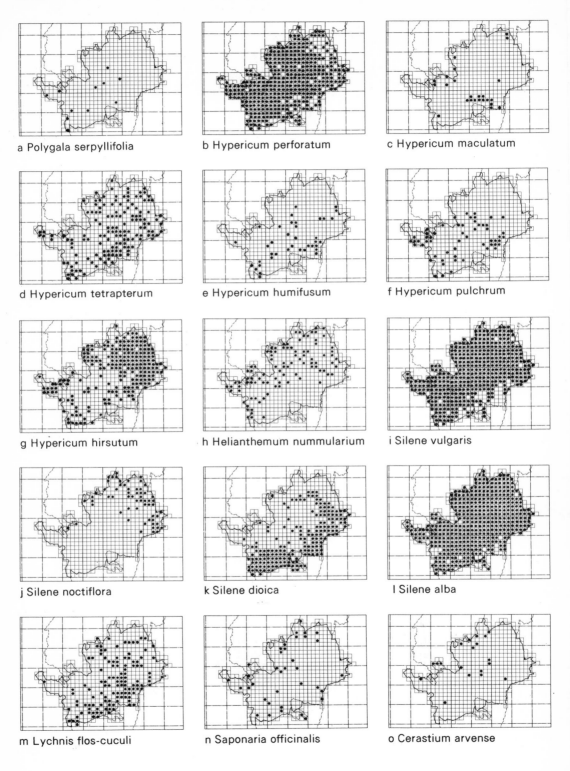

a Polygala serpyllifolia

b Hypericum perforatum

c Hypericum maculatum

d Hypericum tetrapterum

e Hypericum humifusum

f Hypericum pulchrum

g Hypericum hirsutum

h Helianthemum nummularium

i Silene vulgaris

j Silene noctiflora

k Silene dioica

l Silene alba

m Lychnis flos-cuculi

n Saponaria officinalis

o Cerastium arvense

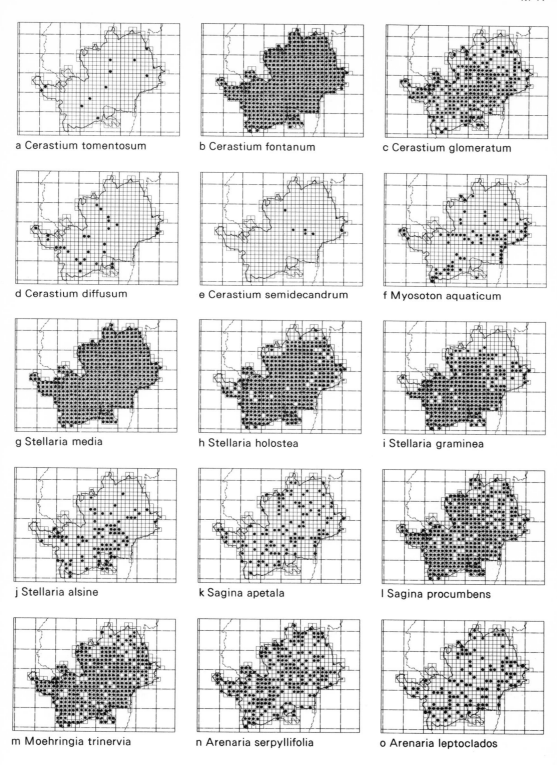

a Cerastium tomentosum

b Cerastium fontanum

c Cerastium glomeratum

d Cerastium diffusum

e Cerastium semidecandrum

f Myosoton aquaticum

g Stellaria media

h Stellaria holostea

i Stellaria graminea

j Stellaria alsine

k Sagina apetala

l Sagina procumbens

m Moehringia trinervia

n Arenaria serpyllifolia

o Arenaria leptoclados

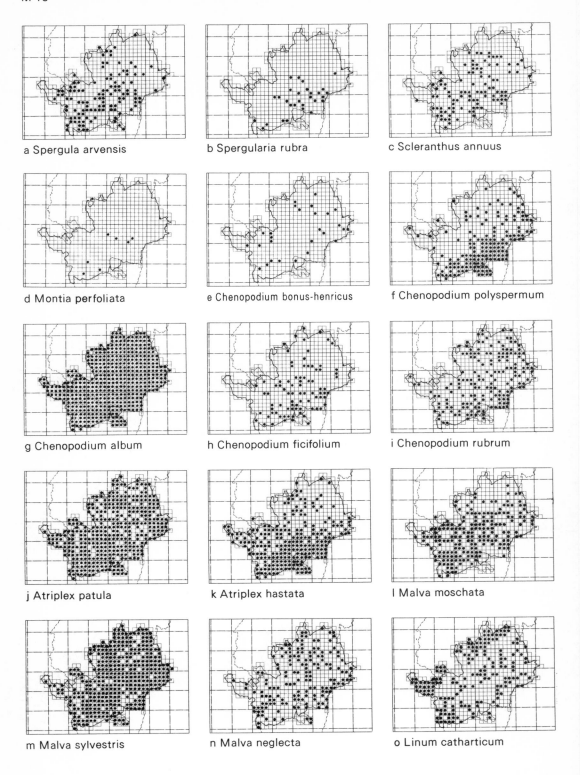

a Spergula arvensis

b Spergularia rubra

c Scleranthus annuus

d Montia perfoliata

e Chenopodium bonus-henricus

f Chenopodium polyspermum

g Chenopodium album

h Chenopodium ficifolium

i Chenopodium rubrum

j Atriplex patula

k Atriplex hastata

l Malva moschata

m Malva sylvestris

n Malva neglecta

o Linum catharticum

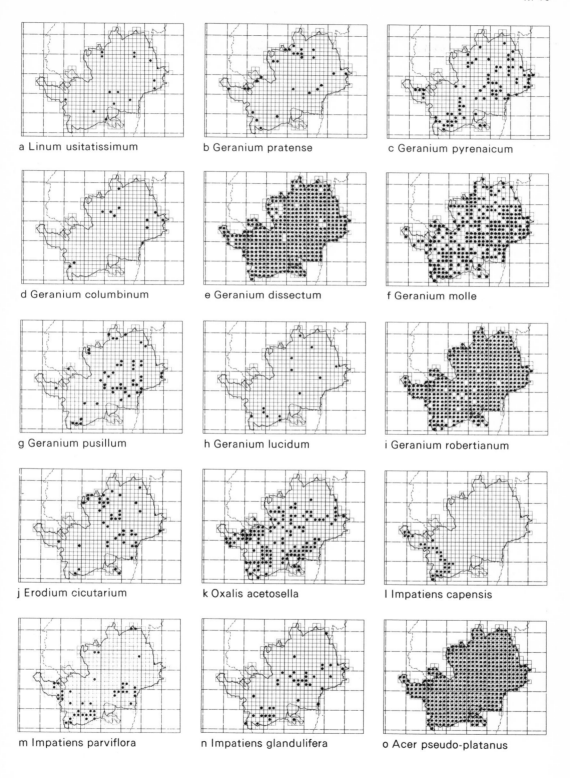

a Linum usitatissimum

b Geranium pratense

c Geranium pyrenaicum

d Geranium columbinum

e Geranium dissectum

f Geranium molle

g Geranium pusillum

h Geranium lucidum

i Geranium robertianum

j Erodium cicutarium

k Oxalis acetosella

l Impatiens capensis

m Impatiens parviflora

n Impatiens glandulifera

o Acer pseudo-platanus

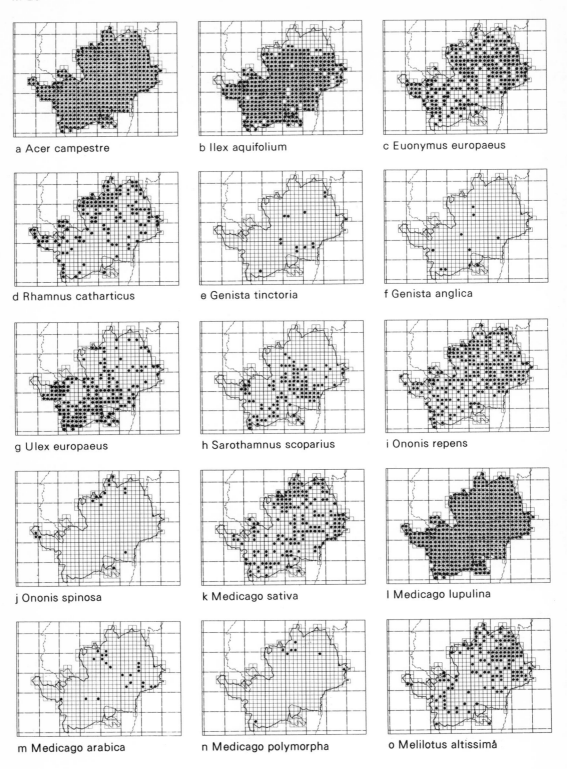

a Acer campestre

b Ilex aquifolium

c Euonymus europaeus

d Rhamnus catharticus

e Genista tinctoria

f Genista anglica

g Ulex europaeus

h Sarothamnus scoparius

i Ononis repens

j Ononis spinosa

k Medicago sativa

l Medicago lupulina

m Medicago arabica

n Medicago polymorpha

o Melilotus altissimá

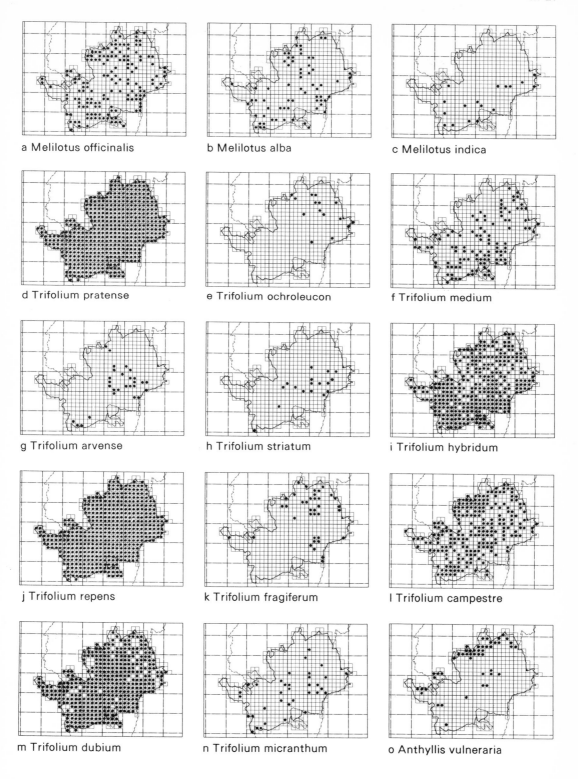

a Melilotus officinalis

b Melilotus alba

c Melilotus indica

d Trifolium pratense

e Trifolium ochroleucon

f Trifolium medium

g Trifolium arvense

h Trifolium striatum

i Trifolium hybridum

j Trifolium repens

k Trifolium fragiferum

l Trifolium campestre

m Trifolium dubium

n Trifolium micranthum

o Anthyllis vulneraria

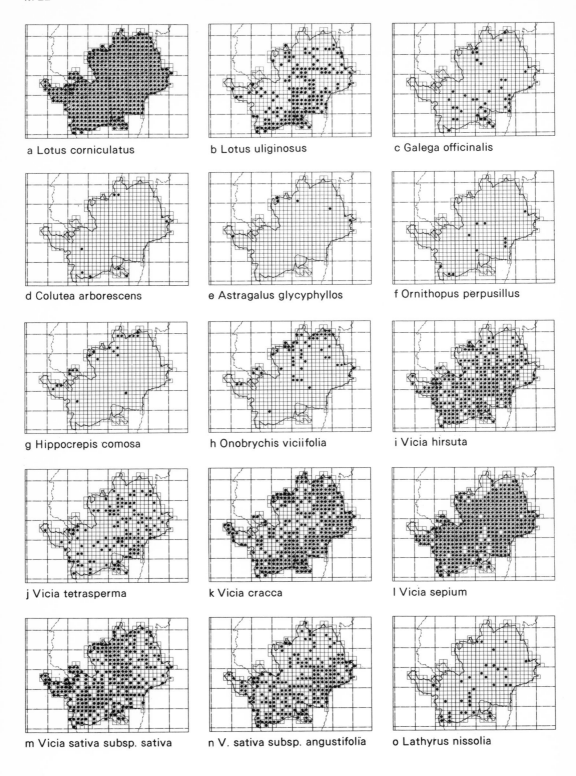

a Lotus corniculatus

b Lotus uliginosus

c Galega officinalis

d Colutea arborescens

e Astragalus glycyphyllos

f Ornithopus perpusillus

g Hippocrepis comosa

h Onobrychis viciifolia

i Vicia hirsuta

j Vicia tetrasperma

k Vicia cracca

l Vicia sepium

m Vicia sativa subsp. sativa

n V. sativa subsp. angustifolia

o Lathyrus nissolia

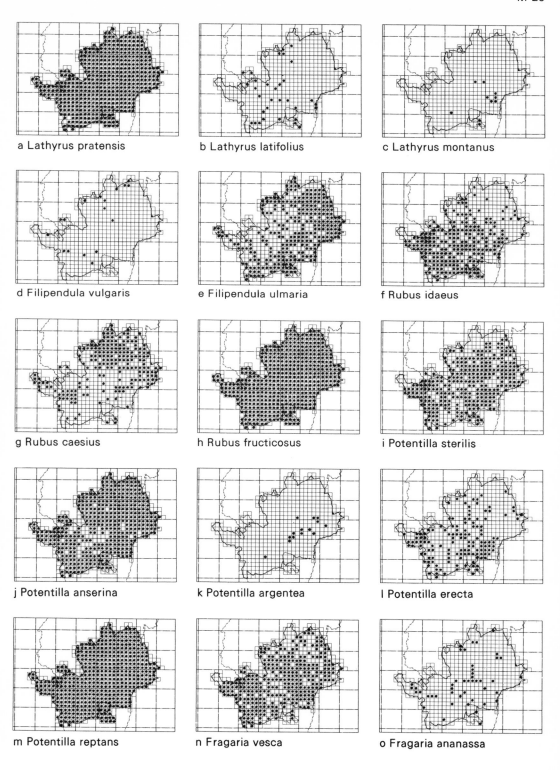

a Lathyrus pratensis

b Lathyrus latifolius

c Lathyrus montanus

d Filipendula vulgaris

e Filipendula ulmaria

f Rubus idaeus

g Rubus caesius

h Rubus fructicosus

i Potentilla sterilis

j Potentilla anserina

k Potentilla argentea

l Potentilla erecta

m Potentilla reptans

n Fragaria vesca

o Fragaria ananassa

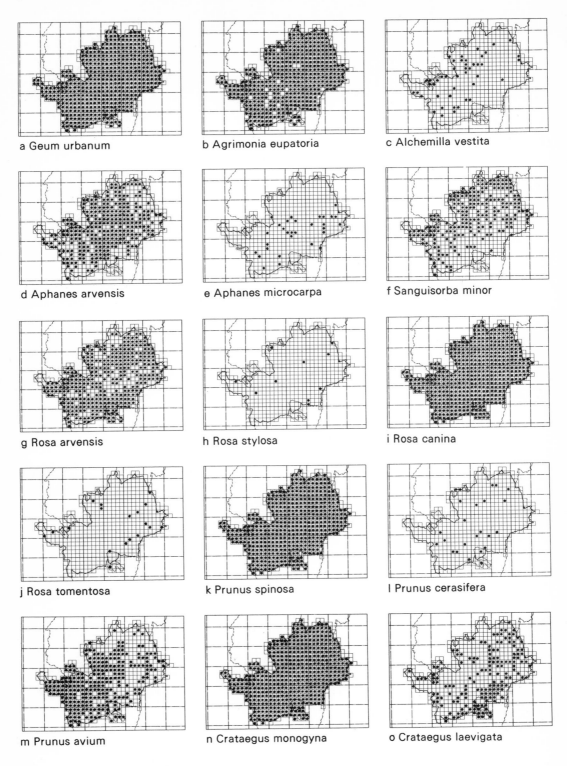

a Geum urbanum

b Agrimonia eupatoria

c Alchemilla vestita

d Aphanes arvensis

e Aphanes microcarpa

f Sanguisorba minor

g Rosa arvensis

h Rosa stylosa

i Rosa canina

j Rosa tomentosa

k Prunus spinosa

l Prunus cerasifera

m Prunus avium

n Crataegus monogyna

o Crataegus laevigata

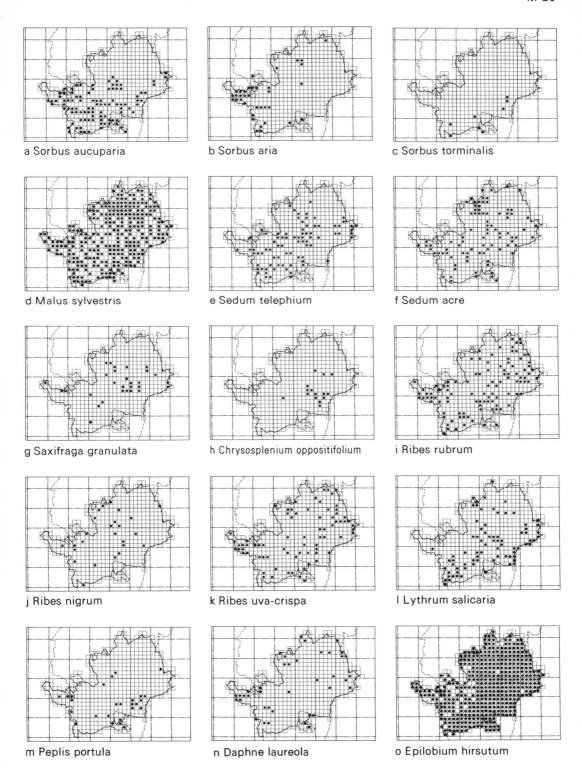

a Sorbus aucuparia

b Sorbus aria

c Sorbus torminalis

d Malus sylvestris

e Sedum telephium

f Sedum acre

g Saxifraga granulata

h Chrysosplenium oppositifolium

i Ribes rubrum

j Ribes nigrum

k Ribes uva-crispa

l Lythrum salicaria

m Peplis portula

n Daphne laureola

o Epilobium hirsutum

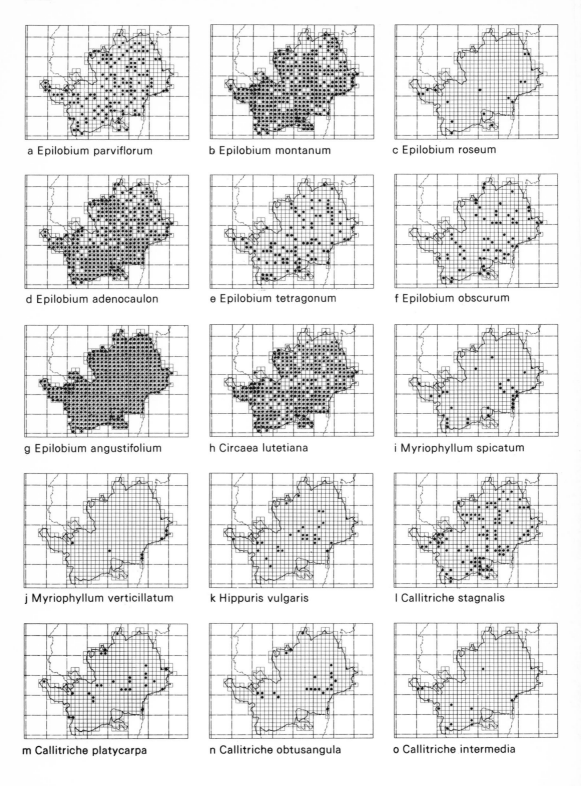

a Epilobium parviflorum

b Epilobium montanum

c Epilobium roseum

d Epilobium adenocaulon

e Epilobium tetragonum

f Epilobium obscurum

g Epilobium angustifolium

h Circaea lutetiana

i Myriophyllum spicatum

j Myriophyllum verticillatum

k Hippuris vulgaris

l Callitriche stagnalis

m Callitriche platycarpa

n Callitriche obtusangula

o Callitriche intermedia

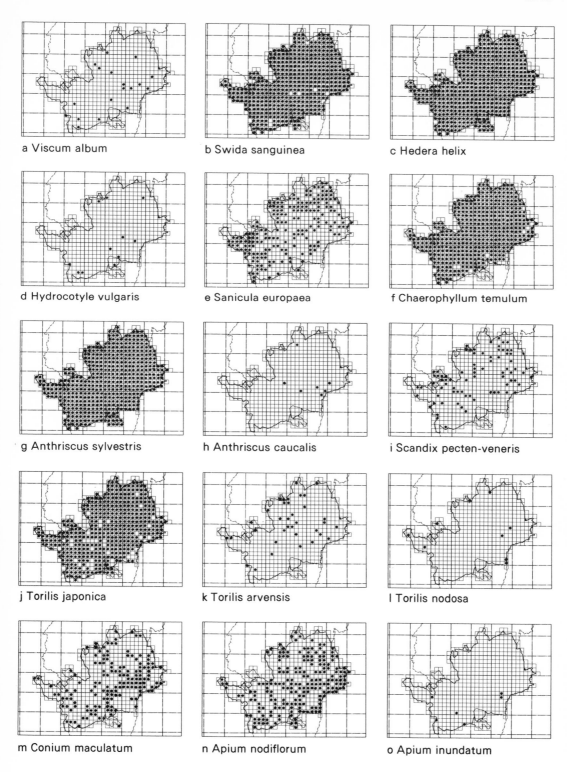

a Viscum album

b Swida sanguinea

c Hedera helix

d Hydrocotyle vulgaris

e Sanicula europaea

f Chaerophyllum temulum

g Anthriscus sylvestris

h Anthriscus caucalis

i Scandix pecten-veneris

j Torilis japonica

k Torilis arvensis

l Torilis nodosa

m Conium maculatum

n Apium nodiflorum

o Apium inundatum

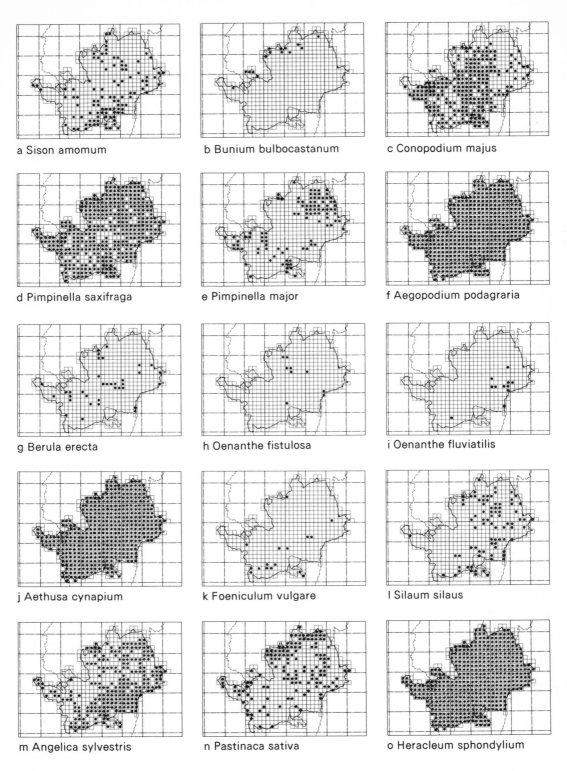

a Sison amomum

b Bunium bulbocastanum

c Conopodium majus

d Pimpinella saxifraga

e Pimpinella major

f Aegopodium podagraria

g Berula erecta

h Oenanthe fistulosa

i Oenanthe fluviatilis

j Aethusa cynapium

k Foeniculum vulgare

l Silaum silaus

m Angelica sylvestris

n Pastinaca sativa

o Heracleum sphondylium

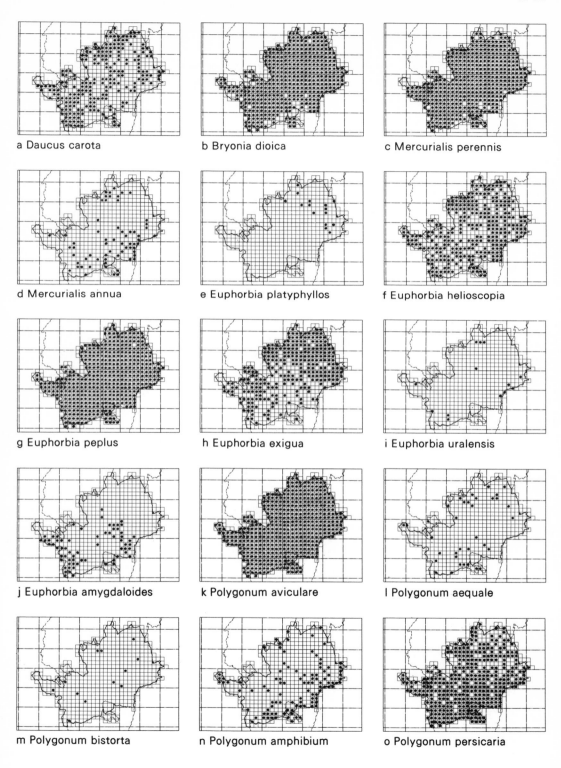

a Daucus carota

b Bryonia dioica

c Mercurialis perennis

d Mercurialis annua

e Euphorbia platyphyllos

f Euphorbia helioscopia

g Euphorbia peplus

h Euphorbia exigua

i Euphorbia uralensis

j Euphorbia amygdaloides

k Polygonum aviculare

l Polygonum aequale

m Polygonum bistorta

n Polygonum amphibium

o Polygonum persicaria

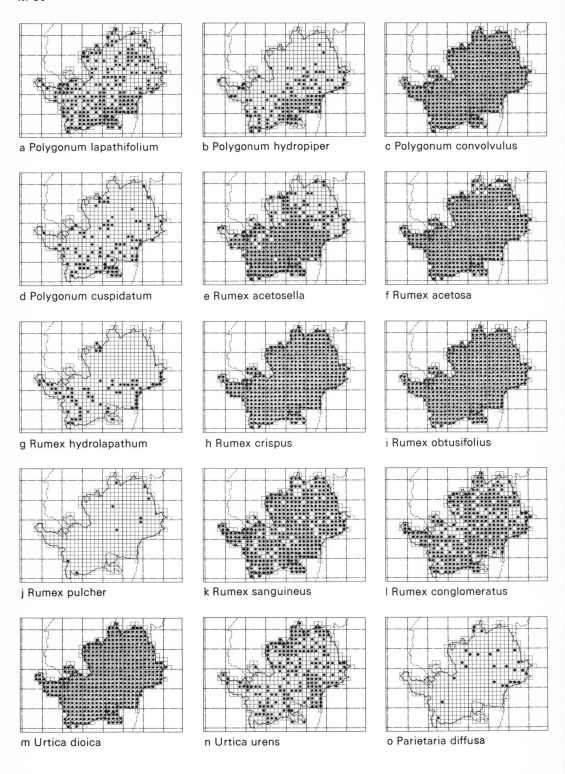

a Polygonum lapathifolium

b Polygonum hydropiper

c Polygonum convolvulus

d Polygonum cuspidatum

e Rumex acetosella

f Rumex acetosa

g Rumex hydrolapathum

h Rumex crispus

i Rumex obtusifolius

j Rumex pulcher

k Rumex sanguineus

l Rumex conglomeratus

m Urtica dioica

n Urtica urens

o Parietaria diffusa

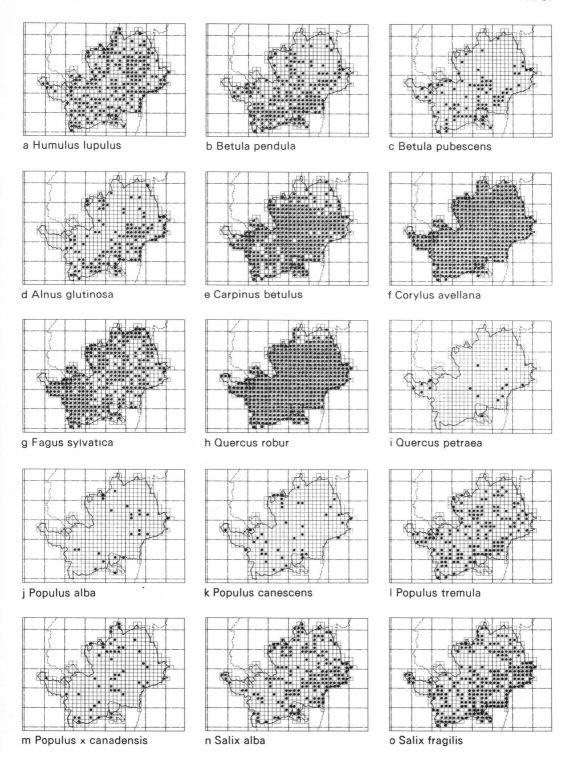

a Humulus lupulus

b Betula pendula

c Betula pubescens

d Alnus glutinosa

e Carpinus betulus

f Corylus avellana

g Fagus sylvatica

h Quercus robur

i Quercus petraea

j Populus alba

k Populus canescens

l Populus tremula

m Populus × canadensis

n Salix alba

o Salix fragilis

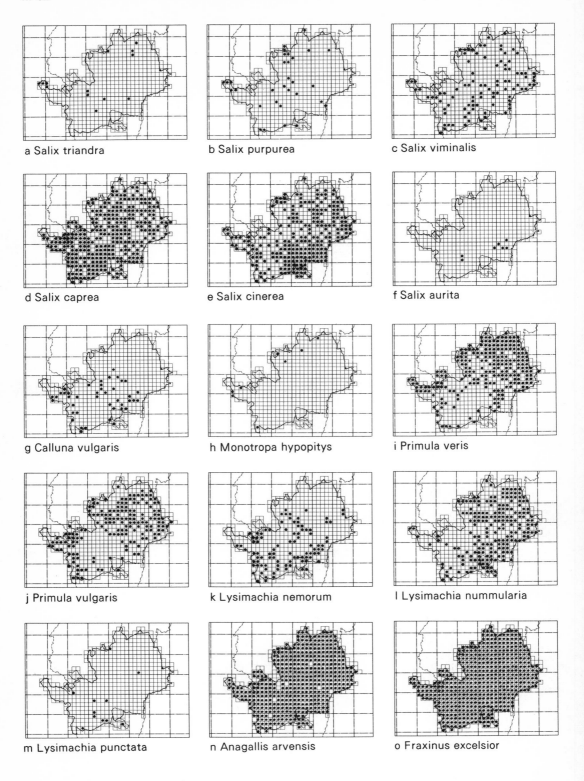

a Salix triandra

b Salix purpurea

c Salix viminalis

d Salix caprea

e Salix cinerea

f Salix aurita

g Calluna vulgaris

h Monotropa hypopitys

i Primula veris

j Primula vulgaris

k Lysimachia nemorum

l Lysimachia nummularia

m Lysimachia punctata

n Anagallis arvensis

o Fraxinus excelsior

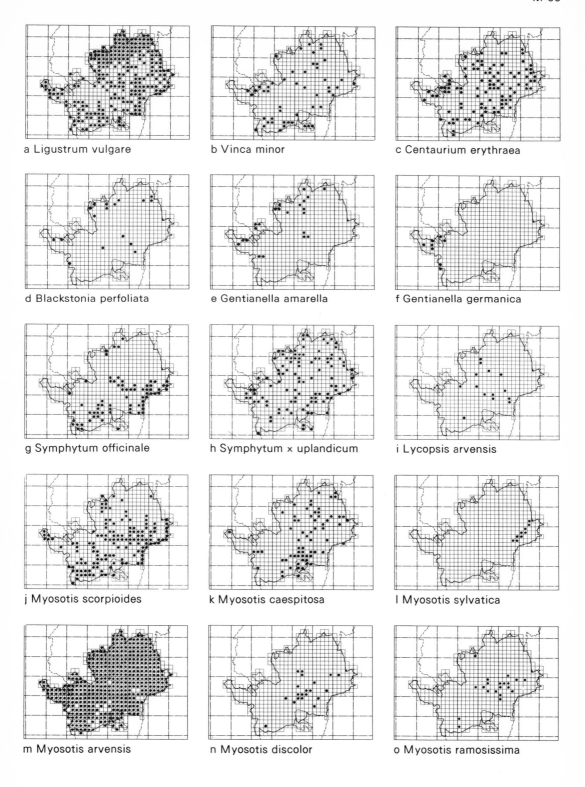

a Ligustrum vulgare

b Vinca minor

c Centaurium erythraea

d Blackstonia perfoliata

e Gentianella amarella

f Gentianella germanica

g Symphytum officinale

h Symphytum × uplandicum

i Lycopsis arvensis

j Myosotis scorpioides

k Myosotis caespitosa

l Myosotis sylvatica

m Myosotis arvensis

n Myosotis discolor

o Myosotis ramosissima

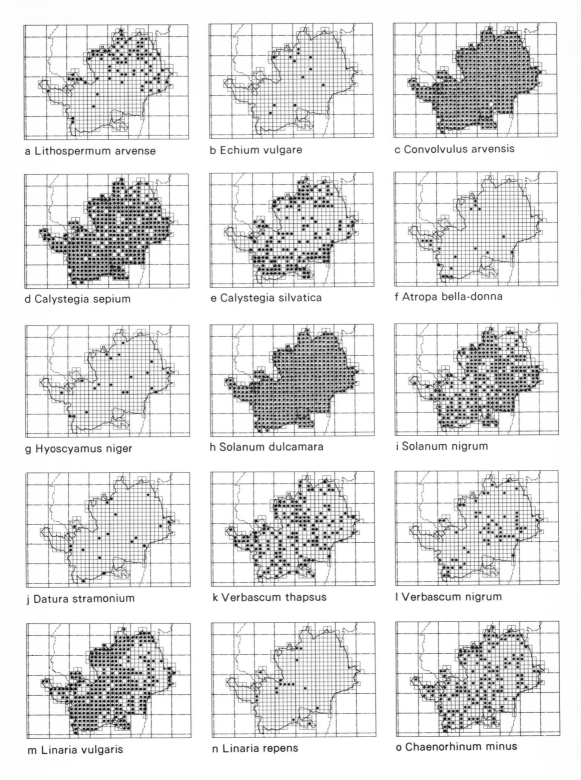

a Lithospermum arvense

b Echium vulgare

c Convolvulus arvensis

d Calystegia sepium

e Calystegia silvatica

f Atropa bella-donna

g Hyoscyamus niger

h Solanum dulcamara

i Solanum nigrum

j Datura stramonium

k Verbascum thapsus

l Verbascum nigrum

m Linaria vulgaris

n Linaria repens

o Chaenorhinum minus

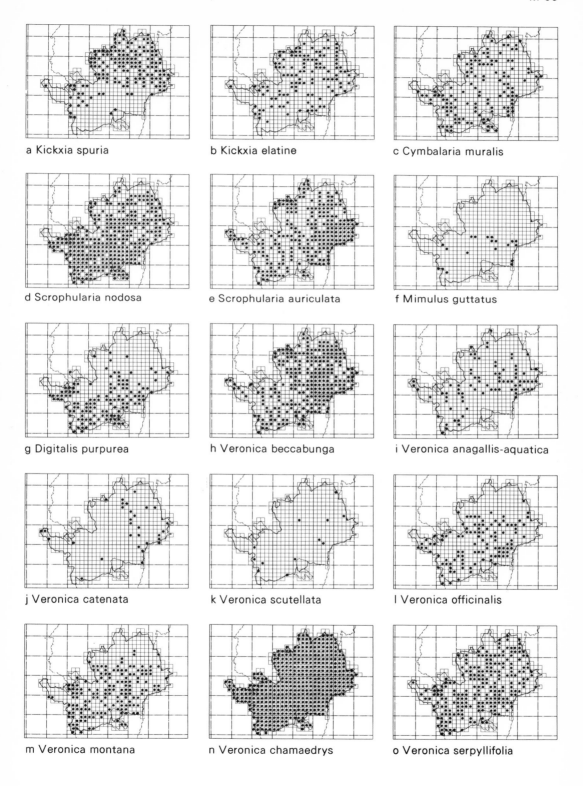

a Kickxia spuria

b Kickxia elatine

c Cymbalaria muralis

d Scrophularia nodosa

e Scrophularia auriculata

f Mimulus guttatus

g Digitalis purpurea

h Veronica beccabunga

i Veronica anagallis-aquatica

j Veronica catenata

k Veronica scutellata

l Veronica officinalis

m Veronica montana

n Veronica chamaedrys

o Veronica serpyllifolia

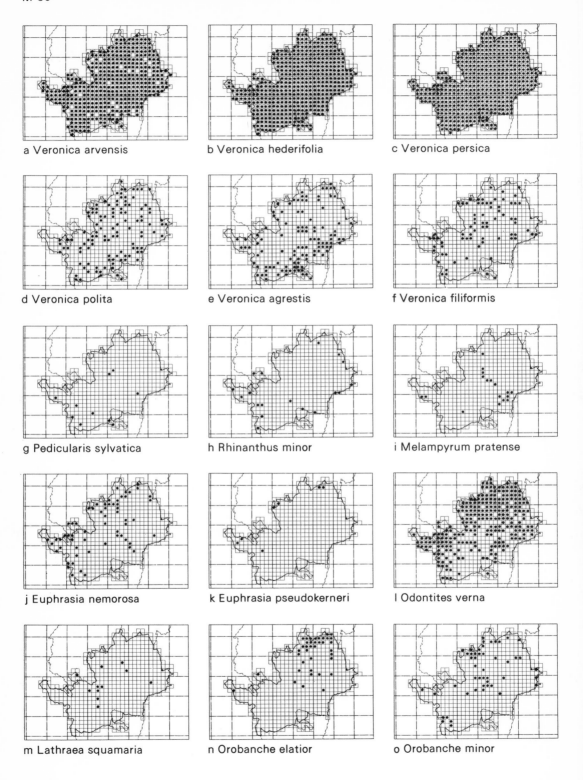

a Veronica arvensis

b Veronica hederifolia

c Veronica persica

d Veronica polita

e Veronica agrestis

f Veronica filiformis

g Pedicularis sylvatica

h Rhinanthus minor

i Melampyrum pratense

j Euphrasia nemorosa

k Euphrasia pseudokerneri

l Odontites verna

m Lathraea squamaria

n Orobanche elatior

o Orobanche minor

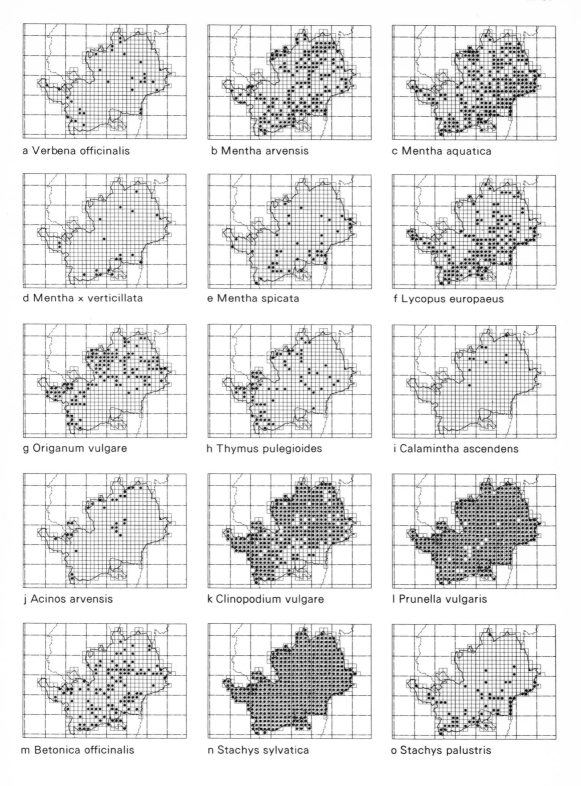

a Verbena officinalis

b Mentha arvensis

c Mentha aquatica

d Mentha x verticillata

e Mentha spicata

f Lycopus europaeus

g Origanum vulgare

h Thymus pulegioides

i Calamintha ascendens

j Acinos arvensis

k Clinopodium vulgare

l Prunella vulgaris

m Betonica officinalis

n Stachys sylvatica

o Stachys palustris

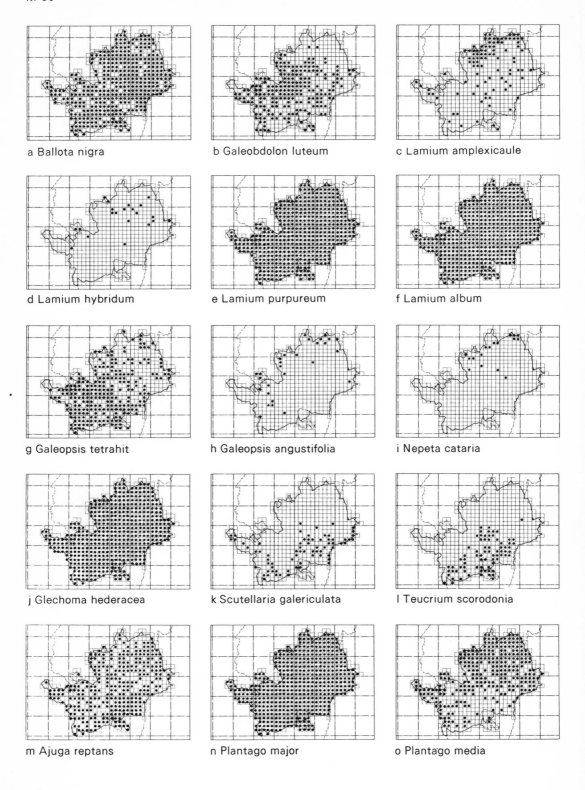

a Ballota nigra

b Galeobdolon luteum

c Lamium amplexicaule

d Lamium hybridum

e Lamium purpureum

f Lamium album

g Galeopsis tetrahit

h Galeopsis angustifolia

i Nepeta cataria

j Glechoma hederacea

k Scutellaria galericulata

l Teucrium scorodonia

m Ajuga reptans

n Plantago major

o Plantago media

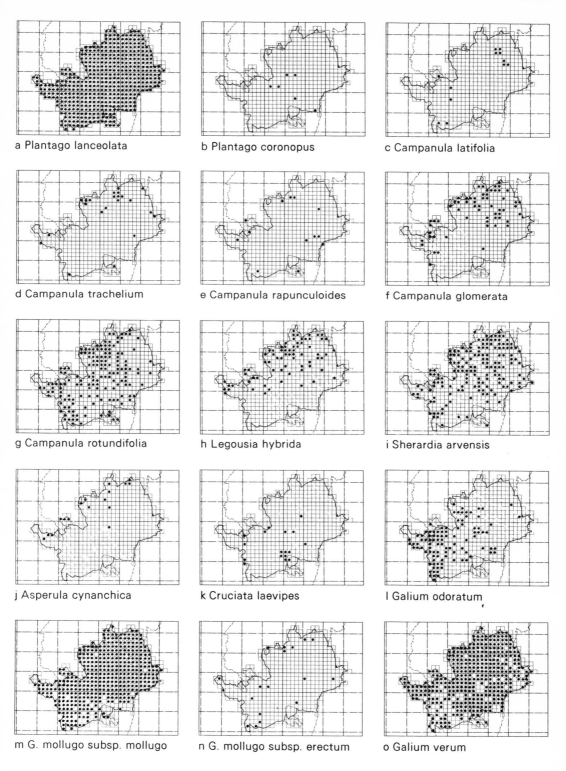

a Plantago lanceolata

b Plantago coronopus

c Campanula latifolia

d Campanula trachelium

e Campanula rapunculoides

f Campanula glomerata

g Campanula rotundifolia

h Legousia hybrida

i Sherardia arvensis

j Asperula cynanchica

k Cruciata laevipes

l Galium odoratum

m G. mollugo subsp. mollugo

n G. mollugo subsp. erectum

o Galium verum

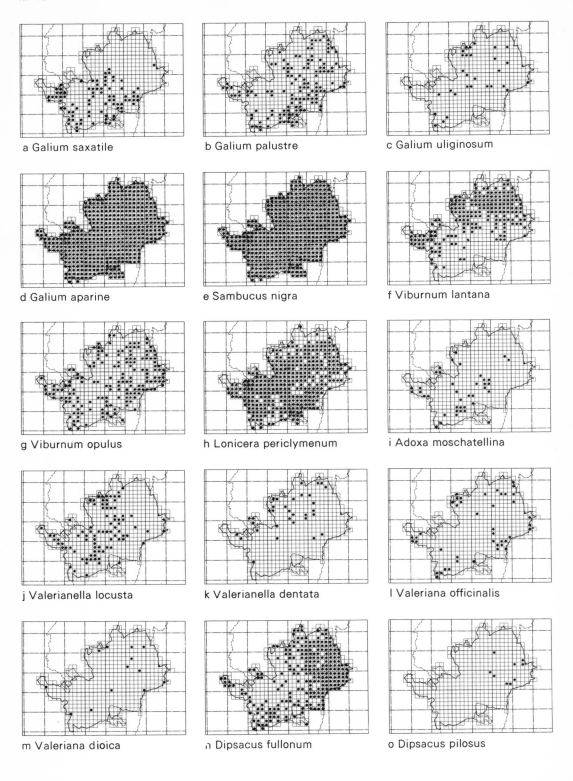

a Galium saxatile

b Galium palustre

c Galium uliginosum

d Galium aparine

e Sambucus nigra

f Viburnum lantana

g Viburnum opulus

h Lonicera periclymenum

i Adoxa moschatellina

j Valerianella locusta

k Valerianella dentata

l Valeriana officinalis

m Valeriana dioica

n Dipsacus fullonum

o Dipsacus pilosus

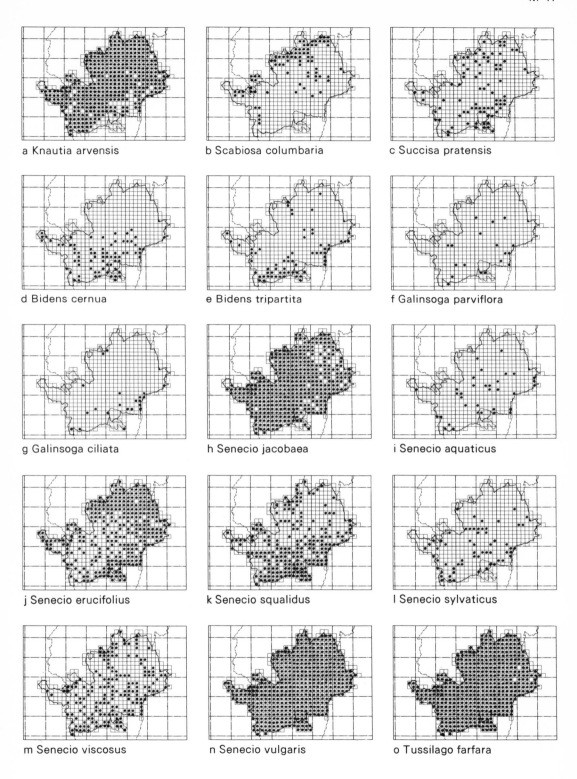

a Knautia arvensis

b Scabiosa columbaria

c Succisa pratensis

d Bidens cernua

e Bidens tripartita

f Galinsoga parviflora

g Galinsoga ciliata

h Senecio jacobaea

i Senecio aquaticus

j Senecio erucifolius

k Senecio squalidus

l Senecio sylvaticus

m Senecio viscosus

n Senecio vulgaris

o Tussilago farfara

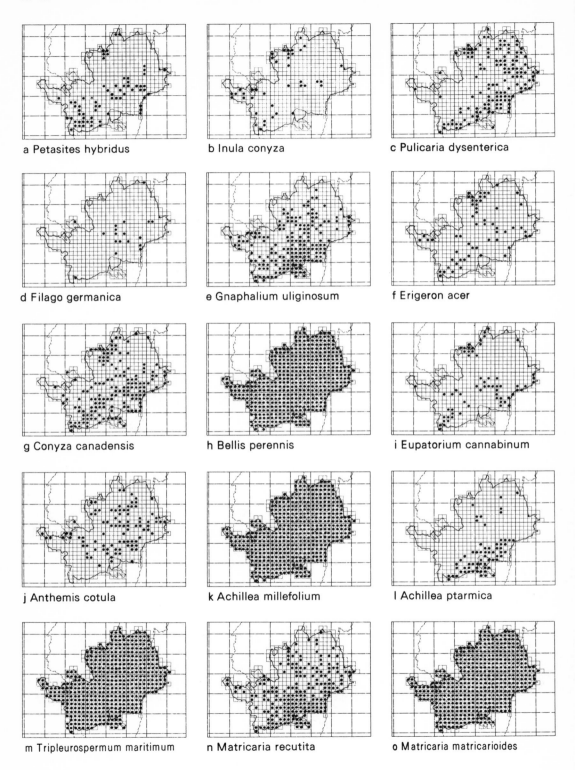

a Petasites hybridus

b Inula conyza

c Pulicaria dysenterica

d Filago germanica

e Gnaphalium uliginosum

f Erigeron acer

g Conyza canadensis

h Bellis perennis

i Eupatorium cannabinum

j Anthemis cotula

k Achillea millefolium

l Achillea ptarmica

m Tripleurospermum maritimum

n Matricaria recutita

o Matricaria matricarioides

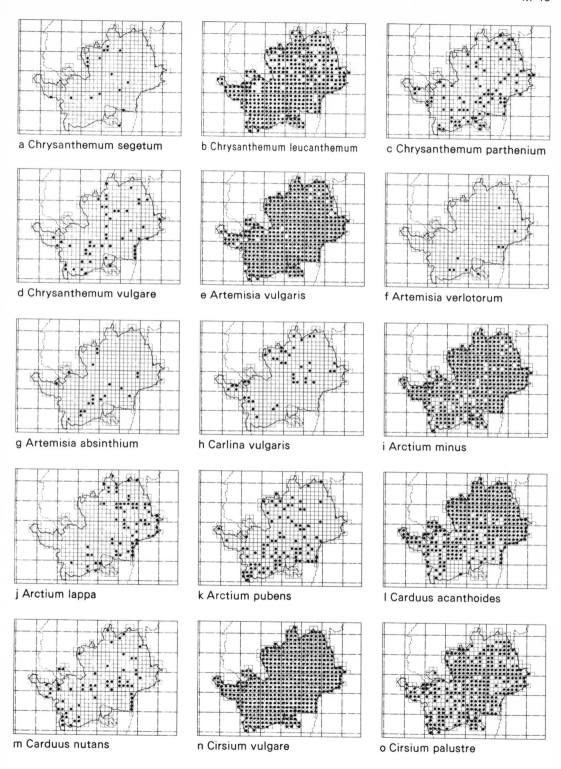

a Chrysanthemum segetum

b Chrysanthemum leucanthemum

c Chrysanthemum parthenium

d Chrysanthemum vulgare

e Artemisia vulgaris

f Artemisia verlotorum

g Artemisia absinthium

h Carlina vulgaris

i Arctium minus

j Arctium lappa

k Arctium pubens

l Carduus acanthoides

m Carduus nutans

n Cirsium vulgare

o Cirsium palustre

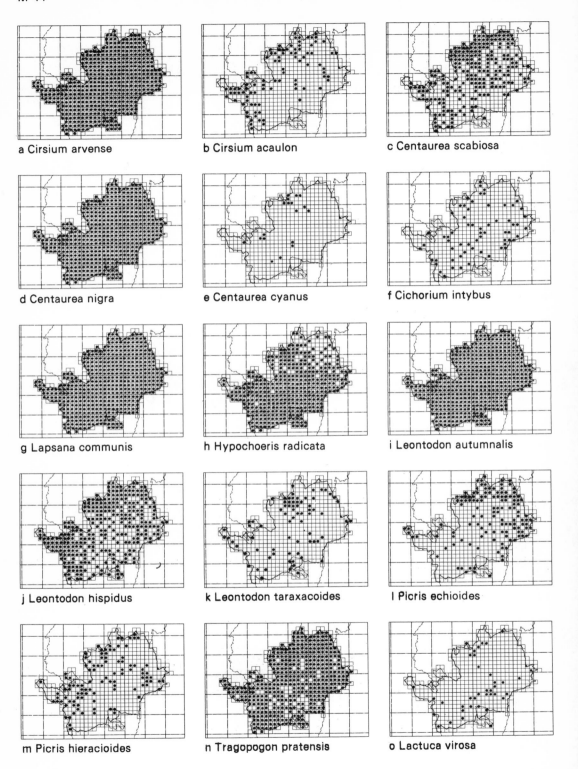

a Cirsium arvense

b Cirsium acaulon

c Centaurea scabiosa

d Centaurea nigra

e Centaurea cyanus

f Cichorium intybus

g Lapsana communis

h Hypochoeris radicata

i Leontodon autumnalis

j Leontodon hispidus

k Leontodon taraxacoides

l Picris echioides

m Picris hieracioides

n Tragopogon pratensis

o Lactuca virosa

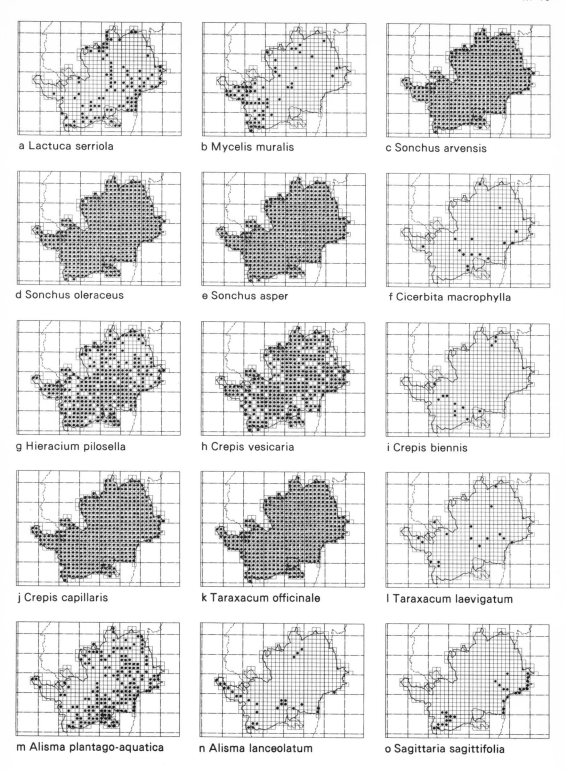

a Lactuca serriola

b Mycelis muralis

c Sonchus arvensis

d Sonchus oleraceus

e Sonchus asper

f Cicerbita macrophylla

g Hieracium pilosella

h Crepis vesicaria

i Crepis biennis

j Crepis capillaris

k Taraxacum officinale

l Taraxacum laevigatum

m Alisma plantago-aquatica

n Alisma lanceolatum

o Sagittaria sagittifolia

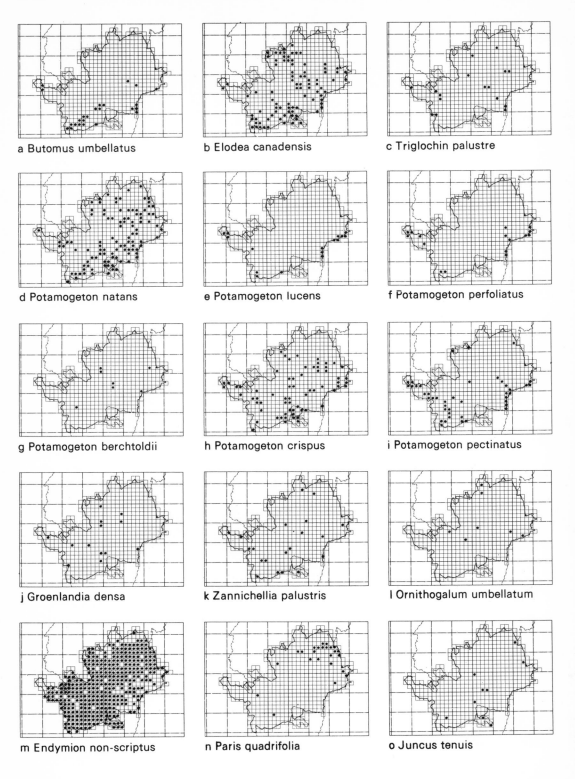

a Butomus umbellatus

b Elodea canadensis

c Triglochin palustre

d Potamogeton natans

e Potamogeton lucens

f Potamogeton perfoliatus

g Potamogeton berchtoldii

h Potamogeton crispus

i Potamogeton pectinatus

j Groenlandia densa

k Zannichellia palustris

l Ornithogalum umbellatum

m Endymion non-scriptus

n Paris quadrifolia

o Juncus tenuis

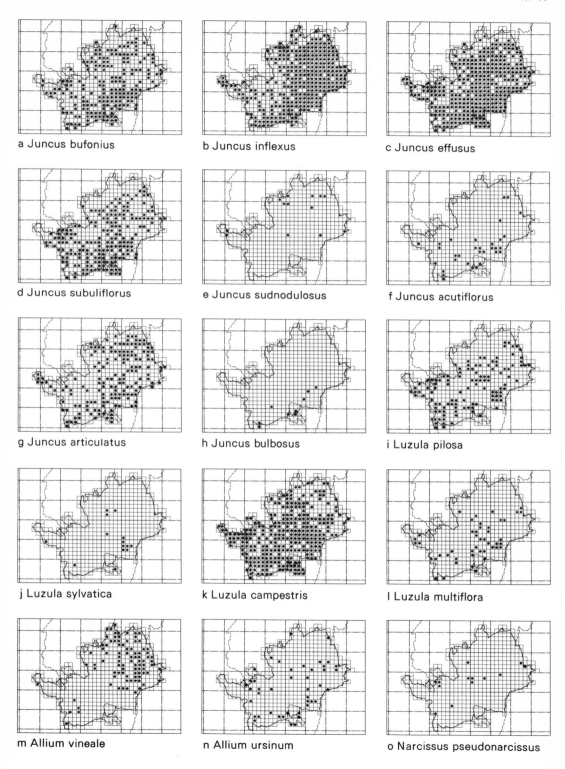

a Juncus bufonius

b Juncus inflexus

c Juncus effusus

d Juncus subuliflorus

e Juncus sudnodulosus

f Juncus acutiflorus

g Juncus articulatus

h Juncus bulbosus

i Luzula pilosa

j Luzula sylvatica

k Luzula campestris

l Luzula multiflora

m Allium vineale

n Allium ursinum

o Narcissus pseudonarcissus

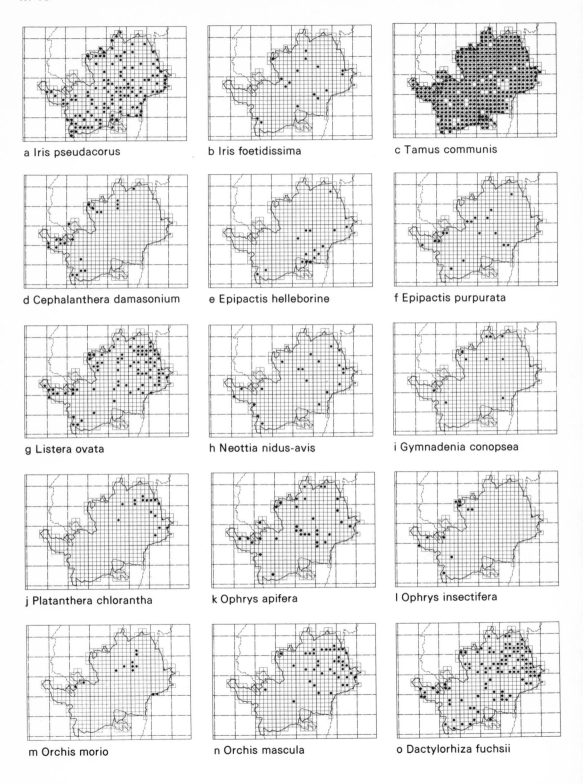

a Iris pseudacorus

b Iris foetidissima

c Tamus communis

d Cephalanthera damasonium

e Epipactis helleborine

f Epipactis purpurata

g Listera ovata

h Neottia nidus-avis

i Gymnadenia conopsea

j Platanthera chlorantha

k Ophrys apifera

l Ophrys insectifera

m Orchis morio

n Orchis mascula

o Dactylorhiza fuchsii

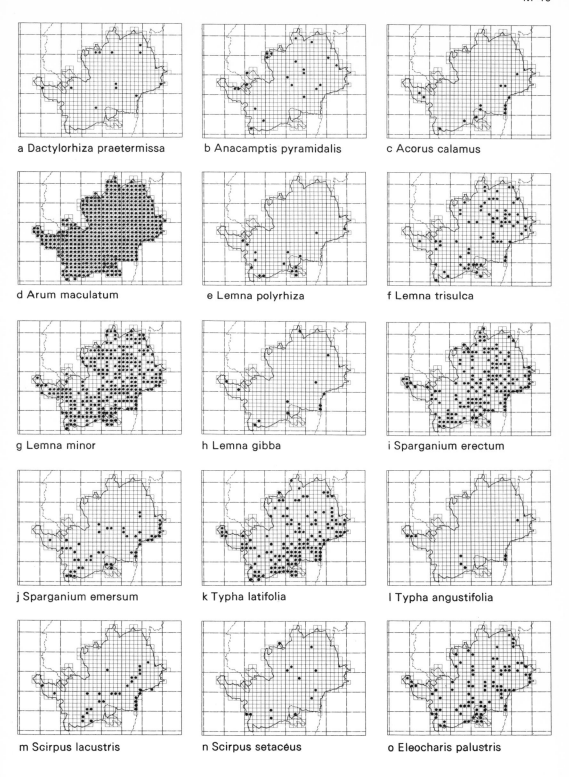

a Dactylorhiza praetermissa

b Anacamptis pyramidalis

c Acorus calamus

d Arum maculatum

e Lemna polyrhiza

f Lemna trisulca

g Lemna minor

h Lemna gibba

i Sparganium erectum

j Sparganium emersum

k Typha latifolia

l Typha angustifolia

m Scirpus lacustris

n Scirpus setaceus

o Eleocharis palustris

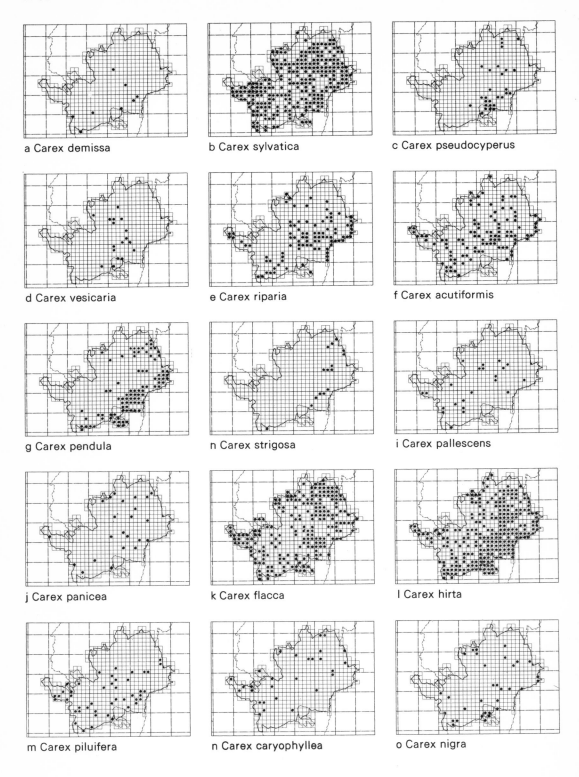

a Carex demissa

b Carex sylvatica

c Carex pseudocyperus

d Carex vesicaria

e Carex riparia

f Carex acutiformis

g Carex pendula

n Carex strigosa

i Carex pallescens

j Carex panicea

k Carex flacca

l Carex hirta

m Carex piluifera

n Carex caryophyllea

o Carex nigra

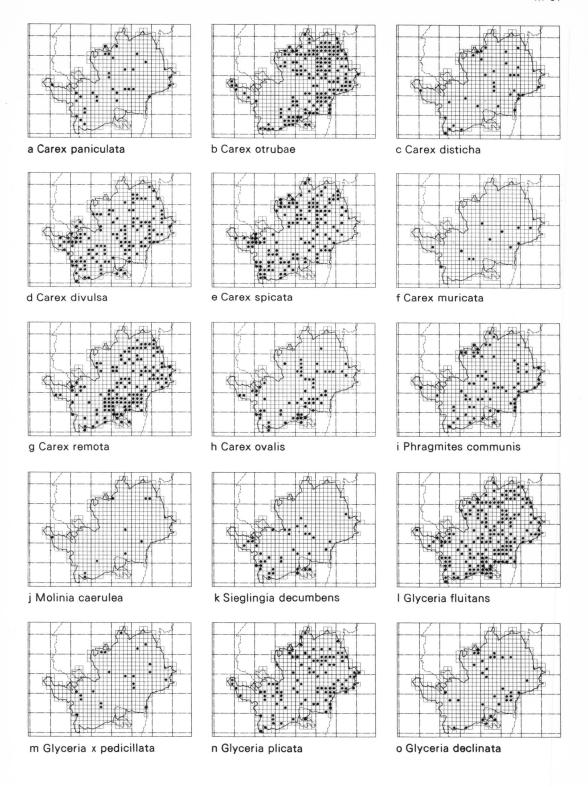

a Carex paniculata

b Carex otrubae

c Carex disticha

d Carex divulsa

e Carex spicata

f Carex muricata

g Carex remota

h Carex ovalis

i Phragmites communis

j Molinia caerulea

k Sieglingia decumbens

l Glyceria fluitans

m Glyceria x pedicillata

n Glyceria plicata

o Glyceria declinata

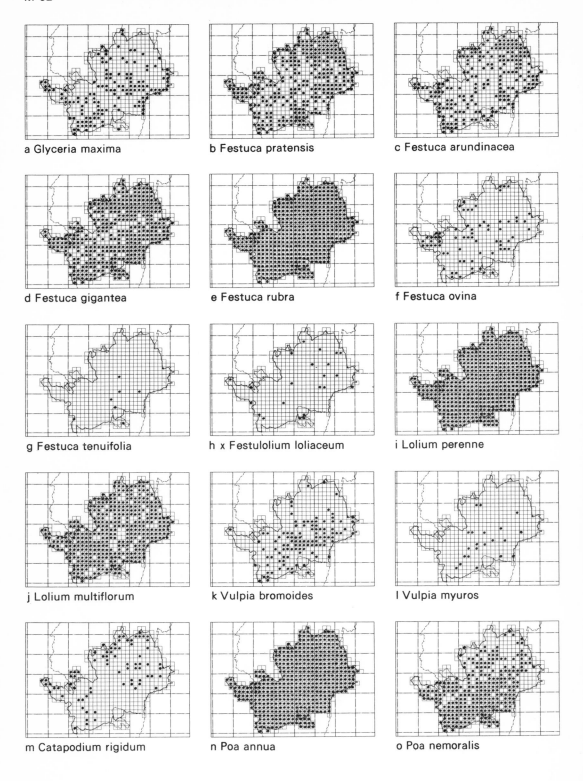

a Glyceria maxima

b Festuca pratensis

c Festuca arundinacea

d Festuca gigantea

e Festuca rubra

f Festuca ovina

g Festuca tenuifolia

h x Festulolium loliaceum

i Lolium perenne

j Lolium multiflorum

k Vulpia bromoides

l Vulpia myuros

m Catapodium rigidum

n Poa annua

o Poa nemoralis

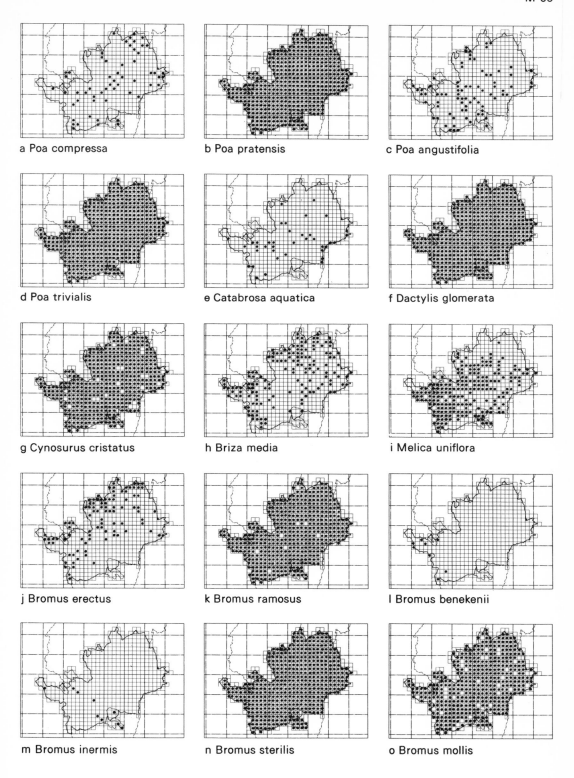

a Poa compressa

b Poa pratensis

c Poa angustifolia

d Poa trivialis

e Catabrosa aquatica

f Dactylis glomerata

g Cynosurus cristatus

h Briza media

i Melica uniflora

j Bromus erectus

k Bromus ramosus

l Bromus benekenii

m Bromus inermis

n Bromus sterilis

o Bromus mollis

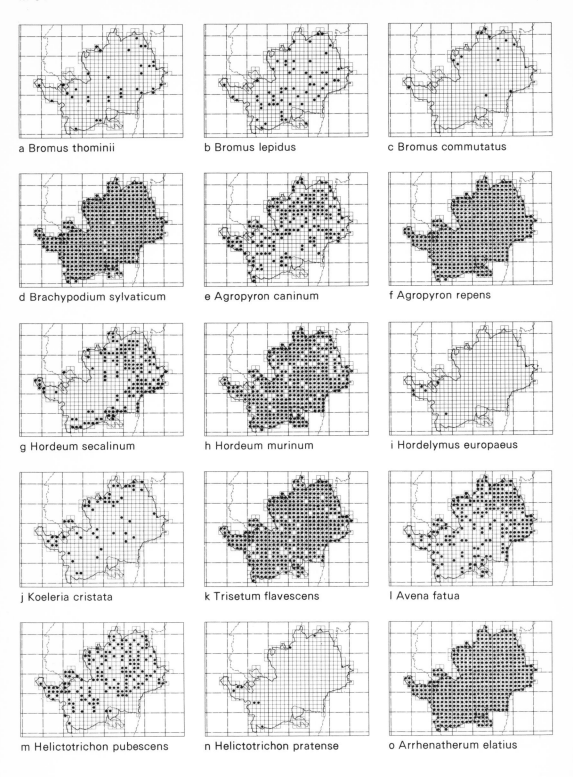

a Bromus thominii

b Bromus lepidus

c Bromus commutatus

d Brachypodium sylvaticum

e Agropyron caninum

f Agropyron repens

g Hordeum secalinum

h Hordeum murinum

i Hordelymus europaeus

j Koeleria cristata

k Trisetum flavescens

l Avena fatua

m Helictotrichon pubescens

n Helictotrichon pratense

o Arrhenatherum elatius

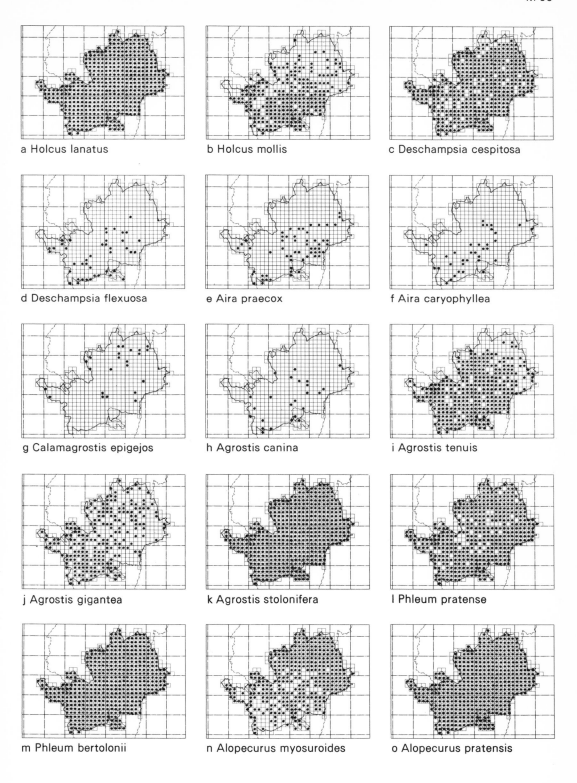

a Holcus lanatus

b Holcus mollis

c Deschampsia cespitosa

d Deschampsia flexuosa

e Aira praecox

f Aira caryophyllea

g Calamagrostis epigejos

h Agrostis canina

i Agrostis tenuis

j Agrostis gigantea

k Agrostis stolonifera

l Phleum pratense

m Phleum bertolonii

n Alopecurus myosuroides

o Alopecurus pratensis

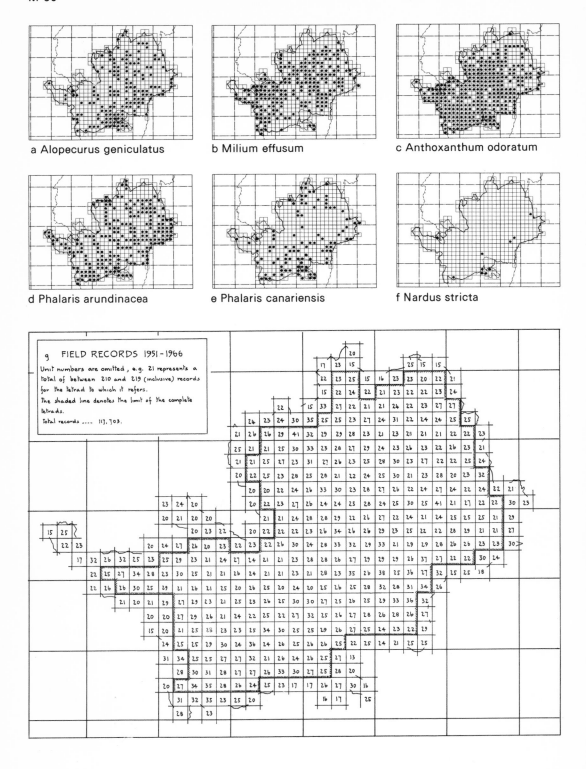

a Alopecurus geniculatus

b Milium effusum

c Anthoxanthum odoratum

d Phalaris arundinacea

e Phalaris canariensis

f Nardus stricta

g FIELD RECORDS 1951-1966

Unit numbers are omitted, e.g. 21 represents a total of between 210 and 219 (inclusive) records for the tetrad to which it refers.

The shaded line denotes the limit of the complete tetrads.

Total records .... 117,703.

Bibliography

ANON. 1855 Notes on a day's botanizing about Tring. *Phytologist (New Series)* 1: 105.

— 1855 An elm called Hertfordshire Elm. *Ibid.* 440.

ANSELL, J. 1846 On the occurrence of Juncus diffusus near Hoddesdon, and on its specific distinctness from J. glaucus. *Phytologist* 2: 662–3.

AVERY, B. W. see THOMASSON, A. J. and AVERY, B. W.

BISHOP'S STORTFORD AND DISTRICT NATURAL HISTORY SOCIETY 1952 *List of vascular plants of Bishop's Stortford and district.*

BLOOM, E. F. D. see HINE, R. L.

BOULGER, G. S. 1911 The Hertfordshire Elms. *South Eastern Nat. and Antiq.* 14: 27–30.

BRITTEN, J. 1920 Scilla campanulata (at Watford). *J. Bot.* 58: 227.

BRITTEN, J. and BOULGER, G.S. 1931 *A biographical index of deceased British and Irish botanists.* Second edition revised by A. B. Rendle. London.

BENSON, R. B. 1940 Some plant records from Bricket Wood. *Trans. Herts. Nat. Hist. Soc.* 21: 175.

BLACKSTONE, J. 1737 *Fasciculus plantarum circa Harefield sponte nascentium.* London.

CAMDEN, W. 1695 *Britannia* (Gibson's translation 1695, Gough's translation 1806). London.

CHAMBERS, R. 1838 Catalogue of the rarer indigenous plants growing in the neighbourhood of Tring. *Mag. Nat. Hist.* 2: 38–40.

CLUTTERBUCK, R. 1815 *History and antiquities of the county of Hertford.* 1: iv–v. Rare plants found in the county. J. Sabine.

[COCKFIELD, J.] 1815 *The botanist's guide. A catalogue of scarce plants found in the neighbourhood of London.* London.

COLES, W. 1657 *Adam in Eden.* London.

COLEMAN, W. H. 1843 see WEBB, R. H. and COLEMAN, W. H.

— 1848 On the geographical distribution of British plants. *Phytologist* 3: 217–221.

— 1848 The authorship of the Flora Hertfordiensis. *Ibid.* 320.

— 1848–49 see WEBB, R. H. and COLEMAN, W. H.

COOK, M. 1676 *The manner of raising . . . trees.* London.

COTTAM, A. 1875 Notes on the flora of the Watford district. *Trans. Watford Nat. Hist. Soc.* 1: 14–16.

CRESPIGNY, E. de 1877 *A new London Flora.* London.

CULPEPER, N. 1652 *The English physician.* London.

DANDY, J.E. 1958 *List of British Vascular plants.* London.

DONY, J. G. 1953 *Flora of Bedfordshire.* Luton.

— 1959 Some Hertfordshire plant records. *London Naturalist* 38: 74–76.

— 1959 *Comparative plant records for Hertfordshire and Bedfordshire.* Luton.

— 1961 The Oxlip in Hertfordshire. *Proc. Bot. Soc. Brit. Isl.* 4: 149–150.

— 1963 Botanists in Hertfordshire. *Hertfordshire, Past and Present* 3: 39–44.

— 1963 The expectation of plant records from prescribed areas. *Watsonia* 5: 377–385.

DRUCE, G. C. 1926 *Flora of Buckinghamshire.* Arbroath.

EDEN, T. 1924 Edaphic factors accompanying the succession after burning on Harpenden Common. *J. Ecol.* 12: 267–286.

EDWARDS, E. 1857 Additions to the Additional Supplement to the Flora Hertfordiensis. *Phytologist (New Series)* 2: 197–202.

— 1860 A list of the ferns of the neighbourhood of Wheathampstead. *Ibid.* 4: 40–41.

ELLIS, W. 1733 *Chiltern and vale farming explained.* London.

— 1738 *The timber tree improved* (second part 1742).

London.

ENGLISH, R. D. S. 1955 Botanical observations on Bricket Wood. *Trans. Herts. Nat. Hist. Soc.* 24: 146–156.

GEE, R. 1878 Famous trees in Hertfordshire. *Trans. Watford Nat. Hist. Soc.* 2: 1–16.

GERARD, J. 1597 *The herball or generall historie of plantes.* London.

GIBBS, A. E. 1881 Plants not previously recorded as growing in certain districts near St. Albans. *Trans. Herts. Nat. Hist. Soc.* 1: 143–4.

— 1902 see HOPKINSON, J.

GIBSON, G. S. 1862 *Flora of Essex.* London.

GOVER, J. E. B., MAWER, A. and STENTON, F. M. 1938 *Place names in Hertfordshire.* Cambridge.

GRAVESON, W. 1925 see WILMORE, A.

GREGORY, P. H. 1951–55 The Fungi of Hertfordshire. *Trans. Herts. Nat. Hist. Soc.* 23: 137–208. Supplement 1. *Ibid.* 24: 38–41.

Supplement 2 by M. Holden. *Ibid.* 26: 157–160.

HAILEYBURY NATURAL SCIENCE SOCIETY 1888 *The Fauna and Flora of Haileybury* (F. W. Headley, Editor). Second Edition 1902. Third Edition (E. D. Wainwright, Editor) 1926. Hertford.

HILL, D. 1911 'Burnt Oak' and other famous trees in the neighbourhood of Watford. *Trans. Herts. Nat. Hist. Soc.* 14: 129–134.

HILL, J. 1756–57 *The British herbal.* London.

HINE, R. L. (Editor) 1934 *The Natural History of the Hitchin Region.* Hitchin (Botany by J. E. Little, Aromatic and medicinal herbs by E. F. D. Bloom).

HOLDEN, M. 1955 see GREGORY, P. H.

HOPKINSON, J. 1890 Hertfordshire Plant Records, 1886–89, *Trans. Herts. Nat. Hist. Soc.* 6: 74–75.

— 1902 Botany, in *Victoria County History of the county of Hertfordshire.* 1: 43–66 (Mosses and liverworts by A. E. Gibbs, Mycetozoa by J. Saunders).

HOW, W. 1650 *Phytologia Britannica.* London.

HUGHES, W.R. 1936 *A Hertfordshire Wood (Sherrards Park Wood).* Welwyn Garden City.

JACKSON, B. D. 1897 Some overlooked records of Hertfordshire plants. *Trans. Herts. Hist. Nat. Soc.* 9: 121–125.

— 1904 Some Hertfordshire naturalists and their work. *Ibid.* 12: 77–88.

KENT, D. H. and LOUSLEY, J. E. 1951–57 A handlist of the plants of the London area. *London Naturalist* 30–36.

KENT, D. H. 1957 (a) An interesting 19th century hortus siccus. *Proc. Bot. Soc. Brit. Isl.* 2: 365–66.

— 1957 (b) *British Herbaria.* London.

KINGSTON, A. 1883 Flowering of plants at Royston in 1882. *Trans. Herts. Nat. Hist. Soc.* 2: 240.

— 1904 *Royston Heath, its history, its beauty and its typical wild flowers* (reprinted 1961). Royston.

LETCHWORTH NATURALISTS' SOCIETY. 1963 *In and around Letchworth* (Flowers and trees by D. and H. Meyer).

LITTLE, J. E. 1916 Hertfordshire poplars. *J. Bot.* 54: 233–236.

— 1917 Supplementary notes to the Hertfordshire Flora. *Ibid.* 55: 44–52, 74–77.

— 1922 Notes on north Herts. willows. *Ibid.* 60: 78–80.

— 1923 Alnus incana. *Ibid.* 61: 146–147.

— 1933 A sketch of the botany of the Ivel district of Hertfordshire. *Bot. Exch. Club 1932 Rep.* 375–387.

— 1934 see HINE, R. L. [LITTLE (1933) and LITTLE (1934) are identical].

— 1953 Lamium hybridum Vill. *Watsonia* 2: 361–68 (this paper was written in 1928 and published eighteen years after the author's death).

LITTLEBOY, J. E. 1876 A few words about our local ferns. *Trans. Watford Nat. Hist. Soc.* 1: 83–88.

LOUSLEY, J. E. see KENT, D. H. and LOUSLEY, J. E.

LUCAS, J. 1892 *Kalm's visit to England, 1748.* London.

MEYER, D. and H. see LETCHWORTH NATURALISTS' SOCIETY.

PARKINSON, J. 1640 *Theatrum Botanicum.* London.

PEARSALL, W. H. 1945 Leaf fall in Hertfordshire woodlands. *Trans. Herts. Nat. Hist. Soc.* 22: 97–98.

PERRING, F. H. and WALTERS, S. M. (Editors) 1962 *Atlas of the British flora.* London.

PERRING, F. H., SELL, P. D., WALTERS, S. M. and WHITEHOUSE, H. L. K. 1964 *A Flora of Cambridgeshire.* Cambridge.

PRYOR, A. R. 1874–75 Additions to the flora of Hertfordshire. *J. Bot.* 12: 22, Ibid. 13: 212.

— 1875 (a) Notes on a proposed re-issue of the Flora of Hertfordshire with supplementary remarks on the botany of the Watford district. *Trans. Watford Nat. Hist. Soc.* 1: 17–32.

— 1875 (b) Notes. *Ibid.* 63.

— 1876 (a) Notes on some Hertfordshire Carices. *J. Bot.* 14: 365.

— 1876 (a) On the botanical work of the past season. *Trans. Watford Nat. Hist. Soc.* 1: 65–77.

— 1881 Hertfordshire oaks. *J. Bot.* 19: 152.

— 1887 (a) Notes on some Hertfordshire Carices. *Trans. Herts. Nat. His. Soc.* 4: 121–128.

— 1887 (b) *Flora of Hertfordshire* (B. D. Jackson, editor). London and Hertford.

PUGSLEY, H. W. 1941 Arable weeds in east Hertfordshire. *J. Bot.* 79: 105.

RICHENS, R. H. 1959 The village elms of Hertfordshire. *Forestry* 32: 138–154.

SABINE, J. see CLUTTERBUCK, R.

SALISBURY, E. J. 1911– Botanical observations in Hertfordshire in 1909. *Trans. Herts. Nat. Hist. Soc.* 14: 177–78; in 1910. *Ibid.* 301–02; in 1911 and 1912. *Ibid.* 15: 172; in 1913. *Ibid.* 239; in 1914. *Ibid.* 16: 75–78; in 1915. *Ibid.* 157–60; in 1916. *Ibid.* 13–15. in 1917. *Ibid.* 143–45.

— 1911 Botany in 'St. Albans and its neighbourhood'. *Ibid.* 14: 209–54.

— 1913 (a) British woodlands. *Ibid.* 15: 15–18.

— 1913 (b) The competition of furze and bracken particularly on Harpenden Common. *Ibid.* 71–72.

— 1914 Hertfordshire gentians. *Ibid.* 169–70.

— 1915–18 The oak-hornbeam woods of Hertfordshire. *J. Ecol.* 4: 83–117, 6: 14–52.

— 1916 Variations in Anemone nemorosa. *Annals of Botany* 30: 525.

— 1918 The ecology of scrub in Hertfordshire. *Trans. Herts. Nat. Hist. Soc.* 17: 53–63.

— 1921 Botanical report for the year 1918. *Ibid.* 248–49.

— 1924(a) The effect of coppicing as illustrated by the woods of Hertfordshire. *Ibid.* 18: 1–21.

— 1924 (b) Changes in the Hertfordshire flora – a consideration of the influences of man. *Ibid.* 51–58.

— 1933 On the occurrence of blue pimpernel in Hertfordshire. *Ibid.* 19: 204–05.

— 1936 Some effects of drought upon vegetation. *Ibid.* 20: 47–50.

— 1940 The phanerogamic flora of Bricket Wood. *Ibid.* 21: 159–160.

— 1960 Variation in the flowers of Ranunculus circinatus. *Kew Bulletin* 14: 34–36.

SAUNDERS, J. 1897 Notes on some plants collected in Hertfordshire by Miss Maria Ransom (1830–40). *Trans. Herts. Nat. Hist. Soc.* 9: 167–68.

— 1902 see HOPKINSON, J.

SELBY, A. 1883 Flowering plants and ferns observed in Hertfordshire in 1882. *Trans. Herts. Nat. Hist. Soc.* 2: 237–39.

— 1884 List of flowering plants observed in Hertfordshire during the year 1883. *Ibid.* 3: 101–2.

SIMPSON, N. D. 1960 *A bibliographical index of the British flora.* Bournemouth.

SWINSCOW, T. D. V. (1959) A bryophyte flora of Hertfordshire. *Trans. Brit. Bryological Soc.* 3: 509–557.

THOMASSON, A. J. and AVERY, B. W. 1963. The soils of Hertfordshire. *Trans. Herts. Nat. Hist. Soc.* 25: 247–263.

TURNER, D. and DILLWYN, L. W. 1805 *The botanist's guide.* London.

TRIMEN, H. and DYER, W. T. T. 1869 *Flora of Middlesex.* London.

TRIMEN, H. 1877 Blysmus compressus in Herts. *J. Bot.* 15: 282.

WALTERS, S. M. see PERRING, F. H. and WALTERS, S. M.

WALTON, I. and COTTON, C. 1653 *The compleat angler.* London.

WATSON, H. C. 1835 *The new botanist's guide.* London.

WATT, A. S. 1934 The vegetation of the Chiltern Hills with special reference to their seral relationship. *J. Ecol.* 22: 230–270.

WEBB, R. H. 1857 Additional supplement to the Flora Hertfordiensis 1851–57. *Phytologist* (New Series) 2: 156–163.

WEBB, R. H., BENTLEY, R. and OTHERS 1858 Additions to the Hertfordshire flora. *Ibid.* 492–499.

WEBB, R. H. and COLEMAN, W. H. 1843 *A report of the progress made in the . . . flora of Hertfordshire, with a catalogue of species . . .* Hertford.

— 1848–49 *Flora Hertfordiensis.* London (Supplement 1, 1851; Supplement 2 by R. H. Webb, 1859).

WILMORE, A. and OTHERS 1925 *The natural history of Hertfordshire* (The plants of Hertfordshire by W. Graveson).

WITHERING, W. 1776 *A botanical arrangement of all the vegetables . . . in Great Britain* (Second edition edited by J. Stokes, 1787–92). Birmingham.

MANUSCRIPTS WITH THEIR PLACE OF DEPOSIT

BRUNT MS. Records for Flora of North Herts. and South Beds. By A. G. Brunt, c. 1906–1912. *Letchworth Museum.*

COLEMAN MS. A catalogue of plants observed near Hertford. By W. H. Coleman, 1839. *Linnean Society of London.*

DRUCE MS. Annotated copy of Flora of Hertfordshire (Pryor) made by G. C. Druce *Botany School, Oxford.*

EVANS and DONY MS. Card index of Hertfordshire plant records being a list of records added to copies of Flora of Hertfordshire (Pryor) cut up and fixed to cards. Begun by G. L. Evans (1951) and continued by J. G. Dony (1955). *Hitchin Museum.*

FRANKS MS. 'List of Augustus W. Franks' herbarium' entered in a copy of the Botanical Pocket-book (T. F. Forster). From the library of Sir Augustus W. Franks. *Department of Botany, British Museum (Natural History).*

LETCHWORTH MS. Card index of plants found within twelve miles of Letchworth. *Letchworth Museum.*

MORELL MS. Annotated sheets from Turner and Dillwyn's *Botanist's guide.* By J. D. Morell, 1832–5. *Hitchin Museum.*

LITTLE MS. Records supplementary to the Flora of Hertfordshire (Pryor). By J. E. Little. Four bound volumes. A valuable source of information. *Hitchin Museum.*

NEWBOULD MS. Annotated copy of Flora Hertfordiensis (Webb and Coleman) made by W. W. Newbould. *Luton Museum.*

STEELE MS. A catalogue of some plants spontainiously growing near Barkhamsted or Gadsden. (Gough Herts MS4). *Bodleian Library, Oxford.*

TROWER DRAWINGS. Drawings of British plants. 35 volumes. By Charlotte G. Trower. *Bodleian Library, Oxford.*

Hitchin Museum. Begun by G. L. Evans in 1951 and continued by J. G. Dony in 1955. To it has been added the local specimens in Joseph Pollard's herbarium and some of J. E. Little's specimens. There are also at Hitchin Museum the Phillips herbarium and two smaller collections made by unidentified Quakers c. 1840.

Letchworth Museum. Contains specimens collected by various local botanists.

Haileybury College. Contains specimens collected by J. A. Hankey, Miss Blake (unlocalised) and W. H. Coleman. Most of this collection was presented to the Druce Herbarium but much is still at Haileybury. There is also at the college a collection made over a number of years by scholars.

Druce Herbarium, Botany School, Oxford. Contains the collections of Blake and John Ansell in addition to specimens from Haileybury and additions made by Druce, Hayllar, Higgens, etc.

Botany School, Cambridge. Contains J. E. Little's collection and additional plants by various collectors.

Bolton Museum. Contains a number of W. H. Coleman's specimens which had apparently been added to P. B. Mason's herbarium.

Franks Herbarium. The local specimens were presented to Luton Museum where it is kept as a separate collection.

Phillips Herbarium. A large collection made by the Phillips family and containing a number of local specimens. It is now at Hitchin Museum with a list of its contents in a bound volume.

A. W. Graveson Herbarium. This contains a number of interesting Hertfordshire specimens. Mr. Graveson intends to present it to Bridport Museum.

J. E. Smith Herbarium. At the rooms of the Linnean Society of London.

British Museum (Natural History) Contains the Samuel Rudge and D. Martha Higgins collections in addition to specimens of various collectors.

Kew. This apparently contains no major Hertfordshire collection but it has not been searched thoroughly to see what local material it does contain. The H. C. Watson Herbarium which is housed separately at Kew includes specimens sent to Watson by Isaac Brown and other Hertfordshire botanists.

There are a number of private herbaria containing some local material and these include those of J. E. Lousley, R. M. Payne (now incorporated in the collection of S. T. Jermyn), R. M. Harley (including R. A. Graham's specimens), P. J. Ellison, J. L. Fielding and B. Wurzell.

Index